Cat
Encounters

Peg Woffington, the famous Irish actress (1714–1760) whose manager, Rich, had twenty-seven cats. Drawn by F. Smallfield and engraved by G. C. Finden.

Cat Encounters

A CAT-LOVER'S ANTHOLOGY

Selected by Seon Manley & Gogo Lewis
Illustrated with engravings

Lothrop, Lee & Shepard Books
New York

This book is for
Lolly and Terry Hayes
and their cat
Tigger-Lucille

Illustration p. i: Detail of "Puss in Boots" by Gustav Doré, from Les
Contes de Perrault, *Paris, 1862, courtesy of The Pierpont Morgan Library.*

Library of Congress Cataloging in Publication Data
Main entry under title:
Cat encounters.
    SUMMARY: More than 40 stories and essays about cats by famous writers.
    1. Cats—Legends and stories. 2. Cats—Addresses, essays, lectures. [1. Cats—Fiction.
2. Cats] 1. Manley, Seon. II. Lewis, Gogo.
SF445.5.C378   808.8'036   79-2437
ISBN 0-688-41914-3

ACKNOWLEDGMENTS

We are grateful to the authors, agents, and publishers who have given us permission to reprint the following selections:

"The Christmas Cat" (Chapter 9) from *All Things Wise and Wonderful* by James Herriot. Reprinted by permission of St. Martin's Press, Inc., and Harold Ober Associates Incorporated. Copyright © 1976, 1977 by James Herriot. Copyright © 1977 by St. Martin's Press. Title for Chapter 9 supplied by the editors with the permission of the author, his agent and publisher.

"The Sin of Madame Phloi" by Lilian Jackson Braun. First published in *Ellery Queen's Mystery Magazine,* copyright © 1962 by Davis Publications, Inc. Reprinted by permission of the author and her agent, Blanche C. Gregory, Inc.

Chapter One of *Cat's Company* by Michael Joseph. Reprinted by permission of Mrs. Michael Joseph.

"The Cat That Went to Trinity" by Robertson Davies from *One Half of Robertson Davies*. Copyright © 1977 by Robertson Davies. Reprinted by permission of Viking Penguin Inc. and The Macmillan Company of Canada Limited.

"Podolo" by L. P. Hartley. Reprinted by permission of the author and the author's agents, Scott Meredith Literary Agency, Inc., 845 Third Avenue, New York, New York.

"The Cat in the Lifeboat" by James Thurber. Copyright © 1956 by James Thurber. From *Further Fables for Our Time,* published by Simon & Schuster. Originally printed in *The New Yorker.* Reprinted by permission of Helen Thurber.

"Spooner" by Eleanor Farjeon. Reprinted by permission of Harold Ober Associates Incorporated. Copyright 1952 by Eleanor Farjeon.

"The Cat and the Cornfield" from *The Red Petticoat and Other Stories* by Bryan MacMahon. Copyright © 1955 by Bryan MacMahon. Reprinted by permission of the publisher, E. P. Dutton.

"The Yellow Cat" by Michael Joseph. Reprinted by permission of Mrs. Michael Joseph.

"My Father, The Cat" by Henry Slesar. Copyright © 1957 by King-Size Publications, Inc. Reprinted by permission of the author.

"The Attic" from *Tales of the Mysterious and Macabre* by Algernon Blackwood. Reprinted by permission of the Estate of Algernon Blackwood and the Hamlyn Publishing Group.

"Sylvia the First" from *Cats' Company* by Compton MacKenzie. Reprinted by permission of The Society of Authors as the literary representative of the Estate of Compton MacKenzie.

"Death of a Favorite" by J. F. Powers, from *The Presence of Grace,* 1956; the story originally appeared in *The New Yorker.* Reprinted by permission of the author.

Our thanks also to Betty Shalders; Barbara-Ann Colgan; Allyson Belcher; the staff of the Bellport Memorial Library, Bellport, New York; the staff of the Patchogue Library, Patchogue, New York; the staff of the Greenwich Library, Greenwich, Connecticut; our husbands, Robert R. Manley and William W. Lewis; our daughters, Shivaun Manley, Sara Lewis, and Carol Lewis; and, of course, our many cats.

CONTENTS

INTRODUCTION   ix

THE CHRISTMAS CAT, *by James Herriot*   1

MY LINE OF FAMILY CATS, *by Sarah Orne Jewett*   9

THE SIN OF MADAME PHLOI, *by Lilian Jackson Braun*   14

CAT'S COMPANY, *by Michael Joseph*   26

THE PHILANTHROPIST AND THE HAPPY CAT, *by Saki*   41

THE CAT THAT WENT TO TRINITY, *by Robertson Davies*   48

A CAT CALLED JOHN HARVARD, *by Helen M. Winslow*   59

THE EGYPTIANS AND THEIR CATS, *by Herodotus*   61

AN ASSORTMENT OF CATS, *by Jerome K. Jerome*   64

A CAT AND A BIRD OF OLD NEW ORLEANS, *by A Correspondent*   75

"HEY DIDDLE DIDDLE, THE CAT . . . ," *by Eden Phillpotts*   78

THE CHINESE CAT, *by Pierre Loti*   95

PODOLO, *by L. P. Hartley*   98

PUDDLES OF PORTSMOUTH, *by Francis Buckland*   111

A KITTEN, *by Agnes Repplier*   116

CALVIN—HIS LIFE AND DEATH, *by Charles Dudley Warner*   126

THE CAT IN THE LIFEBOAT, *by James Thurber*   140

"Midshipman," The Cat, *by John Coleman Adams*   143

Spooner, *by Eleanor Farjeon*   154

The Strange Cat, *by John Oxenford*   168

The Cat and the Cornfield, *by Bryan MacMahon*   170

The Yellow Cat, *by Michael Joseph*   180

A Discourse on Cats, *by Bill Nye*   194

Cats of the New York *Sun, by Charles Dana*   198

He Wrote to the Rats, *by Julian Ralph*   202

The Black Cat, *by William Wintle*   207

The Conscientious Cat, *by Agnes A. Sandham*   217

Ye Marvellous Legend of Tom Connor's Cat,
    by Samuel Lover   224

The *"Century"* Cat, *by Mary F. Honeyman*   234

Juno, *by Harriet Beecher Stowe*   239

My Father's Cat, *by William Rossetti*   243

My Father, the Cat, *by Henry Slesar*   245

Moquo, *by Madame Michelet*   254

Are Cats People?, *by Oliver Herford*   257

My Grandmother's Cat, *by Edna Dean Proctor*   261

The Attic, *by Algernon Blackwood*   265

Sylvia the First, *by Compton MacKenzie*   273

Pretty Lady, *by Helen M. Winslow*   282

My Mother's Cat, *by Louise Chandler Moulton*   296

Death of a Favorite, *by J. F. Powers*   298

Miss Spot and Others, *by Harriet Prescott Spofford*   321

On Observing His Cats, *by Andrew Lang*   326

Rumpel, *by Robert Southey*   329

The Last Words, *by Thomas Janvier*   331

The Achievement of the Cat, *by Saki*   332

Biographical Notes   336

INTRODUCTION

Our family has delighted in and been kept and taught by some fifty cats, all with distinct and magnificent personalities of their own. Some were outgoing; others were introspective. Some enjoyed the outside world. They watched the snow coming down with that curious electrical sense of excitement that cats get during any storm. No matter how old they were, they could barely wait until they bounded forth to walk on top of it, as gingerly as any arctic explorer, into a world of whiteness and play. Except for a white cat named Polar, who belied his name. He loathed the cold, and waited until the thaw because he rejoiced in black mud.

One dynasty of our cats disdained the outside altogether. They were inside cats devoted to typewriters, tops of manuscripts, bookshelves. One was called "Bookie," because he was born on a bookshelf; others showed particular affection toward authors who were fond of cats. They slept on the books of such writers as James Herriot and James Thurber (one such cat was called Jimmie). Another had the pomposity of Herodotus, but was forever known as Cat. She was truly a cultured feline. Their less literary siblings answered to Tom, Dick, and Harry, but all of that remarkable litter were "bookish."

Cats seem to bring out the best in writers; cats are classy, cultivated and independent. Most writers like to feel they are the same. Over the years we have encountered cats in stories and reminiscences that were rare and wonderful. We began to notice how often writers were awakened to a new sensitivity, a felicity of expression, by their love and affection for cats. Cats have inspired writers with joy, compassion, mystery, humor; with grace, often with genius, and always with imagination.

Cats have regaled artists as well—from J. G. Francis, who so enjoyed the antics of his cats, to Madame Ronner whose favorite models were her own "Jem" and "Monmouth." It seemed fitting that we should share our pictorial encounters as well. Why not? We had one cat who was not at all keen on the printed word, but was delighted by pictures. He was a gentle cat and his name, for the record, was Thunder.

An Assortment of Kittens. Artist unknown.

Cat Encounters

The Night Before Christmas, by Thomas Nast (1840–1902). Nast was the creator of today's Santa Claus image.

THE CHRISTMAS CAT
(From ALL THINGS WISE AND WONDERFUL)

James Herriot

When Cecil Frances Alexander, in the mid-nineteenth century, wrote the lines, "All Things Bright and Beautiful/All Things Great and Small/All Things Wise and Wonderful," she was expressing the concern and compassion for animals that at that time was a new development.

In our time there is no greater writer about animals, no writer who better uses as a theme the indefinable chemistry between person and animal, than James Herriot. Appropriately, Herriot chose Alexander's lines for the titles of his three magnificent books. Herriot, a veterinarian, has doctored every size animal, but his writing has never seemed more gifted than it does in "The Christmas Cat."

I had plenty of company for Christmas that year. We were billeted in the Grand Hotel, the massive Victorian pile which dominated Scarborough in turreted splendour from its eminence above the sea, and the big dining room was packed with several hundred shouting airmen. The iron discipline was relaxed for a few hours to let the Yuletide spirit run free.

1

It was so different from other Christmases I had known that it ought to have remained like a beacon in my mind, but I know that my strongest memory of Christmas will always be bound up with a certain little cat.

I first saw her one autumn day when I was called to see one of Mrs. Ainsworth's dogs, and I looked in some surprise at the furry black creature sitting before the fire.

"I didn't know you had a cat," I said.

The lady smiled. "We haven't, this is Debbie."

"Debbie?"

"Yes, at least that's what we call her. She's a stray. Comes here two or three times a week and we give her some food. I don't know where she lives but I believe she spends a lot of her time around one of the farms along the road."

"Do you ever get the feeling that she wants to stay with you?"

"No." Mrs. Ainsworth shook her head. "She's a timid little thing. Just creeps in, has some food then flits away. There's something so appealing about her but she doesn't seem to want to let me or any-body into her life."

I looked again at the little cat. "But she isn't just having food today."

"That's right. It's a funny thing but every now and again she slips through here into the lounge and sits by the fire for a few minutes. It's as though she was giving herself a treat."

"Yes . . . I see what you mean." There was no doubt there was something unusual in the attitude of the little animal. She was sit-ting bolt upright on the thick rug which lay before the fireplace in which the coals glowed and flamed. She made no effort to curl up or wash herself or do anything other than gaze quietly ahead. And there was something in the dusty black of her coat, the half-wild scrawny look of her, that gave me a clue. This was a special event in her life, a rare and wonderful thing; she was lapping up a com-fort undreamed of in her daily existence.

As I watched she turned, crept soundlessly from the room and was gone.

2

"That's always the way with Debbie," Mrs. Ainsworth laughed. "She never stays more than ten minutes or so, then she's off."

Mrs. Ainsworth was a plumpish, pleasant-faced woman in her forties and the kind of client veterinary surgeons dream of; well off, generous, and the owner of three cosseted Basset hounds. And it only needed the habitually mournful expression of one of the dogs to deepen a little and I was round there post haste. Today one of the Bassets had raised its paw and scratched its ear a couple of times and that was enough to send its mistress scurrying to the phone in great alarm.

So my visits to the Ainsworth home were frequent but undemanding, and I had ample opportunity to look out for the little cat that had intrigued me. On one occasion I spotted her nibbling daintily from a saucer at the kitchen door. As I watched she turned and almost floated on light footsteps into the hall then through the lounge door.

The three Bassets were already in residence, draped snoring on the fireside rug, but they seemed to be used to Debbie because two of them sniffed her in a bored manner and the third merely cocked a sleepy eye at her before flopping back on the rich pile.

Debbie sat among them in her usual posture; upright, intent, gazing absorbedly into the glowing coals. This time I tried to make friends with her. I approached her carefully but she leaned away as I stretched out my hand. However, by patient wheedling and soft talk I managed to touch her and gently stroked her cheek with one finger. There was a moment when she responded by putting her head on one side and rubbing back against my hand but soon she was ready to leave. Once outside the house she darted quickly along the road then through a gap in a hedge and the last I saw was the little black figure flitting over the rain-swept grass of a field.

"I wonder where she goes," I murmured half to myself.

Mrs. Ainsworth appeared at my elbow. "That's something we've never been able to find out."

It must have been nearly three months before I heard from Mrs.

Ainsworth, and in fact I had begun to wonder at the Bassets' long symptomless run when she came on the 'phone.

It was Christmas morning and she was apologetic. "Mr. Herriot, I'm so sorry to bother you today of all days. I should think you want a rest at Christmas like anybody else." But her natural politeness could not hide the distress in her voice.

"Please don't worry about that," I said. "Which one is it this time?"

"It's not one of the dogs. It's . . . Debbie."

"Debbie? She's at your house now?"

"Yes . . . but there's something wrong. Please come quickly."

Driving through the market place I thought again that Darrowby on Christmas Day was like Dickens come to life; the empty square with the snow thick on the cobbles and hanging from the eaves of the fretted lines of roofs; the shops closed and the coloured lights of the Christmas trees winking at the windows of the clustering houses, warmly inviting against the cold white bulk of the fells behind.

Mrs. Ainsworth's home was lavishly decorated with tinsel and holly, rows of drinks stood on the sideboard and the rich aroma of turkey and sage and onion stuffing wafted from the kitchen. But her eyes were full of pain as she led me through to the lounge.

Debbie was there all right, but this time everything was different. She wasn't sitting upright in her usual position; she was stretched quite motionless on her side, and huddled close to her lay a tiny black kitten.

I looked down in bewilderment. "What's happened here?"

"It's the strangest thing," Mrs. Ainsworth replied. "I haven't seen her for several weeks then she came in about two hours ago—sort of staggered into the kitchen, and she was carrying the kitten in her mouth. She took it through to the lounge and laid it on the rug and at first I was amused. But I could see all was not well because she sat as she usually does, but for a long time—over an hour—then she lay down like this and she hasn't moved."

I knelt on the rug and passed my hand over Debbie's neck and

4

ribs. She was thinner than ever, her fur dirty and mudcaked. She did not resist as I gently opened her mouth. The tongue and mucous membranes were abnormally pale and the lips ice-cold against my fingers. When I pulled down her eyelid and saw the dead white conjunctiva a knell sounded in my mind.

I palpated the abdomen with a grim certainty as to what I would find and there was no surprise, only a dull sadness as my fingers closed around a hard lobulated mass deep among the viscera. Massive lymphosarcoma. Terminal and hopeless. I put my stethoscope on her heart and listened to the increasingly faint, rapid beat then I straightened up and sat on the rug looking sightlessly into the fireplace, feeling the warmth of the flames on my face.

Mrs. Ainsworth's voice seemed to come from afar. "Is she ill, Mr. Herriot?"

I hesitated. "Yes . . . yes, I'm afraid so. She has a malignant growth." I stood up. "There's absolutely nothing I can do. I'm sorry."

"Oh!" Her hand went to her mouth and she looked at me wide-eyed. When at last she spoke her voice trembled. "Well, you must put her to sleep immediately. It's the only thing to do. We can't let her suffer."

"Mrs. Ainsworth," I said. "There's no need. She's dying now—in a coma—far beyond suffering."

She turned quickly away from me and was very still as she fought with her emotions. Then she gave up the struggle and dropped on her knees beside Debbie.

"Oh, poor little thing!" she sobbed and stroked the cat's head again and again as the tears fell unchecked on the matted fur. "What she must have come through. I feel I ought to have done more for her."

For a few moments I was silent, feeling her sorrow, so discordant among the bright seasonal colours of this festive room. Then I spoke gently.

"Nobody could have done more than you," I said. "Nobody could have been kinder."

5

"But I'd have kept her here—in comfort. It must have been terrible out there in the cold when she was so desperately ill—I daren't think about it. And having kittens, too—I . . . I wonder how many she did have?"

I shrugged. "I don't suppose we'll ever know. Maybe just this one. It happens sometimes. And she brought it to you, didn't she?"

"Yes . . . that's right . . . she did . . . she did." Mrs. Ainsworth reached out and lifted the bedraggled black morsel. She smoothed her finger along the muddy fur and the tiny mouth opened in a soundless miaow. "Isn't it strange? She was dying and she brought her kitten here. And on Christmas Day."

I bent and put my hand on Debbie's heart. There was no beat.

I looked up. "I'm afraid she's gone." I lifted the small body, almost feather light, wrapped it in the sheet which had been spread on the rug and took it out to the car.

When I came back Mrs. Ainsworth was still stroking the kitten. The tears had dried on her cheeks and she was brighteyed as she looked at me.

"I've never had a cat before," she said.

I smiled. "Well it looks as though you've got one now."

And she certainly had. That kitten grew rapidly into a sleek handsome cat with a boisterous nature which earned him the name of Buster. In every way he was the opposite to his timid little mother. Not for him the privations of the secret outdoor life; he stalked the rich carpets of the Ainsworth home like a king and the ornate collar he always wore added something more to his presence.

On my visits I watched his development with delight but the occasion which stays in my mind was the following Christmas Day, a year from his arrival.

I was out on my rounds as usual. I can't remember when I haven't had to work on Christmas Day because the animals have never got round to recognising it as a holiday; but with the passage of the years the vague resentment I used to feel has been replaced by philosophical acceptance. After all, as I tramped around the hillside barns in the frosty air I was working up a better appetite for my turkey than all the millions lying in bed or slumped by the fire; and this was aided by the innumerable aperitifs I received from the hospitable farmers.

I was on my way home, bathed in a rosy glow. I had consumed several whiskies—the kind the inexpert Yorkshiremen pour as though it was ginger ale—and I had finished with a glass of old Mrs. Earnshaw's rhubarb wine which had seared its way straight to my toenails. I heard the cry as I was passing Mrs. Ainsworth's house.

"Merry Christmas, Mr. Herriot!" She was letting a visitor out of the front door and she waved at me gaily. "Come in and have a drink to warm you up."

I didn't need warming up but I pulled in to the kerb without hesitation. In the house there was all the festive cheer of last year and the same glorious whiff of sage and onion which set my gastric juices surging. But there was not the sorrow; there was Buster.

He was darting up to each of the dogs in turn, ears pricked, eyes blazing with devilment, dabbing a paw at them then streaking away.

Mrs. Ainsworth laughed. "You know, he plagues the life out of them. Gives them no peace."

She was right. To the Bassets, Buster's arrival was rather like the intrusion of an irreverent outsider into an exclusive London club. For a long time they had led a life of measured grace; regular sedate walks with their mistress, superb food in ample quantities and long snoring sessions on the rugs and armchairs. Their days followed one upon another in unruffled calm. And then came Buster.

He was dancing up to the youngest dog again, sideways this time, head on one side, goading him. When he started boxing with both paws it was too much even for the Basset. He dropped his dignity and rolled over with the cat in a brief wrestling match.

"I want to show you something." Mrs. Ainsworth lifted a hard rubber ball from the sideboard and went out to the garden, followed by Buster. She threw the ball across the lawn and the cat bounded after it over the frosted grass, the muscles rippling under the black sheen of his coat. He seized the ball in his teeth, brought it back

7

to his mistress, dropped it at her feet and waited expectantly. She threw it and he brought it back again.

I gasped incredulously. A feline retriever!

The Bassets looked on disdainfully. Nothing would ever have induced them to chase a ball, but Buster did it again and again as though he would never tire of it.

Mrs. Ainsworth turned to me. "Have you ever seen anything like that?"

"No," I replied. "I never have. He is a most remarkable cat."

She snatched Buster from his play and we went back into the house where she held him close to her face, laughing as the big cat purred and arched himself ecstatically against her cheek.

Looking at him, a picture of health and contentment, my mind went back to his mother. Was it too much to think that that dying little creature with the last of her strength had carried her kitten to the only haven of comfort and warmth she had ever known in the hope that it would be cared for there? Maybe it was.

But it seemed I wasn't the only one with such fancies. Mrs. Ainsworth turned to me and though she was smiling her eyes were wistful.

"Debbie would be pleased," she said.

I nodded. "Yes she would. . . . It was just a year ago today she brought him, wasn't it?"

"That's right." She hugged Buster to her again. "The best Christmas present I ever had."

Christmas Pudding, by J. G. Francis.

MY LINE OF FAMILY CATS

Sarah Orne Jewett

Sarah Orne Jewett, one of the most important writers of the last century, was the daughter of a country doctor. She accompanied him on his rounds from the time she was a small child, and grew intimate with many patients and their pets. The cats of Maine were special—and throughout the rest of her life, cats to her were an absolute necessity.

I look back over so long a line of family cats, from a certain poor Spotty who died an awful death in a fit on the flagstones under the library window when I was less than five years old, to a lawless, fluffy, yellow and white coon cat now in my possession, that I find it hard to single out the most interesting pussy of all. I shall have to speak of two cats at least, one being the enemy and the other the friend of my dog Joe. Joe and I grew up together and were fond companions, until he died of far too early old age and left me to take my country walks alone.

Polly, the enemy, was the best mouser of all: quite the best business cat we ever had, with an astonishing intellect and a shrewd way of gaining her ends. She caught birds and mice as if she

9

foraged for our whole family: she had an air of responsibility and a certain impatience of interruption and interference such as I have never seen in any other cat, and a scornful way of sitting before a person with fierce eyes and a quick, ominous twitching of her tail. She seemed to be measuring one's incompetence as a mouse-catcher in these moments, or to be saying to herself, "What a clumsy, stupid person; how little she knows, and how I should like to scratch her and hear her squeak." I sometimes felt as if I were a larger sort of helpless mouse in these moments, but sometimes Polly would be more friendly, and even jump into our laps, when it was a pleasure to pat her hard little head with its exquisitely soft, dark tortoise-shell fur. No matter if she almost always turned and caught the caressing hand with teeth and claws, when she was tired of its touch, you would always be ready to pat her next time; there was such a fascination about her that any attention on her part gave a thrill of pride and pleasure. Every guest and stranger admired her and tried to win her favor: while we of the household hid our wounds and delighted in her cleverness and beauty.

Polly was but a small cat to have a mind. She looked quite round and kittenish as she sat before the fire in a rare moment of leisure, with her black paws tucked under her white breast and her sleek back looking as if it caught flickers of firelight in some yellow streaks among the shiny black fur. But when she walked abroad she stretched out long and thin like a little tiger, and held her head high to look over the grass as if she were threading the jungle. She lashed her tail to and fro, and one turned out of her way instantly. You opened a door for her if she crossed the room and gave you a look. She made you know what she meant as if she had the gift of speech: at most inconvenient moments you would go out through the house to find her a bit of fish or to open the cellar door. You recognized her right to appear at night on your bed with one of her long-suffering kittens, which she had brought in the rain, out of a cellar window and up a lofty ladder over the wet, steep roofs and down through a scuttle into the garret, and still down into warm shelter. Here she would leave it and with one or

10

Comrades, by Pruett Share.

two loud, admonishing purrs would scurry away upon some errand that must have been like one of the border frays of old.

She used to treat Joe, the dog, with sad cruelty, giving him a sharp blow on his honest nose that made him meekly stand back and see her add his supper to her own. A child visitor once rightly complained that Polly had pins in her toes, and nobody knew this better than poor Joe. At last, in despair, he sought revenge. I was writing at my desk one day, when he suddenly appeared, grinning in a funny way he had, and wagging his tail, until he enticed me out to the kitchen. There I found Polly, who had an air of calling everything in the house her own. She was on the cook's table, gobbling away at some chickens which were being made ready for the oven and had been left unguarded. I caught her and cuffed her, and she fled through the garden door, for once tamed and vanquished, though usually she was so quick that nobody could administer justice upon these depredations of a well-fed cat. Then I turned and saw poor old Joe dancing about the kitchen in perfect delight. He had been afraid to touch Polly himself, but he knew the difference between right and wrong, and had called me to see what a wicked cat she was, and to give him the joy of looking on at the flogging.

It was the same dog who used sometimes to be found under a table where his master had sent him for punishment in his young days of lawless puppyhood for chasing the neighbor's chickens. These faults had long been overcome, but sometimes, in later years, Joe's conscience would trouble him, we never knew why, and he would go under the table of his own accord, and look repentant and crestfallen until some forgiving and sympathetic friend would think he had suffered enough and bid him come out to be patted and consoled.

After such a house-mate as Polly, Joe had great amends in our next cat, yellow Danny, the most amiable and friendly pussy that ever walked on four paws. He took Danny to his heart at once: they used to lie in the sun together with Danny's head on the dog's big paws, and I sometimes used to meet them walking as coy as

12

lovers, side by side, up one of the garden walks. When I could not help laughing at their sentimental and conscious air, they would turn aside into the bushes for shelter. They respected each other's suppers, and ate together on the kitchen hearth, and took great comfort in close companionship. Danny always answered if you spoke to him, but he made no sound while always opening his mouth wide to mew whenever he had anything to say, and looking up into your face with all his heart expressed. These affectations of speech were most amusing, especially in so large a person as yellow Danny. He was much beloved by me and by all his family, especially poor Joe, who must sometimes have had the worst of dreams about old Polly, and her sharp, unsparing claws.

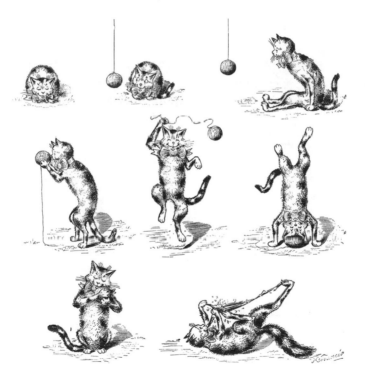

Drawings by Joseph G. Francis of Brookline, a stockbroker of the last century. He developed the "Francis Cat" to delight his Bostonian friends. His inimitable cats became world-famous.

THE SIN OF MADAME PHLOI

Lilian Jackson Braun

One of the favorite Siamese cats of our acquaintance is called simply "Madame." In many ways, that is the only name that any female Siamese requires. Her very attitude demands respect and a certain restraint to familiarity.

Lilian Jackson Braun is the most famous writer to combine cat and mystery; her Madame Phloi made a name for herself in a handful of memorable stories.

From the very beginning Madame Phloi felt an instinctive distaste for the man who moved into the apartment next door. He was fat, and his trouser cuffs had the unsavory odor of fire hydrant.

They met for the first time in the decrepit elevator as it lurched up to the tenth floor of the old building, once fashionable but now coming apart at the seams. Madame Phloi had been out for a stroll in the city park, chewing city grass and chasing faded butterflies, and as she and her companion stepped on the elevator for the slow ride upward, the car was already half filled with the new neighbor.

The fat man and the Madame presented a contrast that was not

*Nineteenth-century engraving, artist unknown. We do know,
however, that one cat was called Cupid and the other, Bess.*

unusual in this apartment house, which had a brilliant past and
no future. He was bulky, uncouth, sloppily attired. Madame Phloi
was a long-legged, blue-eyed aristocrat whose creamy fawn coat
shaded into brown at the extremities.

The Madame deplored fat men. They had no laps, and of what
use is a lapless human? Nevertheless, she gave him the common
courtesy of a sniff at his trouser cuffs and immediately backed away,
twitching her nose and breathing through the mouth.

"*GET* that cat away from me," the fat man roared, stamping his
feet thunderously at Madame Phloi. Her companion pulled on the
leash, although there was no need—the Madame with one backward
leap had retreated to a safe corner of the elevator, which shuddered
and continued its groaning ascent.

"Don't you like animals?" asked the gentle voice at the other
end of the leash.

15

"Filthy, sneaky beasts," the fat man said with a snarl. "Last place I lived, some lousy cat got in my room and et my parakeet."

"I'm sorry to hear that. Very sorry. But you don't need to worry about Madame Phloi and Thapthim. They never leave the apartment except on a leash."

"You got *TWO*? That's just fine, that is! Keep 'em away from me, or I'll break their rotten necks. I ain't wrung a cat's neck since I was fourteen, but I remember how."

And with the long black box he was carrying, the fat man lunged at the impeccable Madame Phloi, who sat in her corner, flat-eared and tense. Her fur bristled, and she tried to dart away. Even when her companion picked her up in protective arms, Madame Phloi's body was taut and trembling.

Not until she was safely home in her modest but well-cushioned apartment did she relax. She walked stiff-legged to the sunny spot on the carpet where Thapthim was sleeping and licked the top of his head. Then she had a complete bath herself—to rid her coat of the fat man's odor. Thapthim did not wake.

This drowsy, unambitious, amiable creature—her son—was a puzzle to Madame Phloi, who was sensitive and spirited herself. She didn't try to understand him; she merely loved him. She spent hours washing his paws and breast and other parts he could easily have reached with his own tongue. At dinnertime she chewed slowly so there would be something left on her plate for his dessert, and he always gobbled the extra portion hungrily. And when he slept, which was most of the time, she kept watch by his side, sitting with a tall, regal posture until she swayed with weariness. Then she made herself into a small bundle and dozed with one eye open.

Thapthim was lovable, to be sure. He appealed to other cats, large and small dogs, people, and even ailurophobes in a limited way. He had a face like a beautiful flower and large blue eyes, tender and trusting. Ever since he was a kitten, he had been willing to purr at the touch of a hand—any hand. Eventually he became so agreeable that he purred if anyone looked at him across the room. What's more, he came when called; he gratefully devoured whatever

16

was served on his dinner plate; and when he was told to get down, he got down.

His wise parent disapproved this uncatly conduct; it indicated a certain lack of character, and no good would come of it. By her own example she tried to guide him. When dinner was served, she gave the plate a haughty sniff and walked away, no matter how tempting the dish. That was the way it was done by any self-respecting feline. In a minute or two she returned and condescended to dine, but never with open enthusiasm.

Furthermore, when human hands reached out, the catly thing was to bound away, lead them a chase, flirt a little before allowing oneself to be caught and cuddled. Thapthim, sorry to say, greeted any friendly overture by rolling over, purring and looking soulful.

From an early age he had known the rules of the apartment:

No sleeping in a cupboard with the pots and pans.
Sitting on the table with the inkwell is permissible.
Sitting on the table with the coffeepot is never allowed.

The sad truth was that Thapthim obeyed these rules. Madame Phloi, on the other hand, knew that a rule was a challenge, and it was a matter of integrity to violate it. To obey was to sacrifice one's dignity. . . . It seemed that her son would never learn the true values in life.

To be sure, Thapthim was adored for his good nature in the human world of inkwells and coffeepots. But Madame Phloi was equally adored—and for the correct reasons. She was respected for her independence, admired for her clever methods of getting her own way, and loved for the cowlick on her white breast, the kink in her tail, and the squint in her delphinium-blue eyes. She was more truly Siamese than her son. Her face was small and perky. By cocking her head and staring with heart-melting eyes, slightly crossed, she could charm a porterhouse steak out from under a knife and fork.

Until the fat man and his black box moved in next door, Madame

17

Phloi had never known an unfriendly soul. She had two companions in her tenth-floor apartment—genial creatures without names who came and went a good deal. One was an easy mark for between-meal snacks; a tap on his ankle always produced a spoonful of cottage cheese. The other served as a hot-water bottle on cold nights and punctually obliged whenever the Madame wished to have her underside stroked or her cheekbones massaged. This second one also murmured compliments in a gentle voice that made one squeeze one's eyes in pleasure.

Life was not all love and cottage cheese, however. Madame Phloi had her regular work. She was official watcher and listener for the household.

There were six windows that needed watching, for a wide ledge ran around the building flush with the tenth-floor window sills, and this was a promenade for pigeons. They strutted, searched their feathers, and ignored the Madame, who sat on the sill and watched them dispassionately but thoroughly through the window screen.

While watching was a daytime job, listening was done after dark and required greater concentration. Madame Phloi listened for noises in the walls. She heard termites chewing, pipes sweating, and sometimes the ancient plaster cracking; but mostly she listened to the ghosts of generations of deceased mice.

One evening, shortly after the incident in the elevator, Madame Phloi was listening, Thapthim was asleep, and the other two were quietly turning pages of books, when a strange and horrendous sound came from the wall. The Madame's ears flicked to attention, then flattened against her head.

An interminable screech was coming out of that wall, like nothing the Madame had ever heard before. It chilled the blood and tortured the eardrums. So painful was the shrillness that Madame Phloi threw back her head and complained with a piercing howl of her own. The strident din even waked Thapthim. He looked about in alarm, shook his head wildly, and clawed at his ears to get rid of the offending noise.

The others heard it, too.

"Listen to that!" said the one with the gentle voice.

"It must be that new man next door," said the other. "It's incredible."

"I can't imagine anyone so crude producing anything so exquisite. Is it Prokofieff he's playing?"

"No, I think it's Bartók."

"He was carrying his violin in the elevator today. He tried to hit Phloi with it."

"He's a nut. . . . Look at the cats—apparently they don't care for violin."

Madame Phloi and Thapthim, bounding from the room, collided with each other as they rushed to hide under the bed.

That was not the only kind of noise which emanated from the adjoining apartment in those upsetting days after the fat man moved in. The following evening, when Madame Phloi walked into the living room to commence her listening, she heard a fluttering sound dimly through the wall, accompanied by highly conversational chirping. This was agreeable music, and she settled down on the sofa to enjoy it, tucking her brown paws neatly under her creamy body.

Her contentment was soon disturbed, however, when the fat man's voice burst through the wall like thunder.

"Look what you done, you dirty skunk!" he bellowed. "Right in my fiddle! Get back in your cage before I brain you."

There was a frantic beating of wings.

"*GET* down off that window, or I'll bash your head in."

This threat brought only a torrent of chirping.

"Shut up, you stupid cluck! Shut up and get back in that cage, or I'll. . . ."

There was a splintering crash, and after that all was quiet except for an occasional pitiful "Peep!"

Madame Phloi was fascinated. In fact, when she resumed her watching the next day, pigeons seemed rather insipid entertainment. She had waked the family that morning in her usual way— by staring intently at their foreheads as they slept. Then she and Thapthim had a game of hockey in the bathtub with a ping pong

19

ball, followed by a dish of mackerel, and after breakfast the Madame took up her post at the living-room window. Everyone had left for the day but not before opening the window and placing a small cushion on the chilly marble sill.

There she sat—Madame Phloi—a small but alert package of fur, sniffing the welcome summer air, seeing all, and knowing all. She knew, for example, that the person who was at that moment walking down the tenth-floor hallway, wearing old tennis shoes and limping slightly, would halt at the door of her apartment, set down his pail, and let himself in with a passkey.

Indeed, she hardly bothered to turn her head when the window washer entered. He was one of her regular court of admirers. His odor was friendly, although it suggested damp basements and floor mops, and he talked sensibly—indulging in none of that falsetto foolishness with which some people insulted the Madame's intelligence.

"Hop down, kitty," he said in a musical voice. "Charlie's gotta take out that screen. See, I brought you some cheese."

He held out a modest offering of rat cheese, and Madame Phloi investigated it. Unfortunately, it was the wrong variety, and she shook one fastidious paw at it.

"Mighty fussy cat," Charlie laughed. "Well, now, you set there and watch Charlie clean this here window. Don't you go jumpin' out on the ledge, because Charlie ain't runnin' after you. No sir! That old ledge, she's startin' to crumble. Some day them pigeons'll stamp their feet hard, and down she goes! . . . Hey, lookit the broken glass out here. Somebody busted a window."

Charlie sat on the marble sill and pulled the upper sash down in his lap, and while Madame Phloi followed his movements carefully, Thapthim sauntered into the room, yawning and stretching, and swallowed the cheese.

"Now Charlie puts the screen back in, and you two guys can watch them crazy pigeons some more. This screen, she's comin' apart, too. Whole buildin' seems to be crackin' up."

Remembering to replace the cushion on the cool, hard sill, he

20

then went on to clean the next window, and the Madame resumed her post, sitting on the very edge of the cushion so that Thapthim could have most of it.

The pigeons were late that morning, probably frightened away by the window washer. It was while Madame Phloi patiently waited for the first visitor to skim in on a blue-gray wing that she noticed the tiny opening in the screen. Every aperture, no matter how small, was a temptation; she had to prove she could wriggle through any tight space, whether there was a good reason or not.

She waited until Charlie had limped out of the apartment before she began pushing at the screen with her nose, first gingerly and then stubbornly. Inch by inch the rusted mesh ripped away from the frame until the whole corner formed a loose flap, and Madame Phloi slithered through—nose and ears, slender shoulders, dainty Queen Anne forefeet, svelte torso, lean flanks, hind legs like steel springs, and finally proud brown tail. For the first time in her life she found herself on the pigeon promenade. She gave a delicious shudder.

Inside the screen the lethargic Thapthim, jolted by this strange turn of affairs, watched his daring parent with a quarter inch of his pink tongue hanging out. They touched noses briefly through the screen, and the Madame proceeded to explore. She advanced cautiously and with mincing step, for the pigeons had not been tidy in their habits.

The ledge was about two feet wide. To its edge Madame Phloi moved warily, nose down and tail high. Ten stories below there were moving objects but nothing of interest, she decided. Walking daintily along the extreme edge to avoid the broken glass, she ventured in the direction of the fat man's apartment, impelled by some half-forgotten curiosity.

His window stood open and unscreened, and Madame Phloi peered in politely. There, sprawled on the floor, lay the fat man himself, snorting and heaving his immense paunch in a kind of rhythm. It always alarmed her to see a human on the floor, which she considered feline domain. She licked her nose apprehensively

21

and stared at him with enormous eyes, one iris hypnotically off-center. In a dark corner of the room something fluttered and squawked, and the fat man waked.

"SHcrrff! *GET* out of here!" he shouted, struggling to his feet.

In three leaps Madame Phloi crossed the ledge back to her own window and pushed through the screen to safety. Looking back to see if the fat man might be chasing her and being reassured that he wasn't, she washed Thapthim's ears and her own paws and sat down to wait for pigeons.

Like any normal cat, Madame Phloi lived by the Rule of Three. She resisted every innovation three times before accepting it, tackled an obstacle three times before giving up, and tried each new activity three times before tiring of it. Consequently she made two more sallies to the pigeon promenade and eventually convinced Thapthim to join her.

Together they peered over the edge at the world below. The sense of freedom was intoxicating. Recklessly Thapthim made a leap at a low-flying pigeon and landed on his mother's back. She cuffed his ear in retaliation. He poked her nose. They grappled and rolled over and over on the ledge, oblivious of the long drop below them, taking playful nips of each other's hide and snarling guttural expressions of glee.

Suddenly and instinctively Madame Phloi scrambled to her feet and crouched in a defensive position. The fat man was leaning from his window.

"Here, kitty, kitty," he was saying in one of those despised falsetto voices, offering some tidbit in a saucer. The Madame froze, but Thapthim turned his beautiful trusting eyes on the stranger and advanced along the ledge. Purring and waving his tail cordially, he walked into the trap. It all happened in a matter of seconds: the saucer was withdrawn, and a long black box was swung at Thapthim like a ball bat, sweeping him off the ledge and into space. He was silent as he fell.

When the family came home, laughing and chattering, with their arms full of packages, they knew at once something was amiss.

No one greeted them at the door. Madame Phloi hunched moodily on the window sill staring at a hole in the screen, and Thapthim was not to be found.

"Look at the screen!" cried the gentle voice.

"I'll bet he got out on the ledge."

"Can you lean out and look? Be careful."

"You hold Phloi."

"Do you see him?"

"Not a sign of him! There's a lot of glass scattered around, and the window's broken next door."

"Do you suppose that man . . . ? I feel sick."

"Don't worry, dear. We'll find him. . . . There's the doorbell! Maybe someone's bringing him home."

It was Charlie standing at the door. He fidgeted uncomfortably. " 'Scuse me, folks," he said. "You missin' one of your kitties?"

"Yes! Have you found him?"

"Poor little guy," said Charlie. "Found him lyin' right under your windows—where the bushes is thick."

"He's dead!" the gentle one moaned.

"Yes, ma'am. That's a long way down."

"Where is he now?"

"I got him down in the basement, ma'am. I'll take care of him real nice. I don't think you'd want to see the poor guy."

Still Madame Phloi stared at the hole in the screen and waited for Thapthim. From time to time she checked the other windows, just to be sure. As time passed and he did not return, she looked behind the radiators and under the bed. She pried open the cupboard door where the pots and pans were stored. She tried to burrow her way into the closet. She sniffed all around the front door. Finally she stood in the middle of the living room and called loudly in a high-pitched, wailing voice.

Later that evening Charlie paid another visit to the apartment.

"Only wanted to tell you, ma'am, how nice I took care of him," he said. "I got a box that was just the right size. A white box, it was. And I wrapped him up in a piece of old blue curtain. The color looked real pretty with his fur. And I buried the little guy right under your window behind the bushes."

And still the Madame searched, returning again and again to watch the ledge from which Thapthim had disappeared. She scorned food. She rebuffed any attempts at consolation. And all night she sat wide-eyed and waiting in the dark.

The living-room window was now tightly closed, but the following day the Madame—after she was left by herself in the lonely apartment—went to work on the bedroom screens. One was new and hopeless, but the second screen was slightly corroded, and she was soon nosing through a slit that lengthened as she struggled out onto the ledge.

Picking her way through the broken glass, she approached the spot where Thapthim had vanished. And then it all happened again. There he was—the fat man—reaching forth with a saucer.

"Here, kitty, kitty."

Madame Phloi hunched down and backed away.

"Kitty want some milk?" It was that ugly falsetto, but she didn't run home this time. She crouched there on the ledge, a few inches out of reach.

"Nice kitty. Nice kitty."

Madame Phloi crept with caution toward the saucer in the out-stretched fist, and stealthily the fat man extended another hand, snapping his fingers as one would call a dog.

The Madame retreated diagonally—half toward home and half toward the dangerous brink.

"Here, kitty. Here, kitty," he cooed, leaning farther out. But muttering, he said, "You dirty sneak! I'll get you if it's the last thing I ever do. Comin' after my bird, weren't you?"

Madame Phloi recognized danger with all her senses. Her ears went back, her whiskers curled, and her white underside hugged the ledge.

A little closer she moved, and the fat man made a grab for her. She jerked back a step, with unblinking eyes fixed on his sweating face. He was furtively laying the saucer aside, she noticed, and edging his fat paunch farther out the window.

Once more she advanced almost into his grasp, and again he lunged at her with both powerful arms.

The Madame leaped lightly aside.

"This time I'll get you, you stinkin' cat," he cried, and raising one knee to the window sill, he threw himself at Madame Phloi. As she slipped through his fingers, he landed on the ledge with all his weight.

A section of it crumbled beneath him. He bellowed, clutching at the air, and at the same time a streak of creamy brown flashed out of sight. The fat man was not silent as he fell.

As for Madame Phloi, she was found doubled in half in a patch of sunshine on her living-room carpet, innocently washing her fine brown tail.

The Cat by the Persea Tree Slaying the Serpent of Darkness,
from an ancient Egyptian papyrus. This was a common topic
for cat-worshipping Egyptians.

CAT'S COMPANY

Michael Joseph

Michael Joseph, one of Britain's most famous literary agents, went on to establish a publishing house that represented some of the greatest writers of the twentieth century. He knew intimately many writers and their cats. He had been introduced at times to the famous cats owned by Algernon Blackwood, May Sinclair, Violet Hunt, Elinor Mordaunt, Henry James, William Lyon Phelps, and the poet Edith Sitwell, whose own cat, "the most beautiful cat in the world," corresponded with Michael Joseph's coterie of cats.

I have rarely been without a cat. Even in France during the war I contrived to keep a cat most of the time. One of my trench pets was a jolly black and white kitten, christened Scissors by the mess cook, whose company he regularly patronised. Scissors, whose glossy black fur was ornamented by a neat white waistcoat, was a great favourite and knew his way about the whole of the sector. He used to follow us up the poppy-lined communication trenches and along the front line. Only a narrow strip of No-man's-land separated us there from the German front line and Scissors had a playful but dangerous habit of leaping gracefully on to the parapet and picking his way delicately along the broken ground, through the wire and over the massed sandbags, keeping pace with my orderly and myself as we made our cautious way below along the zig-zag of the front line. It must have been perfectly obvious to "the enemy" that Scissors was accompanying his officer on his morning round—indeed, one fine August morning we distinctly heard a laugh and a shout in guttural German from beyond the wire—but that part of the line was then known to both armies as "peaceful" and no sniper or bomb-thrower tried his skill on the furry target.

Scissors was wounded before we left the Arras sector by a stray fragment of shrapnel. It was, luckily, a flesh wound only, and when he got used to the little bandage I tied round his leg he became quite proud of it and displayed it to all and sundry; a habit which nearly got me into trouble with the Brigade Major, who, evidently disapproving of trench pets in general and bandaged kittens in particular, snorted at Scissors in an apoplectic kind of way which caused me great alarm. I knew that snort! I remember hastily asking a random question about gas masks (which happened to be his particular hobby) and the crisis passed.

Thanks chiefly to a lavish diet of bully beef, which he adored (to the derisive amusement of the men in my machine-gun section) Scissors grew fat and fast. But he never forsook his nightly habit of rat-hunting. Rats in their thousands infested the trenches and dug-outs and gave Scissors plenty of scope. That most of them were larger than Scissors did not in the least deter him. Scissors discovered early in his life that a cornered rat will show fight and he was bitten several times in his nightly encounters. I can see him now, as the flare of the Very lights used to reveal him, streaking along the trench boards in pursuit of a grey rat larger than himself. Scissors hunted for love of the chase; he never attempted to eat his victims. What sensible cat would, with unlimited bully beef at his disposal?

Poor Scissors! He was "missing" when the division moved to another part of the line, and there was no time to search for him. I have often wondered what became of him. Somehow I cannot picture him as a casualty. I prefer to believe that he made friends with one of the officers or men who relieved us, or that he wandered across No-man's-land into the German line. My batman was horrified, I remember, at the mere suggestion, but I never had any qualms. If Scissors could survive the wrath of our Brigade Major he was safe enough with the Bavarians across the way.

When I was invalided home from France I adopted a wistful-looking tabby—or rather she adopted me—and contrary to all the rules and regulations installed her in my hut in camp. For some obscure reason I can no longer remember she was called Lillywhite. Lillywhite (which my camp batman invariably abbreviated to Lilly) was a very intelligent cat. She understood perfectly well that cats were not officially allowed in army huts; and when, as occasionally happened, some senior officer made a tour of inspection of the officers' quarters—this usually occurred during our absence—Lillywhite would promptly disappear through the open top of the window and lie low until the sound of strange boots and spurs had died away. Beaver (my batman) was very proud of this accomplishment of Lillywhite's. "That's a knowing ca-at, sir," he used to say in his broad Lancashire accent.

Lillywhite was also adept at extracting condensed milk out of tins. A small hole punctured in the top of the tin sufficed for my purposes, and Lillywhite soon learned to roll the tin over, sometimes with disastrous results to blankets and boots, and cause a steady stream of thick, sticky juice to flow by pressure of paws on the side of the tin. Beaver was always catching her at it. But then he used to call her by more names than "knowing ca-at."

It was Lillywhite's insatiable appetite that eventually separated us. To be truthful, she deserted me in favour of the sergeants' mess close by, and although she sometimes condescended to pay me a visit, always looking hungry and wistful (how deceptive was the hussy's appearance!—she traded on it, I am sure), our relationship was not the same. I have always attributed her desertion to the bits of raw rabbit for which she rapidly acquired a taste at the door of the sergeants' mess.

*The Curious Cat, by the English painter and illustrator Harrison Weir
(1824–1906)*

For some months after the war I was without a cat of my own. This sad state of affairs was remedied as soon as I was able to find a London flat which permitted a cat—or cats—(the plural is justified as you will presently realise) to share my tenancy. As it turned out, the flat was as ideal for cats as it was thoroughly uncomfortable for humans. It was situated on an invisible line which separated a fashionable neighbourhood from a—well, unfashionable is a charitable description of the slum which lay to the east of the house. It was an old, queer building, and the uncomfortable peculiarity of my flat was that all the rooms led from one to the other in a straight line. Outside there was a narrow strip of "garden," in which nothing ever grew on account of a high brick wall which successfully obscured the sun. This "garden" came to be called the "Strut" and a happy playground it proved to be for Dudley and the Dudley family.

Dudley, a present to me from my favourite aunt, was a little ball of orange fluff, with tiny white paws and a pedigree as long as Piccadilly, which was lost in the post. Under the mistaken impression that she was a gentleman cat, I christened her Dudley, on account of her aristocratic manners. But it presently became manifest that Dudley was no gentleman. And so, like Dickens, whose cat William was rechristened Williamina, we had to call her Lady Dudley. That is to say, we made valiant but futile efforts to give her the additional title, for after a week or so the household reverted to Dudley with the occasional variation of Dudley-Duff.

From the days of her kittenhood it was plain that she would grow into a distinguished cat. On the small side, she was lithe and graceful as a young panther, and correspondingly strong, as many a neighbouring cat and dog subsequently discovered.

The "Strut" captured her fancy from the first. As soon as she was old enough to compass the distance she would spring gracefully through the air from the kitchen window-sill on to the top of the brick wall and there sit sunning herself in splendid isolation. Her tenancy of the wall was, however, promptly disputed by an old grey patriarch of a cat who appeared one morning and stalked along the top of the wall, fur bristling, towards the immobile Dudley.

30

I happened to be looking out of my bedroom window and thus had an excellent view of the subsequent proceedings. The weather-beaten grey was clearly a veteran. One ear was decidedly smaller, and unnaturally so, than the other; and his fur bore unmistakable traces of recent combat. Dudley, on the other hand, apart from a doorstep skirmish or two, was an untried recruit. There was no time for me to go to her rescue, for the battle began almost instantly. And Dudley began it.

Without warning she advanced swiftly to the attack. Her paw flashed out with lightning speed and an infuriated gasp from the old grey paid tribute to the accuracy of her aim. Instantly following up this advantage with a whirlwind onslaught—all I saw was a streak of orange launch itself at the intruder—she gave the grey no time to recover. Spitting rage, he lost his balance and slithered off the wall down to the flower-beds on the other side. Dudley looked serenely in my direction, resumed her former position in the most sun-favoured place on the wall, idly licked her paws and—dozed off to sleep!

That was the beginning of Dudley's fighting career. She was not a quarrelsome cat and never, to my knowledge, fought except to defend herself or her kittens, but when she did have occasion to fight she made a thorough job of it. In the house she was always good-tempered to the point of being placid and used to let the babies play with her as they liked—and everyone knows that no self-respecting human baby can resist a pussycat's tail.

Dudley was an uncommonly intelligent cat. She was voiceless except for a very faint squeak which she managed to produce if really agitated about something. This inability to "miaow" had its practical disadvantages. For instance, she could not audibly attract attention if she were by chance locked out. But she soon learned how to gain admittance.

As I have said, the rooms in my flat led from one to the other, the sequence being drawing-room, dining-room, then a sort of ante-room into which a bathroom had been built, kitchen, bed-room, dressing-room, bedroom. All these rooms, except the bath-room, had windows looking out on to the "Strut." If, as frequently

31

happened, Dudley came home late and found the door shut she would jump on to each window-sill in turn, until she came to the room I was in. Then, sitting upright, she would beat a tattoo on the window pane *with her outstretched claws*. She knew that the thump of a padded paw was not enough. Almost invariably she chose the room I was in, but if I happened to be out, she went on a tour of investigation, finally tapping at the window most likely to be opened for her. Most of my servants have been fond of cats (they have to be!) and Dudley usually had no difficulty in getting in *via* the kitchen, but she never patronised the kitchen window if she disapproved, as she sometimes did, of its occupants.

The bathroom had two doors, one leading into the little ante-room which separated it from the main passage of the flat and another which opened on to the "Strut." This outside door was usually bolted on the inside but in the summer it was often left open or merely latched. Dudley soon learned that if the latch were pressed down, the door would open: that is, if it were not bolted on the inside. It was difficult for her to manipulate the latch because it was just out of her reach when she stood upright and the nearest window-sill was too far away to enable her to operate it from a higher level. So she had to jump up at it. To make it more compli-cated, there were two or three stone steps outside the door; which meant that she had to take a standing jump from the narrow top step. But I never saw her miss her aim. Invariably her small white paw fell neatly on the lever and depressed it. When the door was bolted this naturally had no effect and Dudley appeared to under-stand perfectly that no amount of playing with the latch would open the door, for she would always give it up immediately as a bad job.

Dudley was an undemonstrative cat. Most people she ignored completely. How I remember her look of disdain and the haughty tilt of her head if well-meaning strangers affronted her, however coaxingly, with the words "Puss, puss!" When food was in the offing she answered a call immediately but she rarely answered to her name on other occasions. Most decidedly she was not a sociable

32

cat. If she wanted to go out (and she often did) she would ask to be released, but made it clear she was not asking favours. She just demanded that doors or windows should be opened and if by chance anyone delayed her she would frown (it is the only word that describes her expression) and lash her tail with ladylike annoyance. But she never lost her temper. That would not have been *comme il faut* for a well-bred cat.

I should like to be able to say that Dudley reserved all her love for me. Actually, I had very little of it. She displayed signs of affection for other members of the family when she was in the mood but I was seldom favoured. Her attitude towards me was one of gentle toleration. She may have loved me. I wonder. . . .

One of her few friends was an old man who had a wooden leg and sold matches. His "pitch" was near the house and Dudley used often to visit him. This old man, who was by way of being a friend of mine, used to stand by a brick wall beside a wired-in window, underneath which was a narrow ledge. On this he laid out in cardboard trays his stock of matches, shoe-laces and studs. Dudley was not a pavement cat (when she had to walk along it I was always reminded of a lady of fashion picking her way fastidiously through a common market-place) and she soon took to installing herself on the ledge, the old man considerately moving his stock to make room for her. There she would sit for hours, looking out over her friend's shoulder at the passers-by. In this way she became a well-known local character and was familiarly greeted as "Ginger" by small boys.

Talking to the old man one day, I discovered Dudley's lapse from gentility. He told me that punctually every Saturday night Dudley presented herself on his ledge. He admitted with engaging candour that he was particularly glad to see her then, for it was the busiest night of the week and Dudley improved his "custom." People, he said, would often spend a copper or two because of the cat. The reason for Dudley's Saturday-night appearances, however, was not altruistic. The old man went on to tell me that every Saturday night the "girls" and "lads" bought fried fish at the fish-

and-chips shop round the corner, and as by the time they passed his place of business the first edge of their appetite had worn off it had become customary for one or two of the more generously disposed to offer Dudley a piece of fish. Lady Dudley eating fried fish on a Saturday night! She, who would turn up her patrician nose at home if breast of chicken were not to her liking! It was her one fall from grace.

The old man refused to call her Dudley. He obviously thought I was a little wrong in the head to have given so queer a name to a cat who patently had to be called Ginger. To the uninitiated—and especially the low-born Londoner—all orange cats are "ginger." I have heard them referred to as yellow cats and sandy cats and marmalade cats by superior persons, but the voice of the people proclaims them ginger.

When we left the flat Dudley did not forget her friend of the wooden leg. Or it may have been the lure of the fried fish! At any rate she used to visit him at irregular intervals. The first time she appeared he packed up his stock and stumped all the way to my new house about a mile away, carrying her in his arms. He was afraid she had lost her way, and refused to accept any reward. I think he was as fond of Dudley as she was of him.

When Dudley had kittens she surprised me by proving herself a devoted mother. Her supercilious manner at once disappeared. She purred contentedly most of the day and was as proud of her babies as any ordinary cat might be. Indeed, she became almost human. (I mean that figuratively.) For so independent and reserved a cat her devotion to her kittens was remarkable. She never tired of displaying them for our approval. Dudley was a great success as a mother and evidently enjoyed the experience, to judge by the frequent regularity with which she subsequently repeated it.

Her kittens were much admired. Dudley herself was more aristocratic-looking than beautiful, but her offspring, while they inherited their mother's quality, were for the most part uncommonly attractive. Ginnaboi, one of my best-loved cats, was her first-born. Minna Minna Mowbray came much later. Meestah and a kitten who was christened "The Wu" for some odd reason completed the first litter.

"The Wu" was an odd cat for whom I had no special liking. He was tortoiseshell and white with a long tail and no manners. He was greedy and very vain. Meestah was a beauty, with a soft, curiously marked bronze coat and the most placid of tempers. If she was not especially intelligent she made up for it by excessive affection, which was a welcome contrast to Dudley's detachment.

Ginnaboi was my favourite. He was a half-Persian orange, handsome and most lovable. From his kitten days he seemed to realise that I had singled him out for affection and his response was as eager as it was gratifying. With the exception of my Siamese, Charles O'Malley, he was the only cat I have ever had who followed me about, jumped on my knee when I sat down, curled up under the eiderdown on my bed and came regularly to greet me when I opened the front door. I could not have resisted his blandishments if I had wanted to.

His favourite position was lying half-asleep on my chest. I encouraged him to do this when he was a kitten, and he never forsook the habit. He used to lie facing me, his eyes blinking lazily out of his doze and his claws gently thrusting in and out of my dressing-gown. This claw-exercising habit, common to most cats when they are pleased, we used to call "carding." It was hard on my dressing-gown but I did not mind.

Ginnaboi's fur was long and I regret to say he did not take care of it. In truth, he was a lazy cat, although I liked him none the less for that. He cleaned himself irregularly and never thoroughly. His sister Meestah—they were devoted to each other—used to wash him even when he was grown up and ought to have known better. He thoroughly approved of this proceeding and made no bones about letting Meestah perform his toilet. It was a sad day for Ginnaboi when Meestah in her turn had kittens, for then he had shamefacedly to attend to his own ablutions.

It was soon after this that his coat became matted. I had been away from home and was horrified on my return to find Ginnaboi

35

looking more like a sweep than a self-respecting cat. He was so delighted to see me again that I could not scold him. Instead, I took him out into the "Strut" for a good brushing to begin with. Then I discovered the condition of his fur. Every day for a week I spent at least an hour patiently unravelling his matted fur with a comb. It was in such a bad state that the more difficult lumps had to be cut with scissors. Throughout the proceedings Ginnaboi lay placidly on his back, purring with pleasure. Yet he strongly disliked other people even stroking him.

Although majestically beautiful, he was a delicate and particularly sensitive cat. He had no use for strangers and shrank from their attempts to caress him. With his magnificent ruff, big amber eyes, curving white whiskers, and huge plume of a tail which matched his long, vividly orange coat in its richness of colour, he was a strikingly handsome cat. In Dudley's presence he always behaved like a shy, awkward and overgrown boy and it was amusing to watch him with his mother. She looked on him as a big booby, which by her exacting standards I dare say he was. He carefully avoided other tom cats after he had disgracefully been put to flight by an aggressive tabby neighbour much smaller than himself. I am sure that Dudley regarded his conduct as a blot on the otherwise honourable family escutcheon.

As cats go, Ginnaboi was neither brave nor intelligent. He liked food and sleeping in the sun above all things. He inherited from Dudley a fastidious palate, would not eat unless he were really hungry, refused milk unless it were warmed for him, caught neither mice nor birds (his jaw instinctively moved at the sight of a bird but, so far as I know, he never made an attempt to catch one) and rejected such feline luxuries as cream and cod's head.

I used sometimes to tease him, and he hated it. If I made fun of his furry "trousers" when his back was turned he never failed to pretend annoyance by turning round and sweeping his bushy tail from side to side. I can see him now, his blunt little nose wrinkled and his eyes blinking at me with the pretence of displeasure. He was a lovable cat and my best friend in those days.

36

I remember Pansy, one of Dudley's later kittens, particularly well because of a rather amusing episode. Pansy was a brightly coloured tortoiseshell of mischievous disposition who disorganised the whole household by staying out at night when she was little more than a kitten. Where she went I shall never know, but it must have been a place where dirt abounded. It was a very dirty and bedraggled Pansy who was found on the doorstep with the early morning milk. Dudley strongly disapproved of the bad company and late hours her daughter was keeping and scolded her in the best maternal tradition. But Pansy took no notice and went to sleep off the effect of her dissipations.

But one morning Pansy did not return. The day went by without any sign of the truant. There was consternation in the house, for Pansy was a great favourite. The next morning we were still Pansy-less. So I hurried round to a printer's and ordered a quantity of those bills headed by "10/– Reward" in heavy, black type. I described Pansy in detail. The printer kept his word and delivered the leaflets that evening, when I hastily proceeded to paste them up in every possible place in the neighbourhood.

We did not have to wait long for results. Late that night there was a peal at the bell. Going to the door myself, I was confronted by a very dirty urchin whom the prospect of earning ten shillings had apparently reduced to incoherence. But it transpired he was out of breath, having run all the way to the house from the timber-yard where he had seen the truant Pansy. I did not wait to get my hat or explain where I was going but set out at once with my small escort, who informed me I would have to hurry or the night watchman might be asleep and unable to let us in. "He allus goes to sleep 'bout this time," said the dirty small boy. "Too much beer, that's wot it is."

I will draw a veil, as the old-fashioned novelists used to say, over the rest of the evening's performance, or rather I will confine myself to the bare facts. The night watchman was surly and succumbed only to liberal largesse. I bruised my shins in several places stumbling over piles of wood in the dark: and the small boy angrily accused me of not knowing my own cat when we eventually discovered a mangy tabby coiled up asleep on top of a stack of timber.

The next morning the fun began. Writing in retrospect I use the word "fun," but it was not so funny at the time. I have already mentioned our proximity to a slum neighbourhood. From this quarter emerged, at intervals, a procession of dirty and expectant children, carrying cats alleged to tally with the description of Pansy. Dazzled by the prospect of ten whole shillings reward, the entire youthful population had, it seemed, organised themselves into search parties for the missing cat (it was holiday time) and any unfortunate animal bearing the slightest resemblance to my lost Pansy was forthwith seized and dragged to our doorstep.

It was only at the end of a day spent for the most part in opening the front door and repudiating the cats submitted that I realised my mistake. The first arrival had no doubt been genuinely mistaken for Pansy and the youngster who brought the animal was so disappointed that I had naturally rewarded him for his trouble. I also distributed largesse—in decreasing amounts—to those who followed. It was only when I finally lost patience and stopped the donations that the appearance of strange cats on my doorstep significantly ceased.

As for Pansy, she turned up a few days later of her own accord, so filthy as to be almost unrecognisable and with a far-away look in her eye which I will not attempt to interpret. After several other temporary disappearances, to which we soon became accustomed, she finally deserted us. We charitably put it down to wanderlust.

Dudley, as I have observed, was a glutton for motherhood. The kittens which disappeared and were presented to our friends were speedily replaced by new arrivals. We could not keep pace with Dudley's output and it was not long before the kitten problem became acute.

When the cat family totalled fourteen my wife, abetted by my mother-in-law, insisted that something should be done about it. At about this time I met that great friend of cats, Mr. Louis Wain, who told me that he housed over forty! In vain I pointed this out to my wife. She repeated firmly that something must be done.

By this time kittens had been supplied to all the people we knew who wanted them. At best I could only hope to dispose of kittens singly and at intervals, and meanwhile the said kittens were growing up. Some of them at least would have families of their own

Drawing by the French artist
Paul Audra, Paris, 1888.

by the time new homes had been found for them. We were in a vicious circle, with the supply always overtaking the demand.

Then, one day, passing through one of the big department stores, I chanced to stop by the Animal Department. It suddenly occurred to me that here might be an opening for kittens in wholesale quantities. I made discreet enquiries, hurried home, commandeered the baby's pram (my wife being out) and sent off half a dozen. It took me a long time to pick them out, not so much because I had to choose them impartially and with due regard to maternal requirements, but because I simply hated to let them go.

When the pram returned empty I was both relieved and disappointed. The woman in the Animal Department had welcomed them, I gathered, their stock of kittens being low. But in future would I please supply more gentleman kittens than ladies. In future! I thought it advisable to wait a week or so before sending the second batch. With one exception, a rather less beautiful female for whom I luckily found another home, these were also accepted and I was able to look my wife and mother-in-law in the face again. I may perhaps add that, for some illogical feminine reason, I was regarded as personally responsible for the enlargement of our cat family. When I announced the successful disposal of the surplus kittens my mother-in-law (of whom I was really very fond) had a look in her eye which plainly said, "I'm glad you've realised your responsibilities."

Apparently the store could absorb as many kittens as we could produce, provided they continued to be good-looking specimens. It had not occurred to me to ask payment for them; all I wanted was an assurance that they would find their way into comfortable homes. However, about a month later I received a cheque for a sum which agreeably surprised me: and I could not resist flourishing this before my wife and her mother as tangible evidence of the quality of my cats, with a slight emphasis on the word "my." The cheque was followed a few months later by a printed post-card, requesting me to render my semi-annual account (or something of the kind). To my amusement, it was solemnly addressed to Mr. Michael Joseph, Cat Breeder!

THE PHILANTHROPIST AND THE HAPPY CAT

Saki

H. H. Munro, who wrote under the name of Saki, befriended his first cat while he was still a boy. His childhood had been dominated by aunts whom he described as bellowing, prehistoric creatures. Infinitely more sophisticated were his cats, which inspired much of his later writing.

Jocantha Bessbury was in the mood to be serenely and graciously happy. Her world was a pleasant place, and it was wearing one of its pleasantest aspects. Gregory had managed to get home for a hurried lunch and a smoke afterwards in the little snuggery; the lunch had been a good one, and there was just time to do justice to the coffee and cigarettes. Both were excellent in their way, and Gregory was, in his way, an excellent husband. Jocantha rather suspected herself of making him a very charming wife, and more than suspected herself of having a first-rate dressmaker.

"I don't suppose a more thoroughly contented personality is to be found in all Chelsea," observed Jocantha in allusion to herself; "except perhaps Attab," she continued, glancing towards the large tabby-marked cat that lay in considerable ease in a corner of the

41

divan. "He lies there, purring and dreaming, shifting his limbs now and then in an ecstasy of cushioned comfort. He seems the incarnation of everything soft and silky and velvety, without a sharp edge in his composition, a dreamer whose philosophy is sleep and let sleep; and then, as evening draws on, he goes out into the garden with a red glint in his eyes and slays a drowsy sparrow."

"As every pair of sparrows hatches out ten or more young ones in the year, while their food supply remains stationary, it is just as well that the Attabs of the community should have that idea of how to pass an amusing afternoon," said Gregory. Having delivered himself of this sage comment he lit another cigarette, bade Jocantha a playfully affectionate good-bye, and departed into the outer world.

"Remember, dinner's a wee bit earlier tonight, as we're going to the Haymarket," she called after him.

Left to herself, Jocantha continued the process of looking at her life with placid, introspective eyes. If she had not everything she wanted in this world, at least she was very well pleased with what she had got. She was very well pleased, for instance, with the snuggery, which contrived somehow to be cozy and dainty and expensive all at once. The porcelain was rare and beautiful, the Chinese enamels took on wonderful tints in the firelight, the rugs and hangings led the eye through sumptuous harmonies of colouring. It was a room in which one might have suitably entertained an ambassador or an archbishop, but it was also a room in which one could cut out pictures for a scrap-book without feeling that one was scandalizing the deities of the place with one's litter. And as with the snuggery, so with the rest of the house, and as with the house, so with the other departments of Jocantha's life; she really had good reason for being one of the most contented women in Chelsea.

From being in a mood of simmering satisfaction with her lot she passed to the phase of being generously commiserating for those thousands around her whose lives and circumstances were dull, cheap, pleasureless, and empty. Work girls, shop assistants and so forth, the class that have neither the happy-go-lucky freedom of

One of the charming cats by Laura Elizabeth Richards, the daughter of Julia Ward Howe (1819–1910), author and leader of the women's suffrage movement.

the poor nor the leisured freedom of the rich, came specially within the range of her sympathy. It was sad to think that there were young people who, after a long day's work, had to sit alone in chill, dreary bedrooms because they could not afford the price of a cup of coffee and a sandwich in a restaurant, still less a shilling for a theatre gallery.

Jocantha's mind was still dwelling on this theme when she started forth on an afternoon campaign of desultory shopping; it would be rather a comforting thing, she told herself, if she could do something, on the spur of the moment, to bring a gleam of pleasure and interest into the life of even one or two wistful-hearted, empty-pocketed workers; it would add a good deal to her sense of enjoyment at the theatre that night. She would get two upper circle tickets for a popular play, make her way into some cheap tea-shop, and present the tickets to the first couple of interesting work girls with whom she could casually drop into conversation. She could explain matters by saying that she was unable to use the tickets herself and did not want them to be wasted, and, on the other hand, did not want the trouble of sending them back. On further reflection she decided that it might be better to get only one ticket and give it to some lonely-looking girl sitting eating her frugal meal by herself; the girl might scrape acquaintance with her next-seat neighbour at the theatre and lay the foundations of a lasting friendship.

With the Fairy Godmother impulse strong upon her, Jocantha marched into a ticket agency and selected with immense care an upper circle seat for the "Yellow Peacock," a play that was attracting a considerable amount of discussion and criticism. Then she went forth in search of a tea-shop and philanthropic adventure, at about the same time that Attab sauntered into the garden with a mind attuned to sparrow stalking. In a corner of an A.B.C. shop she found an unoccupied table, whereat she promptly installed herself, impelled by the fact that at the next table was sitting a young girl, rather plain of feature, with tired, listless eyes and a general air of uncomplaining forlornness. Her dress was of poor material, but

44

aimed at being in the fashion, her hair was pretty, and her complexion bad; she was finishing a modest meal of tea and scone, and she was not very different in her way from thousands of other girls who were finishing, or beginning, or continuing their teas in London tea-shops at that exact moment. The odds were enormously in favour of the supposition that she had never seen the "Yellow Peacock"; obviously she supplied excellent material for Jocantha's first experiment in haphazard benefaction.

Jocantha ordered some tea and a muffin, and then turned a friendly scrutiny on her neighbour with a view to catching her eye. At that precise moment the girl's face lit up with sudden pleasure, her eyes sparkled, a flush came into her cheeks, and she looked almost pretty. A young man, whom she greeted with an affectionate "Hullo, Bertie," came up to her table and took his seat in a chair facing her. Jocantha looked hard at the new-comer; he was in appearance a few years younger than herself, very much better looking than Gregory, rather better looking, in fact, than any of the young men of her set. She guessed him to be a well-mannered young clerk in some wholesale warehouse, existing and amusing himself as best he might on a tiny salary, and commanding a holiday of about two weeks in the year. He was aware, of course, of his good looks, but with shy self-consciousness, not blatant complacency. He was obviously on terms of friendly intimacy with the girl he was talking to, probably they were drifting towards a formal engagement. Jocantha pictured the boy's home, in a rather narrow circle, with a tiresome mother who always wanted to know how and where he spent his evenings. He would exchange that humdrum thraldom in due course for a home of his own, dominated by a chronic scarcity of pounds, shillings, and pence, and a dearth of most of the things that made life attractive or comfortable. Jocantha felt extremely sorry for him. She wondered if he had seen the "Yellow Peacock"; the odds were enormously in favour of the supposition that he had not. The girl had finished her tea, and would shortly be going back to her work; when the boy was alone it would be quite easy for Jocantha to say: "My husband

45

has made other arrangements for me this evening; would you care to make use of this ticket, which would otherwise be wasted?" Then she could come there again one afternoon for tea, and, if she saw him, ask him how he liked the play. If he was a nice boy and improved on acquaintance he could be given more theatre tickets and perhaps asked to come one Sunday to tea at Chelsea. Jocantha made up her mind that he would improve on acquaintance, and that Gregory would like him, and that the Fairy God-mother business would prove far more entertaining than she had originally anticipated. The boy was distinctly presentable; he knew how to brush his hair, which was possibly an imitative faculty; he knew what colour of tie suited him, which might be intuition; he was exactly the type that Jocantha admired, which of course was accident. Altogether she was rather pleased when the girl looked at the clock and bade a friendly but hurried farewell to her companion. Bertie nodded "good-bye," gulped down a mouthful of tea, and then produced from his overcoat pocket a paper-covered book, bearing the title *Sepoy and Sahib, a Tale of the Great Mutiny.*

The laws of tea-shop etiquette forbid that you should offer theatre tickets to a stranger without having first caught the stranger's eye. It is even better if you can ask to have a sugar basin passed to you, having previously concealed the fact that you have a large and well-filled sugar basin on your own table; this is not difficult to manage, as the printed menu is generally nearly as large as the table, and can be made to stand on end. Jocantha set to work hopefully; she had a long and rather high-pitched discussion with the waitress concerning alleged defects in an altogether blameless muffin, she made loud and plaintive inquiries about the tube service to some impossibly remote suburb, she talked with brilliant insincerity to the teashop kitten, and as a last resort she upset a milk-jug and swore at it daintily. Altogether she attracted a good deal of attention, but never for a moment did she attract the attention of the boy with the beautifully brushed hair, who was some thousands of miles away in the baking plains of

46

Hindostan, amid deserted bungalows, seething bazaars, and riotous barrack squares, listening to the throbbing of tom-toms and the distant rattle of musketry.

Jocantha went back to her house in Chelsea, which struck her for the first time as looking dull and over-furnished. She had a resentful conviction that Gregory would be uninteresting at dinner, and that the play would be stupid after dinner. On the whole her frame of mind showed a marked divergence from the purring complacency of Attab, who was again curled up in his corner of the divan with a great peace radiating from every curve of his body.

But then, he had killed his sparrow.

Nineteenth-century illustration by R. B. Birch.

THE CAT THAT WENT TO TRINITY
A College Ghost Story

Robertson Davies

Robertson Davies, who is the Master of Massey College in Toronto, Canada, has an international reputation as a novelist, a dramatist, a critic, and a wit. He has also revived the wonderful old Christmas tradition of telling stories at the Gaudies—those traditional college parties that originated in the Middle Ages. This enchanting feline Frankenstein made its debut at such a gathering.

Every autumn when I meet my new classes, I look them over to see if there are any pretty girls in them. This is not a custom peculiar to me: all professors do it. A pretty girl is something on which I can rest my eyes with pleasure while another student is reading a carefully researched but uninspiring paper.

This year, in my seminar on the Gothic Novel, there was an exceptionally pretty girl, whose name was Elizabeth Lavenza. I thought it a coincidence that this should also be the name of the heroine of one of the novels we were about to study—no less a work than Mary Shelley's celebrated romance *Frankenstein*. When I mentioned it to her she brushed it aside as of no significance.

'I was born in Geneva,' said she, 'where lots of people are called Lavenza.'

Nevertheless, it lingered in my mind, and I mentioned it to one of my colleagues, who is a celebrated literary critic.

'You have coincidence on the brain,' he said. 'Ever since you wrote that book—*Fourth Dimension* or whatever it was called—you've talked about nothing else. Forget it.'

I tried, but I couldn't forget it. It troubled me even more after I had met the new group of Junior Fellows in this College, for one of them was young Einstein, who was studying Medical Biophysics. He was a brilliant young man, who came to us with glowing recommendations; some mention was made of a great-uncle of his, an Albert Einstein, whose name meant nothing to me, though it appeared to have special significance in the scientific world. It was young Mr. Einstein's given names that roused an echo in my consciousness, for he was called Victor Frank.

For those among you who have not been reading Gothic Novels lately, I may explain that in Mrs. Shelley's book *Frankenstein, or The Modern Prometheus,* the hero's name is also Victor, and the girl he loved was Elizabeth Lavenza. This richness of coincidence might trouble a mind less disposed to such reflection than mine. I held my peace, for I had been cowed by what my friend the literary critic had said. But I was dogged by apprehension, for I know the disposition of the atmosphere of Massey College to constellate extraordinary elements. Thus, cowed and dogged, I kept my eyes open for what might happen.

It was no more than a matter of days when Fate added another figure to this coincidental pattern, and Fate's instrument was none other than my wife. It is our custom to entertain the men of the College to dinner, in small groups, and my wife invites a few girls to each of these occasions to lighten what might otherwise be a too exclusively academic atmosphere. The night that Frank Einstein appeared in our drawing-room he maintained his usual reserved—not to say morose—demeanour until Elizabeth Lavenza entered the room. Their meeting was, in one sense, a melodramatic cliché. But we must remember that things become clichés because they are

49

of frequent occurrence, and powerful impact. Everything fell out as a thoroughly bad writer might describe it. Their eyes met across the room. His glance was electric; hers ecstatic. The rest of the company seemed to part before them as he moved to her side. He never left it all evening. She had eyes for no other. From time to time his eyes rose in ardour, while hers fell in modest transport. This rising and falling of eyes was so portentously and swooningly apparent that one or two of our senior guests felt positively unwell, as though aboard ship. My heart sank. My wife's, on the contrary, was uplifted. As I passed her during the serving of the meal I hissed, 'This is Fate.' 'There is no armour against Fate,' she hissed in return. It is a combination of words not easily hissed, but she hissed it.

We had an unusually fine autumn, as you will recall, and there was hardly a day that I did not see Frank and Elizabeth sitting on one of the benches in the quad, sometimes talking, but usually looking deep into each other's eyes, their foreheads touching. They did it so much that they both became slightly cross-eyed, and my dismay mounted. I determined if humanly possible to avert some disastrous outcome (for I assure you that my intuition and my knowledge of the curious atmosphere of this College both oppressed me with boding) and I did all that lay in my power. I heaped work on Elizabeth Lavenza; I demanded the ultimate from her in reading of the Gothic Novel, as a means both of keeping her from Frank, and of straightening her vision.

Alas, how puny are our best efforts to avert a foreordained event! One day I saw Frank in the quad, sitting on the bench alone, reading a book. Pretending nonchalance, I sat beside him. 'And what are you reading, Mr. Einstein?' I said in honeyed tones.

Taciturn as always, he held out the book for me to see. It was *Frankenstein*. 'Liz said I ought to read it,' he said.

'And what do you make of it?' said I, for I am always interested in the puny efforts of art to penetrate the thoroughly scientific mind. His answer astonished me.

'Not bad at all,' said he. 'The Medical Biophysics aspect of the plot is very old-fashioned, of course. I mean when the hero makes that synthetic human being out of scraps from slaughter-houses. We could do better than that now. A lot better,' he added, and I thought he seemed to be brooding on nameless possibilities. I decided to change the line of our conversation. I began to talk about the College, and some of the successes and failures we had met with in the past.

Among the failures I mentioned our inability to keep a College Cat. In the ten years of our existence we have had several cats here, but not one of them has remained with us. They all run away, and there is strong evidence that they all go to Trinity. I thought at one time that they must be Anglican cats, and they objected to our oecumenical chapel. I went to the length of getting a Persian cat, raised in the Zoroastrian faith, but it only lasted two days. There is a fine Persian rug in Trinity Chapel. Our most recent cat had been christened Episcopuss, in the hope that this thoroughly Anglican title would content it; furthermore, the Lionel Massey Fund provided money to treat the cat to a surgical operation which is generally thought to lift a cat's mind above purely sectarian considerations. But it, too, left us for Trinity. Rationalists in the College suggested that Trinity has more, and richer, garbage than we have, but I still believe our cats acted on religious impulse.

As I spoke of these things Frank Einstein became more animated than I had ever known him. 'I get it,' he said; 'you want a cat that has been specifically programmed for Massey. An oecumenical cat, highly intelligent so that it prefers graduates to undergraduates, and incapable of making messes in the Round Room. With a few hours of computer time it oughtn't to be too difficult.'

I looked into his eyes—though from a greater distance than was usual to Elizabeth Lavenza—and what I saw there caused a familiar shudder to convulse my entire being. It is the shudder I feel when I know, for a certainty, that Massey College is about to be the scene of yet another macabre event.

Nevertheless, in the pressure of examinations and lectures, I forgot my uneasiness, and might perhaps have dismissed the matter

51

from my mind if two further interrelated circumstances—I dare not use the word coincidence in this case—had not aroused my fears again. One autumn morning, reading *The Globe and Mail,* my eye was caught by an item, almost lost at the bottom of a column, which bore the heading 'Outrage at Pound'; it appeared that two masked bandits, a man and a woman, had held up the keeper of the pound at gun-point, while seizing no less than twelve stray cats. Later that same day I saw Frank and Elizabeth coming through the College gate, carrying a large and heavy sack. From the sack dripped a substance which I recognized, with horror, as blood. I picked up a little of it on the tip of my finger; a hasty corpuscle count confirmed my suspicion that the blood was not human.

Night after night in the weeks that followed, I crept down to my study to look across the quad and see if a light was burning in Frank Einstein's room. Invariably it was so. And one morning, when I had wakened early and was standing on my balcony, apostrophizing the dawn, Elizabeth Lavenza stole past me from the College's main gate, her face marked, not by those lineaments of slaked desire so common among our visitors at such an hour, but by the pallor and fatigue of one well-nigh exhausted by intellectual work of the most demanding sort.

The following night I awoke from sleep at around two o'clock with a terrifying apprehension that something was happening in the College which I should investigate. Shouts, the sound of loud music, the riot of late revellers—these things do not particularly disturb me, but there is a quality of deep silence which I know to be the accompaniment of evil. Wearily and reluctantly I rose, wrapped myself in a heavy dressing-gown, and made my way into the quadrangle and there—yes, it was as I had feared—the eerie gleam from Frank Einstein's room was the only light to guide me. For there was a thick fog hanging over the University, and even the cruel light through the arrow-slits of the Robarts Library and the faery radiance from OISE were hidden.

Up to his room I climbed, and tapped on the door. It had not been locked, and my light knock caused it to swing open and there

—never can I forget my shock and revulsion at what I saw!—there were Frank and Elizabeth crouched over a table upon which lay an ensanguined form. I burst upon them.

'What bloody feast is this?' I shouted. 'Monsters, fiends, cannibals, what do I behold?'

'Shhh,' said Elizabeth; 'Frank's busy.'

'I'm making your cat,' said Frank.

'Cat,' I shrieked, almost beside myself; 'that is no cat. It's as big as a donkey. What cat are you talking about?'

'The Massey College cat,' said Frank. 'And it is going to be the greatest cat you have ever seen.'

I shall not trouble you with a detailed report of the conversation that followed. What emerged was this: Frank, beneath the uncommunicative exterior of a scientist, had a kindly heart, and he had been touched by the unlucky history of Massey College and its cats. 'What you said was,' said he to me, 'that the College never seemed to get the right cat. To you, with your simple, emotional, literary approach to the problem, this was an insuperable difficulty: to my finely organized biophysical sensibility, it was simply a matter of discovering what kind of cat was wanted, and producing it. Not by the outmoded method of selective breeding, but by the direct creation of the Ideal College Cat, or ICC as I came to think of it. Do you remember that when you talked to me about it I was reading that crazy book Liz was studying with you, about the fellow who made a man? Do you remember what he said? "Whence did the principle of life proceed? It was a bold question, and one which has ever been considered as a mystery; yet with how many things are we upon the brink of becoming acquainted, if cowardice or carelessness did not restrain our enquiries." That was written in 1818. Since then the principle of life has become quite well known, but most scientists are afraid to work on the knowledge they have. You remember that the fellow in the book decided to make a man, but he found the work too fiddly if he made a man of ordinary size, so he decided to make a giant. Me too. A cat of ordinary size is a nuisance, so I decided to multiply the dimensions by twelve. And

53

like the fellow in the book I got my materials and went to work. Here is your cat, about three-quarters finished.'

The fatal weakness, the tragic flaw, in my character is foolish good-nature, and that, combined with an uninformed but lively scientific curiosity, led me into what was, I now perceive, a terrible mistake. I was so interested in what Frank was doing that I allowed him to go ahead, and instead of sleeping at nights I crept up to his room, where Frank and Elizabeth allowed me, after I had given my promise not to interfere or touch anything, to sit in a corner and watch them. Those weeks were perhaps the most intensely lived that I have ever known. Beneath my eyes the ICC grew and took form. By day the carcass was kept in the freezer at Rochdale, where Elizabeth had a room; each night Frank warmed it up and set to work.

The ICC had many novel features which distinguished it from the ordinary domestic cat. Not only was it as big as twelve ordinary cats; it had twelve times the musculature. Frank said proudly that when it was finished it would be able to jump right over the College buildings. Another of its beauties was that it possessed a novel means of elimination. The trouble with all cats is that they seem to be housebroken, but in moments of stress or laziness they relapse into an intolerable bohemianism which creates problems for the cleaning staff. In a twelve-power cat this could be a serious defect. But Frank's cat was made with a small shovel on the end of its tail with which it could, once a week, remove its own ashes and deposit them behind the College in the parking-space occupied by *The Varsity,* where, it was assumed, they would never be noticed. I must hasten to add that the cat was made to sustain itself on a diet of waste-paper, of which we have plenty, and that what it produced in the manner I have described was not unlike confetti.

But the special beauty of the ICC was that it could talk. This, in the minds of Frank and Elizabeth, was its great feature as a College pet. Instead of mewing monotonously when stroked, it would be able to enter into conversation with the College men, and as we pride ourselves on being a community of scholars, it was to be provided with a class of conversation and a vocabulary infinitely superior to that of, for instance, a parrot.

This was Elizabeth's special care, and because she was by this time deep in my course on the Gothic Novel she decided, as a compliment to me, to so program the cat that it would speak in the language appropriate to that *genre* of literature. I was not so confident about this refinement as were Frank and Elizabeth, for I knew more about Gothic Novels than they, and have sometimes admitted to myself that they can be wordy. But as I have told you, I was a party to this great adventure only in the character of a spectator, and I was not to interfere. So I held my peace, hoping that the cat would, in the fulness of time, do the same.

At last the great night came, when the cat was to be invested with life. I sat in my corner, my eyes fixed upon the form which Frank was gradually melting out with Elizabeth's electric hairdryer. It was a sight to strike awe into the boldest heart.

I never dared to make my doubts about the great experiment known to Frank and Elizabeth, but I may tell you that my misgivings were many and acute. I am a creature of my time in that I fully understand that persons of merely aesthetic bias and training, like myself, should be silent in the presence of men of science, who know best about everything. But it was plain to me that the ICC was hideous. Not only was it the size of twelve cats, but the skins of twelve cats had been made to serve as its outer envelope. Four of these cats had been black, four were white, and four were of a marmalade colour. Frank, who liked things to be orderly, had arranged them so that the cat was piebald in mathematically exact squares. Because no ordinary cat's eyes would fit into the huge skull the eyes of a goat had been obtained—I dared not ask how—and as everyone knows, a goat's eyes are flat and have an uncanny oblong pupil. The teeth had been secured at a bargain rate from a denturist, and as I looked at them I knew why dentists say that these people must be kept in check. The tail, with the shovel at the end of it, was disagreeably naked. Its whiskers were like knitting needles. Indeed, the whole appearance of the cat was monstrous

The Composite Cat, by R. B. Birch.

and diabolical. In the most exact sense of the words, it was the damnedest thing you ever saw. But Frank had a mind above appearances and to Elizabeth, so beautiful herself, whatever Frank did was right.

The moment had arrived when this marvel of science was to be set going. I know that Frank was entirely scientific, but to my old-fashioned eye he looked like an alchemist as, with his dressing-gown floating around him, he began to read formulae out of a notebook, and Elizabeth worked switches and levers at his command. Suddenly there was a flash, of lightning it seemed to me, and I knew that we had launched the ICC upon its great adventure.

'Come here and look,' said Frank. I crept forward, half-afraid yet half-elated that I should be witness to such a triumph of medical biophysics. I leaned over the frightful creature, restraining my revulsion. Slowly, dreamily, the goat's eyes opened and focussed upon me.

'My Creator!' screamed the cat in a very loud voice, that agreed perfectly with the hideousness of its outward person. 'A thousand, thousand blessings be upon Thee. Hallowed be Thy name! Thy

kingdom come! O rapture, rapture thus to behold the golden dawn!'
With which words the cat leapt upon an electric lamp and ate the
bulb.

To say that I recoiled is to trifle with words. I leapt backward
into a chair and cringed against the wall. The cat pursued me,
shrieking Gothic praise and endearment. It put out its monstrous
tongue and licked my hand. Imagine, if you can, the tongue of a
cat which is twelve cats rolled into one. It was weeks before the
skin-graft made necessary by this single caress was completed. But
I am ahead of my story.

'No, no,' I cried; 'my dear animal, listen to reason. I am not your
Creator. Not in the least. You owe the precious gift of life to my
young friend here.'

I waved my bleeding hand toward Frank. In their rapture he
and Elizabeth were locked in a close embrace. That did it. Horrid,
fiendish jealousy swept through the cat's whole being. All its twelve
coats stood on end, the goat's eyes glared with fury, and its shovel
tail lashed like that of a tiger. It sprang at Elizabeth, and with a
single stroke of its powerful forepaws flung her to the ground.

I am proud to think that in that terrible moment I remembered
what to do. I have always loved circuses, and I know that no trainer
of tigers ever approaches his beasts without a chair in his hand. I
seized up a chair and, in the approved manner, drove the monstrous
creature into a corner. But what I said was not in tune with my
action, or the high drama of the moment. I admit it frankly; my
words were inadequate.

'You mustn't harm Miss Lavenza,' I said, primly; 'she is Mr.
Einstein's fiancée.'

But Frank's words—or rather his single word—were even more
inadequate than my own. 'Scat!' he shouted, kneeling by the bleeding form of his fainting beloved.

Elizabeth was to blame for programming that cat with a vocabulary culled from the Gothic Novel. 'Oh, Frankenstein,' it yowled,
in that tremendous voice; 'be not equitable to every other and
trample upon me alone, to whom thy justice and even thy clemency

57

and affection is most due. Remember that I am thy creature; I ought to be thy Adam; dub me not rather the fallen angel, whom thou drivest hence only because I love—nay, reverence—thee. Jealousy of thy love makes me a fiend. Make me happy, and I shall once more be virtuous.'

There is something about that kind of talk that influences everybody that hears it. I was astonished to hear Frank—who was generally contented with the utilitarian vocabulary of the scientific man— say: 'Begone! I will not hear you. There can be no community between thee and me; we are enemies. Cursed be the day, abhorred devil, in which you first saw the light! You have left me no power to consider whether I am just to you or not. Begone! Relieve me of the sight of your detested form!'

Elizabeth was not the most gifted of my students, and the cat's next words lacked something of the true Gothic rhetoric. 'You mean you don't love your own dear little Pussikins best,' it whined. But Frank was true to the Gothic vein. 'This lady is the mistress of my affections, and I acknowledge no Pussikins before her,' he cried.

The cat was suddenly a picture of desolation, of rejection, of love denied. Its vocabulary moved back into high gear. 'Thus I relieve thee, my Creator. Thus I take from thee a sight which you abhor. Farewell!' And with one gigantic bound it leapt through the window into the quadrangle, and I heard the thunderous sound as the College gate was torn from its hinges.

I know where it went, and I felt deeply sorry for Trinity.

A CAT CALLED
JOHN HARVARD

Helen M. Winslow

Cats have a natural bent for meditation. They will purr while you learn, purr while you write, purr while you paint. The cat is creative.

In our long periods at school and college, more than one cat became an important part of our lives. In our boarding school it was Major, a large black, commanding cat who carried himself with the stiff-backed discipline of our headmistress.

Underneath his forbidding name and manner was a cat that comforted many a lonely child. School cats and campus cats have a classical approach to life.

A truly remarkable story of sagacity is told of an old Cambridge (Mass.) cat: although where, in all America, would we expect to find cultured cats if not in that historic town? This cat rejoices in the seemingly appropriate name of John Harvard. When John was a kitten, famed for his beauty and good temper, the family adored him not only for his mental and moral qualities, but for his proud, historic name; but when one day John Harvard presented his owners with a litter of kittens, it was seriously thought that John must

The Rug, by J. L. Dolph.

be disposed of. Steps were being taken to that effect, when one day
John left her litter of kittens, came up from the cellar in hot haste,
and rushed into the kitchen. She began to mew piteously and attracted the attention of the cook and the family by running to the
cellar door, but when it was opened for her she refused to descend:
finally she induced one member of the family to go down with her.
When they got downstairs, a wooden barrel close beside the box
where her kittens were lying was discovered to be in a blaze: a few
minutes more and the house would have been on fire. John Harvard, despite the weakness of her sex, had vindicated the honor of
her name, and since then she has lived on the fat of the land.

THE EGYPTIANS AND THEIR CATS

Herodotus

The ancient historian Herodotus (born about 484 B.C.) was also one of the first anthropologists. He had a particularly discerning eye for the animals of that period and how people treated them; he could tell much from the concern a nation displayed toward its animals. This is one of the very first instances of a Greek writer describing ancient Egypt. Herodotus himself was the earliest Egyptologist.

Egypt, though it borders upon Libya, is not a region abounding in wild animals. The animals that do exist in the country, whether domesticated or otherwise, are all regarded as sacred. If I were to explain why they are consecrated to the several gods, I should be led to speak of religious matters, which I particularly shrink from mentioning; the points whereon I have touched slightly hitherto have all been introduced from sheer necessity. Their custom with respect to animals is as follows:—For every kind there are appointed certain guardians, some male, some female, whose business it is to look after them; and this honour is made to descend from father to

61

The Cat, the Ally of Ra,
from an ancient Egyptian papyrus.

son. The inhabitants of the various cities, when they have made a vow to any god, pay it to his animals in the way which I will now explain. At the time of making the vow they shave the head of the child, cutting off all the hair, or else half, or sometimes a third part, which they then weigh in a balance against a sum of silver; and whatever sum the hair weighs is presented to the guardian of the animals, who thereupon cuts up some fish, and gives it to them for food—such being the stuff whereon they are fed. When a man has killed one of the sacred animals, if he did it with malice prepense, he is punished with death, if unwittingly, he has to pay such a fine as the priests choose to impose. When an ibis, however, or a hawk is killed, whether it was done by accident or on purpose, the man must needs die.

The number of domestic animals in Egypt is very great, and would be still greater were it not for what befalls the cats. As the females, when they have kittened, no longer seek the company of the males, these last, to obtain once more their companionship, practise a curious artifice. They seize the kittens, carry them off, and kill them, but do not eat them afterwards. Upon this the females, being deprived of their young, and longing to supply their place, seek the males once more, since they are particularly fond of their off-spring. On every occasion of a fire in Egypt the strangest prodigy occurs with the cats. The inhabitants allow the fire to rage as it pleases, while they stand about at intervals and watch these animals, which, slipping by the men or else leaping over them, rush headlong into the flames. When this happens, the Egyptians are in deep affliction. If a cat dies in a private house by a natural death, all the inmates of the house shave their eyebrows; on the death of a dog they shave the head and the whole of the body.

The cats on their decease are taken to the city of Bubastis, where they are embalmed, after which they are buried in certain sacred repositories. The dogs are interred in the cities to which they belong, also in sacred burial-places. The same practice obtains with respect to the ichneumons; the hawks and shrew-mice, on the contrary, are conveyed to the city of Buto for burial, and the ibises to Hermopolis. The bears, which are scarce in Egypt, and the wolves, which are not much bigger than foxes, they bury wherever they happen to find them lying.

The Kaffir, or Egyptian cat.
Artist unknown.

63

AN ASSORTMENT OF CATS

Jerome K. Jerome

Jerome K. Jerome, the author of the enchanting book Three Men in a Boat, *was in his day the equal of any humorist in the world. He had a sure knowledge of the world of cats—and, for that matter, the world of dogs as well. He always kept an eye out for a good tale about any animal.*

Here a cat reveals in its own words something that we have wondered about: how a strange cat manages to be "taken in."

"Cats," remarked Jephson to me, one afternoon, as we sat in the punt discussing the plot of our novel, "cats are animals for whom I entertain a very great respect. You might almost think they had a soul."

"They are," I responded, "wonderfully cunning little animals, and it is not by their moral and religious instincts alone that they are so closely linked to man; the marvellous ability they display in taking care of 'number one' is worthy of the human race itself. Some friends of mine had a cat, a big black Tom: they have got half of him still. They had reared him from a kitten, and, in their homely, undemonstrative way, they liked him. There was nothing, however, approaching passion on either side.

"One day a Chinchilla came to live in the neighbourhood, under the charge of an elderly spinster, and the two cats met at a garden wall party.

" 'What sort of diggings have you got?' asked the Chinchilla.

" 'Oh, pretty fair.'

" 'Nice people?'

" 'Yes, nice enough—as people go.'

" 'Pretty willing? Look after you well, and all that sort of thing?'

" 'Yes——oh yes. I've no fault to find with them.'

" 'What's the victuals like?'

" 'Oh, the usual thing, you know, bones and scraps, and a bit of dog-biscuit now and then for a change.'

" 'Bones and dog-biscuits! Do you mean to say you eat bones?'

" 'Yes, when I can get 'em. Why, what's wrong about them?'

" 'Shade of Egyptian Isis, bones and dog-biscuits! Don't you ever get any spring chickens, or a sardine, or a lamb cutlet?'

" 'Chickens! Sardines! What are you talking about? What are sardines?'

" 'What are sardines! Oh, my dear child (the Chinchilla was a lady cat, and always called gentlemen friends a little older than herself 'dear child'), these people of yours are treating you just shamefully. Come, sit down and tell me all about it. What do they give you to sleep on?'

" 'The floor.'

" 'I thought so; and skim milk and water to drink, I suppose?'

" 'It is a bit thin.'

" 'I can quite imagine it. You must leave these people, my dear, at once.'

" 'But where am I to go to?'

" 'Anywhere.'

" 'But who'll take me in?'

" 'Anybody, if you go the right way to work. How many times do you think I've changed my people? Seven!—and bettered myself

65

on each occasion. Why, do you know where I was born? In a pig-sty. There were three of us, mother and I and my little brother. Mother would leave us every evening, returning generally just as it was getting light. One morning she did not come back. We waited and waited, but the day passed on and she did not return, and we grew hungrier and hungrier, and at last we lay down, side by side, and cried ourselves to sleep.

"'In the evening, peeping through a hole in the door, we saw her coming across the field. She was crawling very slowly, with her body close down against the ground. We called to her, and she answered with a low "crroo"; but she did not hasten her pace.

"'She crept in and rolled over on her side, and we ran to her, for we were almost starving. We lay long upon her breasts, and she licked us over and over.

"'I dropped asleep upon her, and in the night I awoke, feeling cold. I crept closer to her, but that only made me colder still, and she was wet and clammy with a dark moisture that was oozing from her side. I did not know what it was at that time, but I have learnt since.

"'That was when I could hardly have been four weeks old, and from that day to this I've looked after myself: you've got to do that in this world, my dear. For awhile, I and my brother lived on in that sty and kept ourselves. It was a grim struggle at first, two babies fighting for life; but we pulled through. At the end of about three months, wandering farther from home than usual, I came upon a cottage, standing in the fields. It looked warm and cosy through the open door, and I went in: I have always been blessed with plenty of nerve. Some children were playing round the fire, and they welcomed me and made much of me. It was a new sensation to me, and I stayed there. I thought the place a palace at the time.

"'I might have gone on thinking so if it had not been that, passing through the village one day, I happened to catch sight of a room behind a shop. There was a carpet on the floor, and a rug before the fire. I had never known till then that there were such luxuries in the world. I determined to make that shop my home, and I did so.'

Country Cats, an engraving by an unknown nineteenth-century artist.

" 'How did you manage it?' asked the black cat, who was growing interested.

" 'By the simple process of walking in and sitting down. My dear child, cheek's the "Open sesame" to every door. The cat that works hard dies of starvation, the cat that has brains is kicked downstairs for a fool, and the cat that has virtue is drowned for a scamp; but the cat that has cheek sleeps on a velvet cushion and dines on cream and horseflesh. I marched straight in and rubbed myself against the old man's legs. He and his wife were quite taken with what they called my "trustfulness," and adopted me with enthusiasm. Strolling about the fields of an evening I often used to hear the children of the cottage calling my name. It was weeks before they gave up seeking for me. One of them, the youngest, would sob herself to sleep of a night, thinking that I was dead: they were affectionate children.

"'I boarded with my shopkeeping friends for nearly a year, and from them I went to some new people who had lately come to the neighbourhood, and who possessed a really excellent cook. I think I could have been very satisfied with these people, but, unfortunately, they came down in the world, and had to give up the big house and the cook, and take a cottage, and I did not care to go back to that sort of life.

"'Accordingly I looked about for a fresh opening. There was a curious old fellow who lived not far off. People said he was rich, but nobody liked him. He was shaped differently from other men. I turned the matter over in my mind for a day or two, and then determined to give him a trial. Being a lonely sort of man, he might make a fuss over me, and if not I could go.

"'My surmise proved correct. I have never been more petted than I was by "Toady," as the village boys had dubbed him. My present guardian is foolish enough over me, goodness knows, but she has other ties, while "Toady" had nothing else to love, not even himself. He could hardly believe his eyes at first when I jumped up on his knees and rubbed myself against his ugly face. "Why Kitty," he said, "do you know you're the first living thing that has ever come to me of its own accord." There were tears in his funny little red eyes as he said that.

"'I remained two years with "Toady," and was very happy indeed. Then he fell ill, and strange people came to the house, and I was neglected. "Toady" liked me to come up and lie upon the bed, where he could stroke me with his long, thin hand, and at first

I used to do this. But a sick man is not the best of company, as you can imagine, and the atmosphere of a sick room not too healthy, so, all things considered, I felt it was time for me to make a fresh move.

" 'Where to go, I did not know. Two or three homes were offered me, but none of them quite suited me. At one place, where I put up for a day, just to see how I liked it, there was a dog; and at another, which would otherwise have done admirably, they kept a baby. Whatever you do, never stop at a house where they keep a baby. If a child pulls your tail or ties a paper bag round your head, you can give it one for itself and nobody blames you. "Well, serve you right," they say to the yelling brat, "you shouldn't tease the poor thing." But if you resent a baby's holding you by the throat and trying to gouge out your eye with a wooden ladle, you are called a spiteful beast, and "shoo'd" all round the garden. If people keep babies, they don't keep me; that's my rule.

" 'After sampling some three or four families, I finally fixed upon a banker. Offers more advantageous from a worldly point of view were open to me. I could have gone to a public-house, where the victuals were simply unlimited, and where the back door was left open all night. But about the banker's (he was also a church-warden, and his wife never smiled at anything less than a joke by the bishop) there was an atmosphere of solid respectability that I felt would be comforting to my nature. My dear child, you will come across cynics who will sneer at respectability: don't you listen to them. Respectability is its own reward—and a very real and practical reward. It may not bring you dainty dishes and soft beds, but it brings you something better and more lasting. Don't you ever let anyone set you against respectability. It's the most satisfying thing I know of in this world—and about the cheapest.

" 'I was nearly three years with this family, and was sorry when I had to go. I should never have left if I could have helped it, but one day something happened at the bank which necessitated the banker's taking a sudden journey to Spain, and, after that, the house became a somewhat unpleasant place to live in. Noisy, dis-agreeable people were continually knocking at the door and making

69

rows in the passage; and at night folks threw bricks at the windows.

" 'I was in a delicate state of health at the time, and my nerves could not stand it. I said good-bye to the town, and making my way back into the country, put up with a county family.

" 'From these people I went to a retired potato merchant. It was a social descent, but a rise so far as comfort and appreciation were concerned. They appeared to be an exceedingly nice family, and to be extremely fond of me. I say they "appeared" to be these things, because the sequel proved that they were neither. Six months after I had come to them they went away and left me. They never asked me to accompany them. They made no arrangements for me to stay behind. It shook my faith—never too robust—in human nature. I determined that, in future, no one should have the opportunity of disappointing my trust in them. I selected my present mistress on the recommendation of a gentleman friend of mine who had formerly lived with her. He said she was an excellent caterer. The only reason he had left her was that she expected him to be in at ten each night, and that hour didn't fit in with his other arrangements. It made no difference to me—as a matter of fact, I do not care for these midnight reunions that are so popular amongst us. There are always too many cats for one properly to enjoy oneself, and sooner or later a rowdy element is sure to creep in. I offered myself to her, and she accepted me gratefully. But I have never liked her, and never shall. She is a silly old woman, and bores me. She is, however, devoted to me, and, unless something extra attractive turns up, I shall stick to her.

" 'That, my dear, is the story of my life, so far as it has gone. I tell it you to show you how easy it is to be "taken in." Fix on your house, and mew piteously at the back door. When it is opened run in and rub yourself against the first leg you come across. Rub hard, and look up confidingly. Nothing gets round human beings, I have noticed, quicker than confidence. They don't get much of it, and it pleases them. Always be confiding. At the same time be prepared for emergencies. If you are still doubtful as to your reception, try and get yourself slightly wet. Why people should prefer a wet cat to a dry one I have never been able to understand; but that a wet cat is practically sure of being taken in and gushed over, while a dry cat is liable to have the garden hose turned upon it, is an undoubted fact. Also, if you can possibly manage it, and it is offered you, eat a bit of dry bread. The Human Race is always stirred to its deepest depths by the sight of a cat eating a bit of dry bread.'

"My friend's black Tom profited by the Chinchilla's wisdom. A catless couple had lately come to live next door. He determined to adopt them on trial. Accordingly, on the first rainy day, he went out soon after lunch and sat for four hours in an open field. In the evening, soaked to the skin, and feeling pretty hungry, he went mewing to their door. One of the maids opened it, he rushed under her skirts and rubbed himself against her legs. She screamed, and down came the master and the mistress to know what was the matter.

" 'It's a stray cat, mum,' said the girl.

" 'Turn it out,' said the master.

" 'Oh no, don't,' said the mistress.

" 'Oh, poor thing, it's wet,' said the housemaid.

" 'Perhaps it's hungry,' said the cook.

" 'Try it with a bit of dry bread,' sneered the master, who wrote for the newspapers, and thought he knew everything.

"A stale crust was proffered. The cat ate it greedily, and afterwards rubbed himself gratefully against the man's light trousers.

"This made the man ashamed of himself, likewise of his trousers. 'Oh, well, let it stop if it wants to,' he said.

"So the cat was made comfortable, and stayed on.

"Meanwhile its own family were seeking for it high and low. They had not cared overmuch for it while they had had it; now it was gone, they were inconsolable. In the light of its absence, it appeared to them the one thing that had made the place home. The shadows of suspicion gathered round the case. The cat's disappearance, at first regarded as a mystery, began to assume the shape of a crime. The wife openly accused the husband of never having liked the animal, and more than hinted that he and the gardener between them could give a tolerably truthful account of its last moments; an insinuation that the husband repudiated with a warmth that only added credence to the original surmise.

"The bull-terrier was had up and searchingly examined. Fortunately for him, he had not had a single fight for two whole days. Had any recent traces of blood been detected upon him, it would have gone hard with him.

"The person who suffered most, however, was the youngest boy. Three weeks before, he had dressed the cat in doll's clothes and taken it round the garden in the perambulator. He himself had forgotten the incident, but Justice, though tardy, was on his track. The misdeed was suddenly remembered at the very moment when unavailing regret for the loss of the favourite was at its deepest, so that to box his ears and send him, then and there, straight off to bed was felt to be a positive relief.

"At the end of a fortnight, the cat, finding he had not, after all, bettered himself, came back. The family were so surprised that at first they could not be sure whether he was flesh and blood, or a spirit come to comfort them. After watching him eat half a pound of raw steak, they decided he was material, and caught him up and hugged him to their bosoms. For a week they over-fed him and made much of him. Then, the excitement cooling, he found himself dropping back into his old position, and didn't like it, and went next door again.

"The next door people had also missed him, and they likewise greeted his return with extravagant ebullitions of joy. This gave the cat an idea. He saw that his game was to play the two families off one against the other; which he did. He spent an alternate fortnight with each, and lived like a fighting cock. His return was always greeted with enthusiasm, and every means were adopted to induce him to stay. His little whims were carefully studied, his favourite dishes kept in constant readiness.

"The destination of his going leaked out at length, and then the two families quarrelled about him over the fence. My friend ac-

cused the newspaper man of having lured him away. The newspaper man retorted that the poor creature had come to his door
wet and starving, and added that he would be ashamed to keep an
animal merely to ill-treat it. They have a quarrel about him twice
a week on the average. It will probably come to blows one of these
days."

Jephson appeared much surprised by this story. He remained
thoughtful and silent. I asked him if he would like to hear any
more, and as he offered no active opposition I went on. (Maybe
he was asleep; that idea did not occur to me at the time.)

I told him of my grandmother's cat, who, after living a blameless life for upwards of eleven years, and bringing up a family of
something like sixty-six, not counting those that died in infancy
and the water-butt, took to drink in her old age, and was run over
while in a state of intoxication (oh, the justice of it!) by a brew-
er's dray. I have read in temperance tracts that no dumb animal
will touch a drop of alcoholic liquor. My advice is, if you wish to
keep them respectable, don't give them a chance to get at it. I
knew a pony— But never mind him; we are talking about my
grandmother's cat.

A leaky beer-tap was the cause of her downfall. A saucer used
to be placed underneath it to catch the drippings. One day the
cat, coming in thirsty, and finding nothing else to drink, lapped up
a little, liked it, and lapped a little more, went away for half an
hour, and came back and finished the saucerful—then sat down
beside it, and waited for it to fill again.

From that day till the hour she died, I don't believe that cat was
ever once sober. Her days she passed in a drunken stupor before
the kitchen fire. Her nights she spent in the beer cellar.

My grandmother, shocked and grieved beyond expression, gave
up her barrel and adopted bottles. The cat, thus condemned to
enforced abstinence, meandered about the house for a day and a
half in a disconsolate, quarrelsome mood. Then she disappeared,
returning at eleven o'clock as tight as a drum.

Where she went, and how she managed to procure the drink,

73

we never discovered; but the same programme was repeated every day. Some time during the morning she would contrive to elude our vigilance and escape; and late every evening she would come reeling home across the fields in a condition that I will not sully my pen by attempting to describe.

It was on Saturday night that she met the sad end to which I have before alluded. She must have been very drunk, for the man told us that, in consequence of the darkness, and the fact that his horses were tired, he was proceeding at little more than a snail's pace.

I think my grandmother was rather relieved than otherwise. She had been very fond of the cat at one time, but its recent conduct had alienated her affection. We children buried it in the garden under the mulberry tree, but the old lady insisted that there should be no tombstone, not even a mound raised. So it lies there, unhonoured, in a drunkard's grave.

Cat and hearth belonging to John Greenleaf Whittier, American poet, during the winter he wrote Snow-Bound *(1866).*

A CAT AND A BIRD OF OLD NEW ORLEANS

A Correspondent

We are often surprised by cats who choose strange companions. We had a cat, Calico by name, who befriended an old horse called Punch. They used to commune together in the stable yard with genuine warmth. Cats, individualistic as always, have befriended chickens, dogs, rabbits, birds, and within the zoo, eased the captivity of elephants.

Some time ago, in a quiet corner way down on Rue Royale, I chanced upon a little Creole shopkeeper whom the neighbors call "Mam'zelle." With her lived Pierre, the cat, and Jeanne, the bird. Pierre was a handsome black and white fellow, with a noble head, and he and the canary, Jeanne, were about the same age. Mam'zelle told me, in her pretty Creole patois, how devoted the two pets were to each other, and I myself saw frequent evidences of their kindly relationship. In a quiet corner of the little shop I have seen Pierre and Jeanne taking their breakfast together from the same plate, and by and by, when the cat would lie dozing in the sunshine, the bird would hop about him or cuddle up snug and comfortable between his outstretched paws. When Mam'zelle was

75

busy, so that she could not keep an eye on the little bird's safety, she would swing the cage in the doorway, while Pierre would stretch himself on the floor beneath, keeping guard over his friend. And woe betide the stray cat that wandered that way. Pierre was always on the alert for squalls, and if a cat came too near to suit him he would send Jeanne hustling into her cage while he chased the offending feline off the street.

Just this very thing happened at least for the thousandth time, but for the first time on record grief followed the move. Pierre and Jeanne were taking their usual game in the sunshine of the little shop door, when a big brindled stranger appeared on the banquette without. Straight as a die, Jeanne was in her cage, and Pierre had gone in hot pursuit of the brindle. The chase was a hard one, and Mam'zelle says Pierre must have been gone a long time, but she was busy serving customers, and by and by she noticed Jeanne hopping about the counter. Thinking that Pierre had returned she took no further notice of the bird. A little later, however, hearing a dreadful commotion out on the banquette, she ran out to witness the sad little tragedy which I, too, arrived just in time to see, but too late to prevent. Taking advantage of Pierre's protracted absence, an ugly tortoise-shell from the next block strolled to the little shop in search of Jeanne. Finding her out hopping about unprotected, he began siege at once. Mam'zelle and I arrived just in time to see the tortoise-shell pounce on poor Jeanne as she perched on top of the swinging cage, and bear her with him to the pavement. Before either of us could interpose, the deed was done, and then in a moment came Pierre rushing around the corner, and as quick as a flash he had taken in the situation. With one fierce bound he sprang upon the tortoise-shell and swept poor Jeanne from his clutches. For a brief moment he sat guarding her, but that moment was long enough to tell him he was too late. Then, letting Mam'zelle take the little corpse from under his paw, he swooped down upon the tortoise-shell. It was only for a little while, but when the little battle was over, both cats lay dead upon the pavement. Pierre had laid down his life to avenge Jeanne's death, and the little Mam'zelle mourns both her pets.

*A Turbulent Family. Painting by the Dutch artist Henriette Ronner.
Madame Ronner's cat pictures are world-famous.*

"HEY DIDDLE DIDDLE, THE CAT..."

Eden Phillpotts

"You have a great feeling for dialogue. You should stick to natural dialogue . . . try and leave your characters alone so that they can speak for themselves."

So wrote the then best-selling writer Eden Phillpotts to the young Agatha Christie.

They are wise words from a wise man. He let his characters speak for themselves, as does this old country gentleman in a heartwarming story of man and cat.

When you be done larning, you might so well stop living, and for my part, though I'm sixty-five, I thank God as I can still gather useful knowledge when it comes my way.

For example, but four years ago, I had my eyes opened about a matter on which I'd thought wrong for more than half a century. I never could understand man or woman who loved a beast; and when I see an old maid dote on her cat, or an old bachelor share the best off his own plate with his dog, I scorned 'em. And when the creatures came to a bad end, as pets so often will, and their owners

In this House lived an Old Woman with a Cat and a Hen. Illustration by Hans Tegner.

weren't above shedding a tear for 'em, I said, in my ignorance, they did ought to be ashamed, and called 'em weak-minded zanies to let a dumb animal reign over 'em in such a fashion. But I don't put on no airs and graces now when I see anybody fretting for a sick or dead creature; because I be in the same boat myself.

As a widow man and pretty well-to-do, I be one of them that count at Ponsworthy, and have always tried to keep up the dignity of the village and be a good neighbour and help on the welfare of us all in my small way. And being addicted to childer, though never blessed or cursed with none, I made friends with the young things and stood well in their opinion.

So it came about that, as I minded their birthdays pretty often, a sharp little maid axed me when mine might be; and I told her, doubting not that she'd forget again. Daisy Bird she was called, the youngest daughter of my particular friend, Martin Bird, of the all-sorts shop.

Well, Daisy remembered, and on my birthday she brought me a kitten just old enough to leave his mother. 'Twas a cat of a well-known mother, but the father was wrapped in mystery, as fathers too often are. The kitling weren't nothing to praise, nor yet to blame—just a very every day young cat, with a piebald face and a bit of yellow and black dabbed about over a white ground. His eyes were doubtful and Daisy promised me as they'd turn a nice green when he'd growed a bit, same as his mother's; and if you'd looked my gift-cat in the mouth, you'd have seen 'twas pink as a rose, with just the beginning of small, pearly teeth coming. No tail to name; but there again Daisy came to the rescue and solemnly vowed that he had the promise of a very fine tail, if I'd only be patient about it.

'Twas to be called "Sunny Jim," and she much hoped I'd take to it and be a kind friend to it; and if I did not, it had got to be drowned.

I paused at that, for I had meant to beg Daisy to carry it home and let me take the kind will for the deed. But when I see the little thing so trustful and so wishful to please, and so well satisfied with me from the first; and when I understood it was a choice between life along with me and death in the river, I hesitated.

Daisy picked him up and put him in my hand; and if he'd showed any sauce, or turned against me, it would have been "good-bye." But he knew 'twas touch and go; and whenever does a cat do a thing that makes against its own prosperity? He looked up in my face and purred, with the little gruff purr as young cats have, and rubbed his small carcass against my waistcoat, as if he'd found the very person he was wanting. So there it stood; I kept him and let him have his run and his fill, and watched him grow into a very ugly cat in other eyes, but not ugly to me—never to me.

I always say that it's a beautiful thing to see the contentment of animals. No doubt it only happens because they've got no wits and no power to compare their lot with any other; but whatever it be— horse or donkey, dog or cat, only let him know he's welcome and have got a man or woman friend, and he'll cleave to the lowliest lot and be just so cheerful and good-hearted and faithful along with a tinker as a king. They'll fit in, make themselves part of the home, feel 'tis the one place in the world that matters, however poor and humble, and go about the troublesome business of being alive, with such pluck and patience and good appetite that they be often a lesson to us grumbling grizzling humans.

No dog or cat will ever look on the dark side of things. Nature have made 'em hopeful. They be quick to scent pleasure, and though there's a good and bad among 'em and some more easily cast down than others, they be prone to welcome life and give of their best in exchange for small mercies.

My Sunny Jim was a very well-named cat. He had what you might call a reasonable mind, and if he'd lacked the many virtues that came out to him, still I'd have been bound in common justice to rate him as a very worthy chap—along of his amazing affection for me. He seemed to know from the first as I had no use for domestic animals, and he said to himself: "Then I'll break you in and make you properly mad about me and conquer your hard heart."

He went about it very cunning, too. He knew I was a terrible clean old man and liked my house to be so spick and span as myself; and so he began by showing me what cleanliness really was; and a more fussy cat from his youth up I have never met. His father must have been a gentleman for sartain. You felt the cat had good blood in him, he was so nice. Never a hair out of place you might say, and he'd lick himself and wash his chops sometimes after a sup and bite till I'd shout at him to let be. Mud was his abomination, and if he come in with a speck on his pads, he'd bite and fidget, as if he was pulling off a pair of gloves; and he never thanked me more grateful nor purred louder than when I gave him his brush and comb. But, to tell truth, I humoured him in that matter, and finding what a godsend it was to him to have a rub from time to time, I met him there and kept an old brush a' purpose.

At six months I knew he'd got me, and I was a lot too fond of the cat; and on his birthday, which Daisy Bird remembered, us gave Sunny Jim a party, and Daisy and half a score of childer agreed to come. 'Twas a great success. Us provided him with three sardines and a drop of cream, and long after the party was over and the childer gone, he sat polishing up. Then, when he felt perfection inside and out, he just give a sigh of satisfaction, and tucked in his paws and sat quite silent thinking over the day's fine doings.

As for mice, he was a very fine performer, but my house never had no mice in it as he soon found, so he went down three doors to Mrs. Wilkinson's, where there were scores of dozens, and he never drawed a blank there. Not that he'd often eat a mouse; but he was a mighty hunter of 'em—a proper mouse-tiger, you might say—though not much a one for birds. He seldom went afield and never laid a paw to fur or feathers, like many a hard-bitten poacher of a cat, as makes a shameful end soon or late on gamekeeper's gallows.

He slept along with me, at my bed-foot, and I'd trained him to come in for his supper an hour or so after dark. But he liked the evening hour and the moth time. Then he'd sit on the party wall and take the air, or join in a cat chorus perhaps, but all like a gentleman; and he never went too far, or done anything to be ashamed of. A wife or two he may have had, but all well within

82

honour; and he wouldn't fight nor nothing like that, for the good reason that he weighed about five pounds heavier than any cat at Ponsworthy, and no other tom in his right senses would have took him on for a moment.

He supped with me, and by ten o'clock we was both to bed. Then when he was stretched at my feet and the candle out, I'd bid him say his prayers, and he'd purr gentle and steady; and for a good few years the last sound I have heard, as I closed my eyes, was Sunny Jim saying his prayers.

Mrs. Wilkinson warned me, strangely enough, just a week before the crash came.

"You be putting that tortoiseshell tom afore your God, Peter Blount," she said to me, "and 'tis terrible dangerous, for the Almighty's jealous as the grave, and you may get a nasty awakener."

A proper prophet the woman was, for seven nights later, just afore the hour when the cat was due—a moony night in autumn, bright and peaceful, with the owls calling each other in Western

The Spy. Drawing by unknown artist of the last century.

Wood—I heard a harsh, sharp sound which I knowed for a heavy air-gun; and not liking it none too well at that late hour, I went in my garden instanter to call Sunny Jim.

The back side of my house gave on waste land that ran up to furze brakes, and I was going to give a look over the wall and see who it might be prowling round, when my cat crawled up to me on three legs. I picked him up and took him in to the lamp; and then I found as he'd got his shoulder all smashed by a bullet.

I kept my head and ministered to the poor soul, and he fixed his eyes upon me and seemed to ask if it was to be a fatal matter. For a time I thought he was sinking, for he lay cruel still with his eyes shut, breathing hard; but then, seeing he weren't in no immediate danger of death, I offered him water, which he lapped, and after that I picked him up so tender as I might, put him in a big vegetable basket, with a bit of blanket in the bottom, and carried him over to see Billy Blades.

Billy weren't a man I liked, being a doubtful customer in many ways, and said to have shortened his wife's life by unkindness; but he was a very clever vet., and properly renowned for his knowledge of four-footed creatures. He was a great dog-fancier without a doubt, and though 'twas whispered he fancied other people's dogs a thought too often, yet the skill was there; so I took Sunny Jim to see the man, and he was home by good luck and gave me all his attention. The cat knew perfectly well what his doctor was up to, and behaved like a Christian under the search.

"His shoulder blade be smashed to pieces," said Billy, "and if the ball had took him an inch lower, it would have gone through the creature and slain him. The man who done this made a bad shot, I reckon, and when he found he'd only winged the cat, he ran for it, knowing the creature would have strength to get home and give the show away."

"But why should any mortal man want for to kill my cat?" I asked.

"For his skin," explained Billy Blades. "Cat and coney be worth money nowadays. A skin like this here will die black and be worth fifteen shillings, or a pound, to any man; and that's why a good few cats have failed to come home lately. But I bain't going to say he won't live. I think he may. He's in good health and in his prime by the look of him, and he's got a patient sort of nature. You see how he bears up. If all goes well and there's no fatal poison in the wound, he'll very likely make a good recovery. Us can't tell yet; but if, as may happen, the wound gets ugly in a few days, then I'll give him a whiff of chloroform and see into the evil and find if the bullet's there."

"I can take hope, then?" I asked.

"You can," he said, "but not too much. He's hard hit."

So all was dreadful suspense, and nought could be done for a time till the extent of the danger showed.

I took Sunny Jim home, and, to my great thanksgiving, he ate a bit of raw mutton as I cut off a leg and minced for him. Not much, but enough to keep up his strength; and he got a little sleep also off and on, though I did not; and in the morning, I carried him down, and he just lay, patient and resigned, on his little mat by the kitchen fire, while I swallowed my breakfast.

But my rage knew no bounds, and if I could have catched the anointed devil as done it, I'd have choked his breath out of him between my hands. I never did feel so properly hard to any fellow-creature before; and to this day when I see the vision of thicky cat crawling home on three legs, with the moonlight on his poor, terrified eyes, I feel a thrill of hate and passion.

Next morning it was round the village like a flame of fire that Sunny Jim had been shot and might die of it, and a proper rally of neighbors—women, children, and men—streamed along to see him and say how cruel vexed they was on my account, and to hope that Sunny Jim might be spared. 'Twas the general opinion that no neighbor could have sunk to such a crime, for none was known to bear me a grudge, nor yet him.

Billy Blades came morning and evening to view the patient. And then he gave me a ray of hope, for, in a week, he believed the wound was clean and wouldn't get no worse. In fact, it began to heal very nice outside, and now the danger was whether Sunny Jim's sinews would join up too, or whether they would not. And much depended upon that. He couldn't put his paw down yet, of course, but Job never beat him for patience. He didn't like me out of his sight, however, and wouldn't let down his victuals for anybody but me.

And then in my wrath I issued an advertisement, for I was death on bringing the sinner to justice and felt if a man had done the crime he must be had up and disgraced afore the magistrates; while if it was only a wicked, hard-hearted boy, then the least they could do to him, for his own salvation and my satisfaction, would be a damned good hiding.

And I wrote with my own hand six advertisements offering £5 reward for the name of the man, or boy, as had shot my famous cat. One I stuck on my front gate, one on the guide post at the cross roads outside Ponsworthy, one in Martin Bird's shop window, one in the post office, one by the upping-stock, outside "The Green Man" public house, and the other in the bar of the same.

People marvelled at the sight of such big money, and they said, behind my back, as I must be a millionaire, or else going weak in my head; but it was a fortnight afore any response reached me, and then I had the surprise of my life on hearing the sinner's name.

I learnt it of a Friday, when Billy Blades dropped in for a look at Sunny Jim, and he said he was very pleased indeed with the cat's progress, and now felt it was safe to assure me he'd make a recovery and was out of danger.

"The ligaments be joined up beautiful," said Billy, "and the bone have growed together. You see how he can use his leg and trust it again; and he could trust it more than he do, only he's nervous yet. But, though he may go a thought lame for life, it will be nothing to interfere with his pleasure. And in time even the lameness may wear off altogether, when the muscles and sinews get used to the change."

Then I thanked Blades with all my heart and shook his hand and told him I thought he was a very clever man and must send in his account.

"And now 'tis all over," he said, "I'll tell you another thing about this here cat, and that's the name of the party as tried to shoot him and failed."

"You know!" I cried out. "Then I thank Providence, Billy; and never shall I part from a five-pound note with better will."

"No you won't," he answered. "You'll hate to part, Peter; but life's life and cats are cats, and a fiver is a fiver, so just you keep your nerve and take it as it comes. I shot your cat. I was poking about in the furzes with a new air-gun, and seeing the beggar airing himself, I thought a quid for his skin was worth while, me being harder up than usual. So I fired to drop him, but he moved and so was saved alive. Then he was gone like a streak; and so was I, because I knowed you'd fetch him along to me so soon as you could, if he weren't done for. But I'm right down glad to have saved him and be nearly so fond of the chap now as you are yourself."

"You God-forgotten villain!" I cried to the wretch, trembling with white rage.

"I know," he answered. "That's all right, and you can lay it on so thick as you please and cuss till you're winded. But you understand the situation, don't you? You summons me, and I get a dressing down and a caution and a fine. And the fine will be ten shillings and sixpence; and time don't stand still and the matter will soon be forgot; and I get your five pounds."

"Hookem snivey beast!" I said to him. "That ban't all, I promise you! My five pound you may have; but I'll ruin your business and set every honest man and woman against you, and hound you out of Ponsworthy. By God's light I will!"

He laughed his hateful, coarse laugh, and his sharp nose grew sharper than ever.

"You do your worstest and welcome, Peter Blount," he said. "I ban't much afraid. There ain't no other vet. within ten miles that I know about, and the farmers don't care how wicked a man may be, so long as he knows how to cure their things. So you give me my fiver, and then have me up for trying to shoot your cat. And always remember that I'm terrible glad I missed his vitals—though how I

87

failed I can't guess, for 'twas bright moonlight and I was as sober as I am now."

I blazed up at that and ordered him out of my house, and he went; and I bided awake three parts of the night thinking on the awful ways of human nature and the hateful surprises that may be hid in your next-door neighbour and familiar friend. In fact I cussed Billy to hell and raged against him something furious; and first thing next morning I went up to Martin Bird and catched him taking down his shutters, and told him the monstrous tale.

It interested him a lot, and he seemed to think it funny in a way, though for my part I didn't see nothing funny to it.

"To give the traitor as shot Sunny Jim four pound ten shilling for his trouble, be a bit of a joke sure enough," said Martin Bird. "Of course, you'll have the satisfaction of getting him up afore the Justices and turning public opinion against him; but after all, as he very truly said, a cat's only a cat—masterpiece though your cat is known to be—and the law must hold an even balance between man and man; and when you think of the dark crimes that human nature will do at a pinch, the law have to keep a bit up its sleeve for the murderers and such like. And so, no doubt, ten and six for a cat be about the justice of it."

"I don't want no vengeance like that," I told Martin. "We all know vengeance be the Lord's; and to speak plain, I'm a lot more set now on keeping my five-pound note than on having that beastly toad afore the beaks. It ain't money, but the shame; for he'll have the laugh against me to my dying day if he gets the cash."

"He will," admitted Martin. "Billy Blades is an artful item best of times, and it would hit him much harder to withhold your money than have him up."

"But how can it be done in honesty?" I asked. "There it is in plain black and white. I offer five pounds to know who shot my cat; and he told me."

Martin Bird said it was a very pretty problem, but he didn't give up all hope of solving it. He was a clever man, as them with a barrow-load of children must be, if they want to keep their young and themselves out of the workhouse, and he promised me he'd look in during the evening if any light struck upon the subject.

"Anyway, 'tis Saturday, and you can well leave his claim unsettled till you decide whether to summon him," said Bird to me.

So I went home to Sunny Jim, and couldn't help feeling that anything less than the law against Billy would be treachery to my cat. And yet again, there was no doubt that Billy had been wondrous clever with the animal, and so healed his shoulder that he was to have the blessing of his leg. For what be the fulness of life to a cat on three legs? Billy had, in fact, made good his own evil work in a manner of speaking, and I was bound to admit that, once the cat was in his hands, he might have finished the murder, and I shouldn't have been none the wiser.

I couldn't see my duty all day, and the more I thought on Billy Blades the more I detested him, for he'd played a devilish part, and not been ashamed to confess it for blood money. So, when Martin strolled in, after he'd shut up his shop, and asked for a spot of whisky, I weren't no forwarder than in the morn. But, if anything, I hated worse than ever the thought of handing my five pounds to the assassin.

Martin stroked Sunny Jim for a bit and watched him walk, and said that by the look of it he was making a very brave recovery.

"The bone be joined up and the sinews going on fine," I told Bird, "and I shall leave him to nature now, for I won't have that cat murderer in my house no more."

"Well," answered Martin, "I believe I see the way out for you. It come to me, like the Light to Paul, while I was cutting off a pound of bacon. If you want to diddle Billy Blades, it can be done, and you've only to say the word."

"I do," I said. "I never felt to want nothing so much."

"Right," he answered. "Say no more, Peter, but just go about your business and leave the rest to me."

'Twas a very puzzling direction, and I asked Martin to speak a thought plainer; but he refused.

"See what happens o' Monday morning," was all he would answer.

89

And so, full of wonder and quite in the dark, I had to leave it at that.

Then Bird went his way after a lot of whisky, but he explained that I needn't grudge it, because he was going to take a tidy bit of trouble on my account. And when he was gone, me and Sunny Jim toddled off to bed. He couldn't quite get upstairs yet, so I had to carry him; and I reckoned that the poor hero had lost about three of his nine lives by this fearful adventure.

Nought happened Sunday, though, as I found afterwards, Martin had been so busy as a bee on my account; and when Monday came, afore I'd done my breakfast, and while the cat was washing his face after his, the mystery began to unfold. But when I say "washing his face" I must tell you that Sunny Jim could only polish up one side as yet, for his right front paw couldn't work to perfection so far; and 'twas among his greatest griefs, while he was recovering, that the right side of his head and his right whisker and right ear had to go untended. I done what I could, but nought to satisfy him.

Then who should come in but Andy White, the water-keeper, a very knowledgeable man with the rare gift to see in the dark.

"Well, White," I axed, "and what might you want?"

"Five pounds," he said. "I know who 'twas tried to slay your cat."

I leapt out of my chair as if I was sitting on fire.

"Guy Fawkes and angels!" I cried. "D'you tell me you done it, Andy?"

"Me done it!" he said. "No, Peter Blount, I ban't a cat shooter as ever I heard tell about. And I'm sorry you think I'd so demean myself. 'Twas Neddy Tutt, that young rip from Falcon Farm. He's got an air-gun and the deed was his."

Well, for the life of me I couldn't see even yet what was afoot, and after Andy had said he'd be round with proofs for his money a bit later, and had gone to work, I sat marvelling at his news.

And then, just as Mrs. Bassett come in to tidy up for me and see after one thing and another, which she performed regular for half-a-crown a week, who should knock at the door but Willie Stockman, the shoesmith.

"Hullo, Willie, and what can I do for you?" I asked the young man. He was rather a favourite of mine, for he had a kind heart and kept his widowed mother.

"Ban't what you can do for me, master, but what I can do for you," he answered. "Come in the garden and I'll tell you something you be wishful to know."

So I stepped out, and Sunny Jim, he stepped out with me. You'd have thought the blessed cat was in the know, for he sat and looked at Willie without winking while he spoke.

" 'Tis no less a job than the business of this poor creature," said Stockman. "I happened to be going home in the moonlight with my young woman, and just as us came through the furze brakes up over, I marked a chap with a gun. He lifted it and let fly, and then he was sloking off, but he came full upon us, Peter, and gave us 'Good night.' And 'twas that poaching rascal, Timothy Bamsey, from Lower Town. So now you know what you want to know. And I may say your five pounds be going to push on our wedding. There's no hurry, however till you've got the proofs of the crime."

Of course, I thanked him very grateful; and when he was gone I beginned slow and sure to see the terrible cunning of Martin Bird. In fact, I'd never have given the man credit for such amazing stratagems; and even that weren't all, for an hour later, as I was digging a few potatoes in the sun, and the cat was practising his game leg gentle, and seeing if he could clean his claws on the stem of my lilac bush according to his daily use, if Timothy Bamsey himself didn't heave up the road! A hugeous young man—six foot three inches of wickedness, by all accounts. I knew him by sight, no more, and I also knew he'd only escaped clink by the skin of his teeth after a row over the pheasants down to Squire Mannering's preserves. But there he was, and he stopped at the gate and asked in a big voice if I could tell him where I lived.

"Do'e know the man round about here what had his cat shot long ago?" said Timothy Bamsey to me, and I left my fork sticking in the ground and went down to him.

"I'm the man," I said, "and what about it?" For I felt sure he was come to own the felony and claim the fiver, same as Billy Blades had done. I felt fierce, I admit, for I was getting in a miz-maze along of all this plotting. I'd almost forgot Billy, and for the moment I felt as if I stood face to face with the real, living villain at last.

But he soon undeceived me.

"Well, I know who shot your cat, master. By chance I was going home along behind these here houses on the night, and just as I came down, I see a man in the moonlight lift a gun and fire—an air-gun it was, for there weren't no explosion, but just a whizz and a jolt, like what air-guns make. Then he runned forward to take up his prey; but he found nought. He cussed something terrible, and was just making off, when he very near ran into me and tried to hide his face. But I see him so plain as I see you this minute."

"And who was the man, Timothy Bamsey?" I asked, so stern as I could.

"Willie Stockman, the shoesmith," he answered. "There ain't no manner of doubt about it, I assure you. And I'll have my fiver, if it's all one, Mr. Blount."

Well, my head was spinning now till I thought it would roll off in the road.

"Us'll talk about this another time," I said to the man. "There's a mystery here, and I must seek my friends afore I do ought in such a dark matter. I'm very much obliged to you, and you'll hear of me again presently; but I don't part with no five-pound notes for the minute, for it begins to look as if I should have to summon half the parish afore I get to the bitter truth."

"I've told 'e the truth," he says, "and you owe me five pounds."

"I may, or I may not; but be sure justice shall be done," I said. And with that he went off, leaving me in a proper confusion of brain till the evening come. Then Martin dropped in to hear the result of his work. And when he did hear it he was terrible pleased.

"Now," he said, "you stand in a firm position, for here be a cloud of witnesses, Peter, and one man's word is as good as another's, and better for that matter. Because everybody knows Billy Blades is a liar, and nobody would take his word against t'others. So all you need to say is that you don't know who the deuce to believe among 'em, which is true. And then you keep your money in your pocket!"

"A masterpiece of politics, Martin!" I said. "And gratefully I thank you for it, but while Sunny Jim's living, it's always in the power of a wicked man to have the last word and lay him out. Don't you forget that."

"I haven't," answered Bird, who fairly staggered me with his wondrous brain power. "I haven't overlooked the future, and what I advise you to do be this, Peter; Ax the whole crew of 'em in to supper one night, and give 'em a tidy feed and a bit of baccy to each, and a bottle of whisky also. Do 'em a treat; then they'll all be your friends for life."

"And Blades also?" I asked.

"Certainly Blades. He's the one that matters most. 'Cause we know he done it in reality. Then, when they be got together and their bellies filled and their pipes drawing suent and their glasses topped up, you can tell 'em, amiable like, that they be a pack of bare-faced liars, and you find such a lot of men shot your cat that you ain't going to make no distinctions, but trust to the goodwill and gentlemanly feeling of 'em all never to do it no more. It will run you in a pound or so, but you're a snug man and won't be none the worse.

"You've took the lead in this matter," I said, "and I'll go through with it according as you direct. All I ask is that you come to the feed with the rest."

Which Martin Bird did do; and, God's my Judge, I never want to spend a pleasanter evening. They all obeyed my invite; and they all laughed fit to die when I told 'em they was a set of low-down, lying blackguards; and Billy Blades had to be seen home after, for he was blind afore the finish, singing shameful songs, as be long gone out of print, thank the watching Lord.

Sunny Jim, he much enjoyed his evening, also, and got nothing but kind words. And rabbit pie being very near his favourite food, he done himself so well as any of us. But the merriment tired him, and you can't blame the dear chap for not seeing the joke quite so clear as Billy and Timothy and Martin and Andy and Neddy and Willie saw it.

'Twas a good night, however, and me and Sunny Jim felt very glad to get to bed when the boys had gone.

And this I can say: no hand was ever lifted to my cat again. He walked on his way rejoicing, and though I ban't going to pretend he was ever quite the same light-hearted, high-spirited party as of old, yet his higher qualities still shine out of him; and he's all the world to me.

Billy Blades was round only a night ago, and he thought as Sunny Jim ought to live a good five year yet. So I be contented in my mind about him; and while there's a purr left in him, I shall be his very willing servant and faithful friend.

But never again! Life be a cloudy and difficult business enough at best without mixing yourself up with the dumb things and letting a creature without a soul into your heart. I won't love nought on four feet no more. They get too terrible a grip upon your vitals— specially if you're a lonely old blid, without much else to set store by, same as me.

The Cat and the Fiddle. Artist unknown.

THE CHINESE CAT

Pierre Loti

The cats belonging to French writers seemed truly to take on poetic qualities. Colette wrote beautifully of her cat. She maintained, "all our best friends are four-footed."

Not only writers, but composers in France took special delight in animals. Camille Saint Saens even composed music with them in mind, and he reminded us that "no animal could be more cajoling or more faithful than a cat, once you merit his good opinion, but he will not tolerate ill treatment, and he is exceedingly jealous."

Pierre Loti is a master in his description of a variety of cats. Here it is a Chinese cat that calls out for attention.

I well remember the day when our relations became really affectionate. It was a melancholy afternoon in September. The first winds of Autumn roughened the sullen seas. We were sailing eastward, and the ship groaned and creaked as she slid into the hollow of the waves. I sat writing in the semi-obscurity of my cabin, which grew darker and darker as the green waters rose and broke into foam over my closed port-hole. Suddenly I saw a little shadow steal from under my berth, very slowly, and as though with infinite hesitation. There was something truly Oriental in its fashion of holding one paw suspended in air, as if uncertain where to place it for the next step. And always it regarded me with a look of fixed and plaintive interrogation.

"What can the cat want?" I said to myself. "She has had her dinner. She is not hungry. What is it she is after?"

In answer to my unspoken question, la Chinoise crept nearer and nearer until she could touch my foot. Then, sitting upright, with her tail curled close about her, she uttered a gentle little cry, gazing meanwhile straight into my eyes which seemed to hold some message she could read. She understood that I was a thinking creature, capable of pity, and accessible to such mute and piteous prayer; and that my eyes were the mirrors in which her anxious little soul must study my good or bad intentions. It is terrifying to think how near an animal comes to us, when it is capable of such intercourse as this.

For the first time I looked attentively at the little visitor who for two weeks had shared my lodgings. She was tawny as a wild hare, and spotted like a leopard. Only her face and neck were white. Certainly an ugly and attenuated cat, yet perhaps her very ugliness had in it a piquancy which appealed to the discriminating mind. For one thing, she was so unlike the beautiful cats of France. (Alas! poor Moumoutte Blanche!) Stealthy and sinuous, with great ears standing erect, and a preposterously long tail, she had nothing attractive save her eyes,—the deep, golden orange eyes of the Orient, unquiet, and wonderfully expressive.

While I watched her, I carelessly laid my hand on her head, and stroked for the first time the yellow fur. It was not mere physical pleasure that she felt in the caress; but a consciousness of protection, of sympathy in her abandonment. It was for this she had crept from her hiding place; it was for this, and not for food or drink, that she had come to beg, after so much wistful hesitation. Her little cat soul implored some company, some friendship in a lonely world.

Where had she learned this need, poor outcast Pussy, never before touched by a kindly hand; never the object of affection,

96

unless, indeed, the paternal junk held some forlorn Chinese child, as joyless, as famished, as friendless as herself;—a child who, perishing of neglect, would leave in that miserable abode no more trace of its feeble existence than she had done.

At last one small paw was lifted, Oh!, so delicately, so discreetly; and, after a long anxious look, Moumoutte, believing the time had now come for venturing all things, took heart of grace, and leaped upon my knee.

There she curled herself, but with subdued tact and reserve, seeming to make her little limbs as light as possible, a mere featherweight—and never taking her eyes from my face. She stayed a long while, inconveniencing me greatly; but I lacked the courage to put her down, as I might have done unhesitatingly, had she been pretty and plump and gay. Nervously aware of my least movement, she watched me with intentness; not as though fearing I would do her harm,—she was far too intelligent to believe me capable of such a thing,—but as though to ask, "Is it possible that I do not weary or offend you?" After a time her expression softened from anxiety to cajolery, and her eyes, lifted to mine, said with charming distinctness: "On this Autumn evening, so dreary to the soul of a cat, since we two are isolated, and lost in the midst of dangers I do not understand, let us bestow upon each other a little of that mysterious something which sweetens misery and softens death, which is called affection, and which expresses itself from time to time by a caress."

Contentment. Artist unknown.

PODOLO

L. P. Hartley

In Japan the cat was called "the tiger who eats from the hand." In Siam, of course, the cat was a royal animal. But in many parts of the world, people's attitudes toward cats are ambiguous.

In Italy, there has long been a feeling that they should not be killed. For that reason, homeless cats were once seen all over that country. Years ago in the Trajan Forum in Rome, cats overran the streets. They were, we are happy to say, removed and given a special home in the suburbs in an effort to handle the overpopulation of cats.

The evening before we made the expedition to Podolo we talked it over, and I agreed there was nothing against it really.

"But why did you say you'd feel safer if Walter was going too?" Angela asked me. And he said, "What good should I be? I can't help to row the gondola, you know."

Then I felt rather silly, for everything I had said about Podolo was merely conversational exaggeration, meant to whet their curiosity, like a newspaper headline: and I knew that when Angela

Cat's Company. Nineteenth-century drawing by F. Bellew.

actually saw the dull little island, its stony and inhospitable shore littered with broken bottles and empty tins, she would think what a fool I was, with my romancing. So I took back everything I said, called my own bluff, as it were, and explained that I only avoided Podolo because of its exposed position: it was four miles from Venice, and if a boisterous bora got up (as it sometimes did, without warning) we should find getting back hard work, and might be home late. "And what will Walter say," I wound up, "if he comes back from Trieste" (he was going there for the day on business) "and finds no wife to welcome him?" Walter said, on the contrary, he had often wished such a thing might happen. And so, after some playful recriminations between this lately married, charming, devoted couple we agreed that Podolo should be the goal for tomorrow's picnic. "You must curb my wife's generous impulses," Walter warned me; "she always wants to do something for somebody. It's an expensive habit." I assured him at Podolo she would

99

The Owl and the Pussy-cat.
Drawing by Edward Lear.

find no calls on her heart or her purse. Except perhaps for a rat or two it was quite uninhabited. Next morning in brilliant sunshine Walter gulped down his breakfast and started for the station. It seemed hard that he should have to spend six hours of this divine day in a stuffy train. I stood on the balcony watching his departure.

The sunlight sparkled on the water; the gondola, in its best array, glowed and glittered. "Say good-bye to Angela for me," cried Walter as the gondolier braced himself for the first stroke. "And what is your postal address at Podolo?"

"Full fathom five," I called out, but I don't think my reply reached him.

Until you get right up to Podolo you can form no estimate of its size. There is nothing nearby to compare it with. On the horizon it looks like a foot-rule. Even now, though I have been there many times, I cannot say whether it is a hundred yards long or two hundred. But I have no wish to go back and make certain.

We cast anchor a few feet from the stony shore. Podolo, I must say, was looking its best, green, flowery, almost welcoming. One side is rounded to form the shallow arc of a circle: the other is straight. Seen from above, it must look like the moon in its first quarter. Seen as we saw it from the water line with the grassy rampart behind, it forms a kind of natural amphitheatre. The slim withy-like acacia trees give a certain charm to the foreground, and to the background where they grow in clumps, and cast darker shadows, an air of mystery. As we sat in the gondola we were like theater-goers in the stalls, staring at an empty stage.

It was nearly two o'clock when we began lunch. I was very hungry, and, charmed by my companion and occupied by my food, I did not let my eyes stray out of the boat. To Angela belonged the honor of discovering the first denizen of Podolo.

"Why," she exclaimed, "there's a cat." Sure enough there was: a little cat, hardly more than a kitten, very thin and scraggy, and mewing with automatic regularity every two or three seconds. Standing on the weedy stones at the water's edge it was a pitiful sight. "It's smelt the food," said Angela. "It's hungry. Probably it's starving."

Mario, the gondolier, had also made the discovery but he received it in a diffident spirit. "*Povera bestia*," he cried in sympathetic accents, but his eyes brightened. "Its owners did not want it. It has been put here on purpose, one sees." The idea that the cat had been left to starve caused him no great concern, but it shocked Angela profoundly.

"How abominable!" she exclaimed. "We must take it something to eat at once."

The suggestion did not recommend itself to Mario, who had to haul up the anchor and see the prospect of his own lunch growing more remote: I, too, thought we might wait till the meal was over. The cat would not die before our eyes. But Angela could brook no delay. So to the accompaniment of a good deal of stamping and heavy breathing the prow of the gondola was turned to land.

Meanwhile the cat continued to miaow, though it had retreated a little and was almost invisible, a thin wisp of tabby fur, against the parched stems of the outermost grasses.

Angela filled her hands with chicken bones.

"I'll try to win its confidence with these," she said, "and then if I can I shall catch it and put it in the boat and we'll take it to Venice. If it's left here it'll certainly starve."

101

She climbed along the knifelike gunwale of the gondola and stepped delicately on to the slippery boulders.

Continuing to eat my chicken in comfort, I watched her approach the cat. It ran away, but only a few yards: its hunger was obviously keeping its fear at bay. She threw a bit of food and it came nearer: another, and it came nearer still. Its demeanor grew less suspicious; its tail rose into the air; it came right up to Angela's feet. She pounced. But the cat was too quick for her; it slipped through her hands like water. Again hunger overpowered mistrust. Back it came. Once more Angela made a grab at it; once more it eluded her. But the third time she was successful. She got hold of its leg.

I shall never forget seeing it dangle from Angela's (fortunately) gloved hand. It wiggled and squirmed and fought, and in spite of its tiny size, the violence of its struggles made Angela quiver like a twig in a gale. And all the while it made the most extraordinary noise, the angriest, wickedest sound I ever heard. Instead of growing louder as its fury mounted, the sound actually decreased in volume, as though the creature was being choked by its own rage. The spitting died away into the thin ghost of a snarl, infinitely malevolent, but hardly more audible from where I was than the hiss of air from a punctured tire.

Mario was distressed by what he felt to be Angela's brutality. "Poor beast!" he exclaimed with pitying looks. "She ought not to treat it like that." And his face gleamed with satisfaction when, intimidated by the whirling claws, she let the cat drop. It streaked away into the grass, its belly to the ground.

Angela climbed back into the boat. "I nearly had it," she said, her voice still unsteady from the encounter. "I think I shall get it next time. I shall throw a coat over it." She ate her asparagus in silence, throwing the stalks over the side. I saw that she was preoccupied and couldn't get the cat out of her mind. Any form of suffering in others affected her almost like an illness. I began to wish we hadn't come to Podolo; it was not the first time a picnic there had gone badly.

"I tell you what," Angela said suddenly, "if I can't catch it I'll kill it. It's only a question of dropping one of these boulders on it. I could do it quite easily." She disclosed her plan to Mario, who was horror-struck. His code was different from hers. He did not mind the animal dying of slow starvation; that was in the course of nature. But deliberately to kill it! "*Poveretto!* it has done no one any harm," he exclaimed with indignation. But there was another reason, I suspected, for his attitude. Venice is overrun with cats, chiefly because it is considered unlucky to kill them. If they fall into the water and are drowned, so much the better, but woe betide anyone who pushed them in.

I expounded the gondolier's point of view to Angela, but she was not impressed. "Of course I don't expect him to do it," she said, "nor you either, if you'd rather not. It may be a messy business but it will soon be over. Poor little brute, it's in a horrible state. Its life can't be any pleasure to it."

"But we don't know that," I urged, still cravenly averse from the deed of blood. "If it could speak, it might say it preferred to live at all costs." But I couldn't move Angela from her purpose.

"Let's go and explore the island," she said, "until it's time to bathe. The cat will have got over its fright and be hungry again by then, and I'm sure I shall be able to catch it. I promise I won't murder it except as a last resource."

The word "murder" lingered unpleasantly in my mind as we made our survey of the island. You couldn't imagine a better place for one. During the war a battery had been mounted there. The concrete emplacement, about as long as a tennis court, remained: but nature and the weather had conspired to break it up, leaving black holes large enough to admit a man. These holes were like crevasses in a glacier, but masked by vegetation instead of snow. Even in the brilliant afternoon sunlight one had to tread cautiously. "Perhaps the cat has its lair down there," I said, indicating a gloomy cavern with a jagged edge. "I suppose its eyes would shine in the dark." Angela lay down on the pavement and peered in. "I thought I heard something move," she said, "but it might be anywhere in this rabbit-warren."

Our bath was a great success. The water was so warm one hardly felt the shock of going in. The only drawback was the mud, which clung to Angela's white bathing shoes, nasty sticky stuff. A little wind had got up. But the grassy rampart sheltered us; we leaned against it and smoked. Suddenly I noticed it was past five.

"We ought to go soon," I said. "We promised, do you remember, to send the gondola to meet Walter's train."

"All right," said Angela, "just let me have a go at the cat first. Let's put the food" (we had brought some remnants of lunch with us) "here where we last saw it, and watch."

There was no need to watch, for the cat appeared at once and made for the food. Angela and I stole up behind it, but I inadvertently kicked a stone and the cat was off like a flash. Angela looked at me reproachfully. "Perhaps you could manage better alone," I said. Angela seemed to think she could. I retreated a few yards, but the cat no doubt scenting a trap, refused to come out.

Angela threw herself on the pavement. "I can see it," she muttered. "I must win its confidence again. Give me three minutes and I'll catch it."

Three minutes passed. I felt concern for Angela, her lovely hair floating over the dark hole, her face, as much as one could see of it, a little red. The air was getting chilly.

"Look here," I said. "I'll wait for you in the gondola. When you've caught it, give a shout and I'll have the boat brought to land." Angela nodded; she dare not speak for fear of scaring her prey.

So I returned to the gondola. I could just see the line of Angela's shoulders; her face of course was hidden. Mario stood up, eagerly watching the chase. "She loves it so much," he said, "that she wants to kill it." I remembered Oscar Wilde's epigram, rather uncomfortably; still, nothing could be more disinterested than Angela's attitude to the cat. "We ought to start," the gondolier warned me. "The signore will be waiting at the station and wonder what has happened."

"What about Walter?" I called across the water. "He won't know what to do."

Cat Alert. Wood engraving by an unknown artist, in 1857 issue of Frank Leslie's Christmas Box.

Her mind was clearly on something else as she said: "Oh, he'll find his own way home."

More minutes passed. The gondolier smiled. "One must have patience with ladies," he said; "always patience."

I tried a last appeal. "If we started at once we could just do it."

She didn't answer. Presently I called out again. "What luck, Angela? Any hope of catching him?"

There was a pause: then I heard her say, in a curiously tense voice: "I'm not trying to *catch* him now."

The need for immediate hurry had passed, since we were irrevocably late for Walter. A sense of relaxation stole over me; I wrapped the rug round me to keep off the treacherous cold sirocco and I fell asleep. Almost at once, it seemed, I began to dream. In my dream it was night; we were hurrying across the lagoon trying to be in time for Walter's train. It was so dark I could see nothing but the dim blur of Venice ahead, and the little splash of whitish water where the oar dipped. Suddenly I stopped rowing and looked around. The seat behind me seemed to be empty. "Angela!" I cried; but there was no answer. I grew frightened. "Mario!" I shouted. "Where's the signora? We have left her behind! We must go back at once!" The gondolier, too, stopped rowing and came towards me: I could just distinguish his face; it had a wild look. "She's there, signore," he said. "But where? She's not on the seat." "She wouldn't stay on it," said the gondolier. And then, as is the way in dreams, I knew what his next words would be. "We loved her so we had to kill her."

An uprush of panic woke me. The feeling of relief at getting back to actuality was piercingly sweet. I was restored to the sunshine. At least I thought so, in the ecstasy of returning consciousness. The next moment I began to doubt, and an uneasiness, not unlike the beginning of nightmare, stirred in me again. I opened my eyes to the daylight but they didn't receive it. I looked out on to darkness. At first I couldn't believe my eyes: I wondered if I was fainting. But a glance at my watch explained everything. It was past seven o'clock. I had slept the brief twilight through and now it was night, though a few gleams lingered in the sky over Fusina.

106

Mario was not to be seen. I stood up and looked around. There he was on the poop, his knees drawn up, asleep. Before I had time to speak he opened his eyes, like a dog.

"Signore," he said, "you went to sleep, so I did too." To sleep out of hours is considered a joke all the world over; we both laughed. "But the signora," he said, "is *she* asleep? Or is she still trying to catch the cat?"

We strained our eyes toward the island which was much darker than the surrounding sky.

"That's where she was," said Mario, pointing, "but I can't see her now."

"Angela!" I called.

There was no answer, indeed no sound at all but the noise of the waves slapping against the gondola.

We stared at each other.

"Let us hope she has taken no harm," said Mario, a note of anxiety in his voice. "The cat was very fierce, but it wasn't big enough to hurt her, was it?"

"No, no," I said. "It might have scratched her when she was putting her face—you know—into one of those holes."

"She was trying to kill it, wasn't she?" asked Mario.

I nodded.

"*Ha fatto male*," said Mario. "In this country we are not accustomed to kill cats."

"*You* call, Mario," I said impatiently. "Your voice is stronger than mine."

Mario obeyed with a shout that might have raised the dead. But no answer came.

"Well," I said briskly, trying to conceal my agitation, "we must go and look for her or else we shall be late for dinner and the signore will be getting worried. She must be a *dormiotta*—a heavy sleeper."

Mario didn't answer.

"*Avanti!*" I said. "*Andiamo! Coraggio!*" I could not understand why Mario, usually so quick to execute an order, did not move. He was staring straight in front of him.

107

"There *is* someone on the island," he said at last, "but it's not the signora."

I must say, to do us justice, that within a couple of minutes we had beached the boat and landed. To my surprise Mario kept the oar in his hand. "I have a pocketknife," he remarked, "but the blade is only so long," indicating the third joint of a stalwart little finger.

"It was a man, then?" said I.

"It looked like a man's head."

"But you're not sure?"

"No, because it didn't walk like a man."

"How then?"

Mario bent forward and touched the ground with his free hand. I couldn't imagine why a man should go on all fours, unless he didn't want to be seen.

"He must have come while we were asleep," I said. "There'll be a boat round the other side. But let's look here first."

We were standing by the place where we had last seen Angela. The grass was broken and bent; she had left a handkerchief as though to mark the spot. Otherwise there was no trace of her.

"Now let's find the boat," I said.

We climbed the grassy rampart and began to walk round the shallow curve, stumbling over concealed brambles.

"Not here, not here," muttered Mario.

From our little eminence we could see clusters of lights twinkling across the lagoon; Fusina three or four miles away on the left, Malamocco the same distance on the right. And straight ahead Venice, floating on the water like a swarm of fireflies. But no boat. We stared at each other, bewildered.

"So he didn't come by water," said Mario at last. "He must have been here all the time."

"But are you quite certain it wasn't the signora you saw?" I asked. "How could you tell in the darkness?"

"Because the signora was wearing a white dress," said Mario. "And this one is all in black—unless he is a Negro."

108

"That's why it's so difficult to see him."

"Yes, we can't see him, but he can see us all right."

I felt a curious sensation up my spine.

"Mario," I said, "he must have seen her, you know. Do you think he's got anything to do with her not being here?"

Mario didn't answer.

"I don't understand why he doesn't speak to us."

"Perhaps he can't speak."

"But you thought he was a man. . . . Anyhow, we are two against one. Come on. You take the right. I'll go to the left."

We soon lost sight of each other in the darkness, but once or twice I heard Mario swearing as he scratched himself on the acacia bushes. My search was more successful than I expected. Right at the corner of the island, close to the water's edge, I found one of Angela's bathing shoes: she must have taken it off in a hurry, for the button was torn away. A little later I made a grisly discovery. It was the cat, dead, its head crushed. The pathetic little heap of fur would never suffer the pangs of hunger again. Angela had been as good as her word.

I was going to call Mario when the bushes parted and something hurled itself upon me. I was swept off my feet. Alternately dragging and carrying me, my captor continued his headlong course. The next thing I knew I was pitched pell-mell into the gondola and felt the boat move under me.

"Mario!" I gasped. And then—absurd question—"What have you done with the oar?"

The gondolier's white face stared down at me.

"The oar? I left it—it wasn't any use, signore. I tried . . . What it wants is a machine gun."

He was rowing frantically with my oar: the island began to recede.

"But we can't go away," I cried.

The gondolier said nothing, but rowed with all his strength. Then he began to talk under his breath. "It was a good oar, too," I heard him mutter. Suddenly he left the poop, climbed over the cushions and sat down beside me.

109

"When I found her," he whispered, "she wasn't quite dead."

I began to speak but he held up his hand.

"She asked me to kill her."

"But, Mario!"

" 'Before it comes back,' she said. And then she said, '*It's* starving too and it won't wait . . .' " Mario bent his head nearer but his voice was inaudible.

"Speak up," I cried. The next moment I implored him to stop.

Mario clambered on to the poop.

"You don't want to go to the island now, signore?"

"No, no. Straight home."

I looked back. Transparent darkness covered the lagoon save for one shadow that stained the horizon black. Podolo . . .

The Black Cat.
Eighteenth-century woodcut by unknown artist.

PUDDLES OF PORTSMOUTH

Francis Buckland

Francis Buckland was one of the most famous naturalists and zoologists of the nineteenth century. He acquired his intense interests and affection for animals as a very young man, and when he went to the university, he shared his room with a bear. This occasioned the remark of one of his provosts that "either you, Buckland, or the bear must go."

In later years, Buckland not only ran zoos in England but carefully studied which animals suffered or thrived in captivity. All kinds of animals lived with him, from monkeys to cats. No matter where he went, he had an eye for a wonderful story. In a way, he was somewhat like James Herriot of today.

One fine warm day in the summer of 1863, being tired out with the heat of London and incessant work, I stretched myself out upon the shingle near Southsea Castle, and was soon dozing in the sun. I was ere long awoke by hearing the splash of an oar, and jumping up hastily, saw, good reader, the scene which, by the aid of the pencil of Mr. Hyde Briscoe, the artist, I am now enabled to reproduce.

I observed a little way from the shore a queer-looking old man

A Canal Cat, by W. H. Drake.

sitting in the smallest boat that could contain a human frame, and gazing fixedly at me. This old man's face was browned by long exposure to the sea-breeze; his grizzled hair, like bunches of sea-weed, hung loosely about from under his cap; his dress consisted principally of rags of old blue sailor's cloth, and he had but one hand, with which he sculled his boat, which contained his rude tackle and himself.

Notwithstanding his dress and turn-out, the old man's countenance was beaming with intelligence, and from under his well-formed forehead brightly gleamed two telescopic eyes, indicating an observant and reflecting mind, showing that (as I afterwards found out) he was no ordinary person.

'By Jove!' said I, 'well, I am lucky; here's Neptune himself! I never thought I should have had this chance. Good morning, my friend.'

'Morning sir,' said he with a touch of his old sea cap.

'What have you been after, if I may ask?'

'Pout* fishing, sir, all night, and terrible bad luck of it I've had, the tide was so cruel strong and the water was so slobby, that I only ketched a few pouts. But I lost such a lobster! I hauled him up alongside, and I got hold of his claw; but it was so big I could not

* Whiting-pout.

112

grasp master Lobster with my one hand; and he was well hooked too, but he gave a jerk and a kick and dragged the hook straight, and he went down starn foremost thinking he had been plenty high enough up. Ah! he *was* a fine lobster, he was all twelve pounds, and worth four shillings to anybody.'

'But what have you done with your other hand?' said I.

'Oh I lost him too,' answered my friend.

'Did you lose him just now?'

'No sir. I lost him thirty years ago, when I was in His Majesty's service as captain of the foretop on board the "Hind" frigate, off Cape Horn, on the coast of Peru. I got him jammed between two water casks, and the doctor took the slack of him off.'

'What's your name?'

'Well, my right name is George Butler, but they call me "Robinson Crusoe" about these parts."

I bought his pouts, and proceeded to examine his boat, which he paddled ashore. Robinson Crusoe told me he had given a sovereign for her seven years ago. Such a boat it was!—more like in size and shape the half of a house water-butt than a boat: so rotten too, that a good kick would have sent it into a thousand pieces. The planks were started in many places, and there were great holes in the sides, mended with bits of old canvas, leather, and tin nailed over them. The bottom was covered with sea grass and shells; yet in this boat old Robinson Crusoe faces weather in which no ordinary boat would live; he has no fear of the waves.

'I think the waves knows me, sir,' said he; 'they never hurts me and my boat. We swims over their tops like an egg-shell, and I am out a-fishing all weathers, particular when a storm bates a bit, because then the water thickens, and the fish bites. My boat never ships a drop of water, not so much as there is rum in this 'ere rum bottle.' The old man winked as he said this. 'If I was a rich man, and got a thousand a year, I would still go out a-fishing, for I likes the sport; and I'd go to Greenwich Hospital, but then I'd lose my fishing. I am a very poor man, but I *must* have my fishing. I generally goes out of a night and fishes all night; but it's terrible cold at night, and then I rigs up my hurricane house. I gets under my old tarpaulin and lies as snug as may be. And the ships sees me better because I looks like a buoy, and keeps clear of me.

I never mind rough weather; but it's the fog as is so deceiving. One morning I was off the Spit, when I thought I saw a man in a boat coming; I paddled up to it and found it was only a bottle cork as was floating with the tide, and at that time a wine bottle floating in the fog looked like a seventy-four. I saved the Irish steamer coming from London the other day when the fog was terrible thick. She was coming into Portsmouth, and I was fishing at the mouth of Langston harbour when I hears her paddle-wheels a-coming. I halloes to her as how she was going stem on to the Lumps Rocks, and so she would have, if it had not been for me; but they never gave me nothing at all for saving of them. It's much more lonely at night now than when I had my Puddles with me.'

'Puddles! what's that?'

'It's my cat, sir, and that's why they call me "Robinson Crusoe" 'cause of my boat and my cat. He was the wonderfullest water cat as ever come out of Portsmouth harbour was Puddles, and he used to go out a-fishing with me every night. On cold nights he would sit in my lap, while I was a-fishing, and poke his head out every now and then, or else I would wrap him up in a sail, and make him lay quiet. He'd lay down on me when I was asleep, and if anybody come he'd swear a good one, and have the face off on 'em if they went to touch me; and he'd never touch a fish, not even a little teeny pout, if you did not give it him. I was obligated to take him out a-fishing, for else he would stand and yowl and marr till I went back and catched him by the poll and shied him into the boat, and then he was quite happy. When it was fine he used to stick up at the bows of the boat and sit a-watching the dogs.* The dogs used to come alongside by thousands at a time, and when they was thick all about he would dive in and fetch them out jammed in his mouth as fast as may be, just as if they were a parcel of rats, and he did not tremble with the cold half as much as a Newfoundland dog: he was used to it. He looked terrible wild about the head

* Dog-fish.

114

when he come up out of the water with the dog-fish. I larnt him the water myself. One day when he was a kitten I took him down to the sea to wash and brush the fleas out of him, and in a week he would swim after a feather or a cork. He was a black cat natural, and I think the sea water made him blacker; his coat was as clean as a smelt, and had a noble gloss on it. I would not grudge a five-pound note, poor man as I am, to have my cat back. Oh dear, my poor cat! My Puddles was as good a cat for a rat as he was for a fish. I cleared out my cellar once, and I found twenty rats' skins as Puddles had killed, all scooped out as clean as your 'bacca-pouch, but the tails was not touched. He was a plaguey cat, though, for he would go out into the harbour to catch rats, and come in all covered with mud and lay on my bed. I used to give *him* the cat. I says, "So you've been up on my bed before you was dry, have you? Now take your punishment like a man." So I takes a nettle, and stands him on his front paws on the bottom step of the stairs, and I gives him his dozen. He stood quiet enought while I gave him a dozen; but if I gave him thirteen, "marr" he'd go, and away he'd fly as savage as could be. It was a bad day when I lost my Puddles; he was the most superbest cat as was ever afloat. I thinks he was taken aboard a ship as went to the West Indies (sailors is terrible fond of cats, least-ways them as has only got one tail), or else he was killed for his fine skin. There was a terrible cry for cats' skins in Gosport at one time, and if I could only catch the beef-headed fellow as killed him, I'd up with my stump and hammer him like a stock fish. Them as is cruel to dumb animals is always cowards; and if I was a judge I'd soon clap the irons on their legs. I am going to bring up another cat to the water. I got a kitten at home now, but he won't act at all. I must get one before he can see, and in with him into the water, and then he will take to it. Cats is terrible hard things to drown. There was a man the other day as wanted to drown a cat, so he tied a five-pound brick round his neck, and hove that ere cat with the brick on him in the water. But when he got home the cat was there fust; so he ties a stone on to the cat, but even *then* he got sheer of the rope, for he gnawed it off with his grinders, and it was three times before he drowned that ere cat.'

A KITTEN

Agnes Repplier

One of the most charming of essayists, Agnes Repplier was the proud owner of an exceptional cat called Agrippina. After the cat's death, she often found herself extolling this remarkable animal. This wonderful evocation of kittenhood is one for which Agrippina's son, Nero, had been an inspiration.

If "The child is father of the man," why is not the kitten father of the cat? If in the little boy there lurks the infant likeness of all that manhood will complete, why does not the kitten betray some of the attributes common to the adult puss? A puppy is but a dog, plus high spirits, and minus common sense. We never hear our friends say they love puppies, but cannot bear dogs. A kitten is a thing apart; and many people who lack the discriminating enthusiasm for cats, who regard these beautiful beasts with aversion and mistrust, are won over easily, and cajoled out of their prejudices by the deceitful wiles of kittenhood.

"The little actor cons another part," and is the most irresistible comedian in the world. Its wide-open eyes gleam with wonder and mirth. It darts madly at nothing at all, and then, as though suddenly checked in the pursuit, prances sideways on its hind legs with

116

ridiculous agility and zeal. It makes a vast pretense of climbing the rounds of a chair, and swings by the curtain like an acrobat. It scrambles up a table leg, and is seized with comic horror at finding itself full two feet from the floor. If you hasten to its rescue, it clutches you nervously, its little heart thumping against its furry sides, while its soft paws expand and contract with agitation and relief;

> And all their harmless claws disclose,
> Like prickles of an early rose.

Yet the instant it is back on the carpet it feigns to be suspicious of your interference, peers at you out of "the tail o' its ee," and scampers for protection under the sofa, from which asylum it presently emerges with cautious trailing steps, as though encompassed by fearful dangers and alarms. Its baby innocence is yet unseared. The evil knowledge of uncanny things which is the dark inheritance of cathood has not yet shadowed its round infant eyes. Where did witches find the mysterious beasts that sat motionless by their fires, and watched unblinkingly the waxen manikins dwindling in the flame? They never reared these companions of their solitude, for no witch could have endured to see a kitten gamboling on her hearthstone. A witch's kitten! That one preposterous thought proves how wide, how unfathomed, is the gap between feline infancy and age.

So it happens that the kitten is loved and cherished and caressed as long as it preserves the beguiling mirthfulness of youth. Richelieu, we know, was wont to keep a family of kittens in his cabinet, that their grace and gaiety might divert him from the cares of state, and from black moods of melancholy. Yet, with short-sighted selfishness, he banished these little friends when but a few months old, and gave their places to younger pets. The first faint dawn of reason, the first indication of soberness and worldly wisdom, the first charming and coquettish pretenses to maturity, were followed by immediate dismissal. Richelieu desired to be amused. He had no conception of the finer joy which springs from mutual companionship and esteem. Even humbler and more sincere admirers,

117

like Joanna Baillie, in whom we wish to believe Puss found a friend and champion, appear to take it for granted that the kitten should be the spoiled darling of the household, and the cat a social outcast, degraded into usefulness, and expected to work for her living. What else can be understood from such lines as these?

> Ah! many a lightly sportive child,
> Who hath, like thee, our wits beguiled,
> To dull and sober manhood grown,
> With strange recoil our hearts disown.
> Even so, poor Kit! must thou endure,
> When thou becomest a cat demure,
> Full many a cuff and angry word,
> Chid roughly from the tempting board.
> And yet, for that thou hast, I ween,
> So oft our favored playmate been,
> Soft be the change which thou shalt prove,
> *When time hath spoiled thee of our love;*
> Still be thou deemed, by housewife fat,
> A comely, careful, mousing cat,
> Whose dish is, for the public good,
> Replenished oft with savory food.

Here is a plain exposition of the utilitarian theory which Shakespeare is supposed to have countenanced because Shylock speaks of the "harmless, necessary cat." Shylock, forsooth! As if he, of all men in Christendom or Jewry, knew anything about cats! Small wonder that he was outwitted by Portia and Jessica, when an adroit little animal could so easily beguile him. But Joanna Baillie should never have been guilty of those snug commonplaces concerning the "comely, careful, mousing cat," remembering her own valiant Tabby who won Scott's respectful admiration by worrying and killing a dog. It ill became the possessor of an Amazonian cat, distinguished by Sir Walter's regard, to speak with such patronizing kindness of the race.

We can make no more stupid blunder than to look upon our pets from the standpoint of utility. Puss, as a rule, is another Nimrod,

118

eager for the chase, and unwearyingly patient in pursuit of her prey. But she hunts for her own pleasure, not for our convenience; and when a life of luxury has relaxed her zeal, she often declines to hunt at all. I knew intimately two Maryland cats, well born and of great personal attractions. The sleek, black Tom was named Onyx, and his snow-white companion Lilian. Both were idle, urbane, fastidious, and self-indulgent as Lucullus. Now, into the house honored, but not served, by these charming creatures came a rat, which secured permanent lodgings in the kitchen, and speedily evicted the maid servants. A reign of terror followed, and after a few days of hopeless anarchy it occurred to the cook that the cats might be brought from their comfortable cushions upstairs and shut in at night with their hereditary foe. This was done, and the next morning, on opening the kitchen door, a tableau rivaling the peaceful scenes of Eden was presented to the view. On one side of the hearth lay Onyx, on the other, Lilian; and ten feet away, upright upon the kitchen table, sat the rat, contemplating them both with tranquil humor and content. It was apparent to him, as well as the rest of the household, that he was an object of absolute, contemptuous indifference to those two lordly cats.

There is none of this superb unconcern in the joyous eagerness of infancy. A kitten will dart in pursuit of everything that is small enough to be chased with safety. Not a fly on the window-pane, not a moth in the air, not a tiny crawling insect on the carpet, escapes its unwelcome attentions. It begins to "take notice" as soon as its eyes are open, and its vivacity, outstripping its dawning intelligence, leads it into infantile perils and wrong doing. I own that when Agrippina brought her first-born son—aged two days— and established him in my bedroom closet, the plan struck me at the start as inconvenient. I had prepared another nursery for the little Claudius Nero, and I endeavored for a while to convince his mother that my arrangements were best. But Agrippina was inflexible. The closet suited her in every respect; and, with charming and irresistible flattery, she gave me to understand, in the mute language I knew so well, that she wished her baby boy to be under

119

The End of Sir Rat.
Drawings by Oliver Herford.

my immediate protection. "I bring him to you because I trust you," she said as plainly as looks can speak. "Downstairs they handle him all the time, and it is not good for kittens to be handled. Here he is safe from harm, and here he shall remain." After a few weak remonstrances, the futility of which I too clearly understood, her persistence carried the day. I removed my clothing from the closet, spread a shawl upon the floor, had the door taken from its hinges, and resigned myself, for the first time in my life, to the daily and hourly companionship of an infant.

I was amply rewarded. People who require the household cat to rear her offspring in some remote attic, or dark corner of the cellar, have no idea of all the diversion and pleasure that they lose. It is delightful to watch the little blind, sprawling, feeble, helpless things develop swiftly into the grace and agility of kittenhood. It is delightful to see the mingled pride and anxiety of the mother, whose parental love increases with every hour of care, and who exhibits her young family as if they were infant Gracchi, the hope of all their race. During Nero's extreme youth, there were times, I admit, when Agrippina wearied both of his companionship and of her own maternal duties. Once or twice she abandoned him at night for the greater luxury of my bed, where she slept tranquilly by my side, unmindful of the little wailing cries with which Nero lamented her desertion. Once or twice the heat of early summer tempted her to spend the evening on the porch roof which lay beneath my windows, and I have passed some anxious hours awaiting her return, and wondering what would happen if she never came back, and I were left to bring up the baby by hand.

But as the days sped on, and Nero grew rapidly in beauty and intelligence, Agrippina's affection for him knew no bounds. She could hardly bear to leave him even for a little while, and always came hurrying back to him with a loud frightened mew, as if fearing he might have been stolen in her absence. At night she purred over him for hours, or made little gurgling noises expressive of ineffable content. She resented the careless curiosity of strangers, and was a trifle supercilious when the cook stole softly in to give vent to her fervent admiration. But from first to last she shared with me her pride and pleasure; and the joy in her beautiful eyes, as she raised them to mine, was frankly confiding and sympathetic. When the infant Claudius rolled for the first time over the ledge of the closet, and lay sprawling on the bedroom floor, it would have been hard to say which of us was the more elated at his prowess. A narrow pink ribbon of honor was at once tied around the small adventurer's neck, and he was pronounced the most daring and agile of kittens. From that day his brief career was a series of brilliant triumphs. He was a kitten of parts. Like one of Miss Austen's heroes, he had air and countenance. Less beautiful than his mother, whom he closely resembled, he easily eclipsed her in vivacity and the specious arts of fascination. Never were mother and son more unlike in character and disposition, and the inevitable contrast between kittenhood and cathood was enhanced in this case by a strong natural dissimilarity which no length of years could have utterly effaced.

Agrippina had always been a cat of manifest reserve. She was only six weeks old when she came to me, and had already acquired that gravity of demeanor, that air of gentle disdain, that dignified and somewhat supercilious composure, which won the respectful admiration of those whom she permitted to enjoy her acquaintance. Even in moments of self-forgetfulness and mirth her recreations resembled those of the little Spanish Infanta, who, not being permitted to play with her inferiors, and having no equals, diverted herself as best she could with sedate and solitary sport. Always chary of her favors, Agrippina cared little for the admiration of her chosen circle; and, with a single exception, she made no friends beyond it.

Claudius Nero, on the contrary, thirsted for applause. Affable, debonair, and democratic to the core, the caresses and commendations of a chance visitor or of a housemaid were as valuable to him as were my own. I never looked at him "showing off," as children say,—jumping from chair to chair, balancing himself on the bedpost, or scrambling rapturously up the forbidden curtains,—without thinking of the young Emperor who contended in the amphitheatre for the worthless plaudits of the crowd. He was impulsive and affectionate,—so, I believe was the Emperor for a time,—and as masterful as if born to the purple. His mother struggled hard to maintain her rightful authority, but it was in vain. He woke her from her sweetest naps; he darted at her tail, and leaped down on her from sofas and tables with the grace of a diminutive panther. Every time she attempted to punish him for these misdemeanors he cried piteously for help, and was promptly and unwisely rescued by some kind-hearted member of the family. After a while Agrippina took to sitting on her tail, in order to keep it out of his reach, and I have seen her many times carefully tucking it out of sight. She had never been a cat of active habits or of showy accomplishments, and the daring agility of the little Nero amazed and bewildered her. "A Spaniard," observes that pleasant gossip James Howell, "walks as if he marched, and seldom looks upon the ground, as if he contemned it. I was told of a Spaniard who, having got a fall by a stumble, and broke his nose, rose up, and in a disdainful manner said, 'This comes of walking on the earth.' "

Now Nero seldom walked on the earth. At least, he never, if he could help it, walked on the floor; but traversed a room in a series of flying leaps from chair to table, from table to lounge, from lounge to desk, with an occasional dash at the mantelpiece, just to show what he could do. It was curious to watch Agrippina during the performance of these acrobatic feats. Pride, pleasure, the anxiety of a mother, and the faint resentment of conscious inferiority struggled for mastership in her little breast. Sometimes, when Nero's radiant self-satisfaction grew almost insufferable, I have seen her eyelids narrow sullenly, and have wondered whether the Roman Empress ever looked in that way at her brilliant and beautiful son, when maternal love was withering slowly under the shadow of coming evil. Sometimes, when Nero had been prancing and paddling about with absurd and irresistible glee, attracting and compelling the attention of everybody in the room, Agrippina would jump up on my lap, and look in my face with an expression I thought I understood. She had never before valued my affection in all her little petted, pampered life. She had been sufficient for herself, and had merely tolerated me as a devoted and useful companion. But now that another had usurped so many of her privileges, I fancied there were moments when it pleased her to know that one subject, at least, was not to be beguiled from allegiance; that to one friend, at least, she always was and always would be the dearest cat in the world.

I am glad to remember that love triumphed over jealousy, and that Agrippina's devotion to Nero increased with every day of his short life. The altruism of a cat seldom reaches beyond her kittens; but she is capable of heroic unselfishness where they are concerned. I knew of a London beast, a homeless, forlorn vagrant, who constituted herself an out-door pensioner at the house of a friendly man of letters. This cat had a kitten, whose youthful vivacity won the hearts of a neighboring family. They adopted it willingly, but refused to harbor the mother, who still came for her daily dole to her only benefactor. Whenever a bit of fish or some other especial dainty was given her, this poor mendicant scaled the wall, and watched her chance to share it with her kitten, her little wealthy, greedy son, who gobbled it up as remorselessly as if he were not living on the fat of the land.

Agrippina would have been swift to follow such an example of devotion. At dinner time she always yielded the precedence to Nero, and it became one of our daily tasks to compel the little lad to respect his mother's privileges. He scorned his saucer of milk, and from tenderest infancy aspired to adult food, making predatory incursions upon Agrippina's plate, and obliging us finally to feed them in separate apartments. I have seen him, when a very young kitten, rear himself upon his baby legs, and with his soft and wicked little paw strike his mother in the face until she dropped the piece of meat she had been eating, when he tranquilly devoured it. It was to prevent the recurrence of such scandalous scenes that two dining-rooms became a necessity in the family. Yet he was so loving and so lovable, poor little Claudius Nero! Why do I dwell on his faults, remembering, as I do, his winning sweetness and affability? Day after day, in the narrow city garden, the two cats played together, happy in each other's society, and never a yard apart. Night after night they retired at the same time, and slept upon the same cushion, curled up inextricably into one soft, furry ball. Many times I have knelt by their chair to bid them both goodnight; and always, when

I did so, Agrippina would lift her charming head, purr drowsily for a few seconds, and then nestle closer still to her first-born, with sighs of supreme satisfaction. The zenith of her life had been reached. Her cup of contentment was full.

It is a rude world, even for little cats, and evil chances lie in wait for the petted creatures we strive to shield from harm. Remembering the pangs of separation, the possibilities of unkindness or neglect, the troubles that hide in ambush on every unturned page, I am sometimes glad that the same cruel and selfish blow struck both mother and son, and that they lie together, safe from hurt or hazard, sleeping tranquilly and always, under the shadow of the friendly pines.

Country Cats, by W. A. Rogers.

CALVIN–HIS LIFE AND DEATH

Charles Dudley Warner

Charles Dudley Warner, at the time Calvin came to live with him, was the editor of one of the oldest newspapers in the United States— The Hartford Courant. *He was the co-author of* The Gilded Age *with Mark Twain, and a dear friend to most of those great literary lights of Hartford which included Twain, Harriet Beecher Stowe, and many others.*

It was Harriet Beecher Stowe who gave Calvin to Charles Dudley Warner. He was a man of unusual sensibility, and he brought out the magnificent qualities of probably one of the most famous cats in American literary history.

Let us have peas. I have been a zealous advocate of the birds. I have rejoiced in their multiplication. I have endured their concerts at four o'clock in the morning without a murmur. Let them come, I said, and eat the worms, in order that we, later, may enjoy the foliage and the fruits of the earth. We have a cat, a magnificent animal (but not a pole-cat),—so large and powerful that, if he were in the army, he would be called Long Tom. He is a cat of fine disposition, the most irreproachable morals I ever saw thrown away in a cat, and a splendid hunter. He spends his nights, not in social dissipation, but in gathering in rats, mice, flying-squirrels, and also birds. When he first brought me a bird, I told him that it was wrong, and tried to convince him, while he was eating it, that he was doing wrong; for he is a reasonable cat, and understands pretty much everything except the binomial theorem and the time down the cycloidal arc. But with no effect. The killing of birds went on, to my great regret and shame.

The other day I went to my garden to get a mess of peas. I had seen the day before that they were just ready to pick. How I had lined the ground, planted, hoed, bushed them! The bushes were very fine,—seven feet high, and of good wood. How I had delighted in the growing, the blowing, the podding! What a touching thought it was that they had all podded for me! When I went to pick them I found the pods all split open, and the peas gone. The dear little birds, who are so fond of the strawberries, had eaten them all. Perhaps there were left as many as I planted; I did not count them. I made a rapid estimate of the cost of the seed, the interest of the ground, the price of labor, the value of the bushes, the anxiety of weeks of watchfulness. I looked about me on the face of Nature. The wind blew from the south so soft and treacherous! A thrush sang in the woods so deceitfully! All Nature seemed fair. But who was to give me back my peas? The fowls of the air have peas; but what has man!

I went into the house. I called Calvin. (That is the name of our cat, given him on account of his gravity, morality, and uprightness. We never familiarly call him John.) I petted Calvin. I lavished upon him an enthusiastic fondness. I told him that he had no fault; that the one action that I had called a vice was an heroic exhibition of regard for my interests. I bade him go and do likewise continually. I now saw how much better instinct is than mere unguided reason. Calvin knew. If he had put his opinion into English (instead of his native catalogue), it would have been, "You need not teach your grandmother to suck eggs." It was only the round of Nature. The worms eat a noxious something in the ground. The birds eat the worms. Calvin eats the birds. We eat—no, we do not eat Calvin. There the chain stops. When you ascend the scale of being, and come to an animal that is, like ourselves, inedible, you have arrived at a result where you can rest. Let us respect the cat. He completes an edible chain. . . .

The pleasure of gardening in these days when the thermometer is at ninety, is one that I fear I shall not be able to make intelligible to my readers, many of whom do not appreciate the delight of soaking in the sunshine. I suppose that the sun, going through a man, as it will on such a day, takes out of him rheumatism, consumption, and every other disease, except sudden death—from sunstroke. But, aside from this, there is an odor from the evergreens, the hedges, the various plants and vines, that is only expressed and set afloat at a high temperature, which is delicious; and, hot as it may be, a little breeze will come at intervals, which can be heard in the tree-tops, and which is an unobtrusive benediction. I hear a quail or two whistling in the ravine; and there is a good deal of fragmentary conversation going on among the birds, even on the warmest days. The companionship of Calvin, also, counts for a good deal. He usually attends me, unless I work too long in one place; sitting down on the turf, displaying the ermine of his breast, and watching my movements with great intelligence. He has a feline and genuine love for the beauties of Nature, and will establish himself where there is a good view, and look on it for hours. He always accompanies us when we go to gather the vegetables, seeming to be desirous to know what we are to have for dinner. He is a connoisseur in the garden; being fond of almost all the vegetables, except the cucumber,—a dietetic hint to man. I believe it is also said that the pig will not eat tobacco. These are important facts. It is singular, however, that those who hold up the pigs as models to us never hold us up as models to the pigs.

I wish I knew as much about natural history and the habits of animals as Calvin does. He is the closest observer I ever saw; and there are few species of animals on the place that he has not analyzed. I think that he has, to use a euphemism very applicable to him, got

The Cat and the Tortoise, by F. Calvert

outside of every one of them, except the toad. To the toad he is entirely indifferent; but I presume he knows that the toad is the most useful animal in the garden. I think the Agricultural Society ought to offer a prize for the finest toad. When Polly comes to sit in the shade near my strawberry-beds, to shell peas, Calvin is always lying near in apparent obliviousness; but not the slightest unusual sound can be made in the bushes that he is not alert, and prepared to investigate the cause of it. It is this habit of observation, so cultivated, which has given him such a trained mind, and made him so philosophical. It is within the capacity of even the humblest of us to attain this.

Calvin is dead. His life, long to him, but short for the rest of us, was not marked by startling adventures, but his character was so uncommon and his qualities were so worthy of imitation, that I have been asked by those who personally knew him to set down my recollections of his career.

His origin and ancestry were shrouded in mystery; even his age was a matter of pure conjecture. Although he was of the Maltese race, I have reason to suppose that he was American by birth as he certainly was in sympathy. Calvin was given to me eight years ago by Mrs. Stowe, but she knew nothing of his age or origin. He walked into her house one day out of the great unknown and became at once at home, as if he had been always a friend of the family. He appeared to have artistic and literary tastes, and it was as if he had inquired at the door if that was the residence of the author of *Uncle Tom's Cabin*, and, upon being assured that it was, had decided to dwell there. This is, of course, fanciful, for his antecedents were wholly unknown, but in his time he could hardly have been in any household where he would not have heard *Uncle Tom's Cabin* talked about. When he came to Mrs. Stowe, he was as large as he ever was, and apparently as old as he ever became. Yet there was in him no appearance of age; he was in the happy maturity of all his powers, and you would have said in that maturity he had found the secret of perpetual youth. And it was as difficult to believe that he would ever be aged as it was to imagine that he had ever been in immature youth. There was in him a mysterious perpetuity.

After some years, when Mrs. Stowe made her winter home in Florida, Calvin came to live with us. From the first moment, he fell into the ways of the house and assumed a recognized position in the family,—I say recognized, because after he became known he was always inquired for by visitors, and in the letters to the other members of the family he always received a message. Although the least obtrusive of beings, his individuality always made itself felt.

His personal appearance had much to do with this, for he was of royal mould, and had an air of high breeding. He was large, but he had nothing of the fat grossness of the celebrated Angora family; though powerful, he was exquisitely proportioned, and as graceful in every movement as a young leopard. When he stood up to open a door—he opened all the doors with old-fashioned latches—he was portentously tall, and when stretched on the rug before the fire he seemed too long for this world—as indeed he was. His coat was the finest and softest I have ever seen, a shade of quiet Maltese; and from his throat downward, underneath, to the tips of his feet, he wore the whitest and most delicate ermine; and no person was ever more fastidiously neat. In his finely formed head you saw something of his aristocratic character; the ears were small and cleanly cut, there was a tinge of pink in the nostrils, his face was handsome, and the expression of his countenance exceedingly intelligent—I should call it even a sweet expression if the term were not inconsistent with his look of alertness and sagacity.

It is difficult to convey a just idea of his gaiety in connection with his dignity and gravity, which his name expressed. As we know nothing of his family, of course it will be understood that Calvin was his Christian name. He had times of relaxation into utter playfulness, delighting in a ball of yarn, catching sportively at stray ribbons when his mistress was at her toilet, and pursuing his own tail, with hilarity, for lack of anything better. He could amuse himself by the hour, and he did not care for children; perhaps something in his past was present to his memory. He had absolutely no bad habits, and his disposition was perfect. I never saw him exactly angry, though I have seen his tail grow to an enormous size when a strange cat appeared upon his lawn. He disliked cats, evidently regarding them as feline and treacherous, and he had no association with them. Occasionally there would be heard a night concert in the shrubbery. Calvin would ask to have the door opened, and you would hear a rush and a "pestzt," and the concert would explode, and Calvin would quietly come in and resume his seat on the hearth. There was no trace of anger in his manner, but he wouldn't have any of that about the house. He had the rare virtue of magnanimity. Although he had fixed notions about his own rights, and extraordinary persistency in getting them, he never showed temper at a repulse; he simply and firmly persisted till he had what he wanted. His diet was one point; his idea was that of the scholars about dictionaries,—to "get the best." He knew as well as anyone what was in the house, and would refuse beef if turkey was to be had; and if there were oysters, he would wait over the turkey to see if the oysters would not be forthcoming. And yet he was not a gross gourmand; he would eat bread if he saw me eating it, and thought he was not being imposed on. His habits of feeding, also, were refined; he never used a knife, and he would put up his hand and draw the fork down to his mouth as gracefully as a grown person. Unless necessity compelled, he would not eat in the kitchen, but insisted upon his meals in the dining room, and would wait patiently, unless a stranger were present; and then he was sure to importune the visitor, hoping that the latter was ignorant of the rule of the house, and would give him something. They used to say that he preferred as his table-cloth on the floor a certain well-known church journal; but this was said by an Episcopalian. So far as I know, he had no religious prejudices, except that he did not like the association with Romanists. He tolerated the servants, because they belonged to the house, and would sometimes linger by the kitchen stove; but the moment visitors came in he rose, opened the door, and marched into the drawing-room. Yet he enjoyed the company of his equals, and never withdrew, no matter how many callers—whom he recognized as of his society—might come into the drawing-room. Calvin was fond of company, but he wanted to choose it; and I have no doubt that his was an aristocratic fastidiousness rather than one of faith. It is so with most people.

The intelligence of Calvin was something phenomenal, in his rank of life. He established a method of communicating his wants, and even some of his sentiments; and he would help himself in many things. There was a furnace register in a retired room, where he used to go when he wished to be alone, that he always opened when he desired more heat; but never shut it, any more than he shut the door after himself. He could do almost everything but speak; and you would declare sometimes that you could see a pathetic longing to do that in his intelligent face. I have no desire to overdraw his qualities, but if there was one thing in him more noticeable than another, it was his fondness for nature. He could content himself for hours at a low window, looking into the ravine and at the great trees, noting the smallest stir there; he delighted, above all things, to accompany me walking about the garden, hearing the birds, getting the smell of the fresh earth, and rejoicing in the sunshine. He followed me and gambolled like a dog, rolling over on the turf and exhibiting his delight in a hundred ways. If I worked, he sat and watched me, or looked off over the bank, and kept his ear open to the twitter in the cherry-trees. When it stormed, he was sure to sit at the window, keenly watching the rain or the snow, glancing up and down at its falling; and a winter tempest always delighted him. I think he was genuinely fond of birds, but, so far as I know, he usually confined himself to one a day; he never killed, as some sportsmen do, for the sake of killing, but only as civilized people do,—from necessity. He was intimate with the flying-squirrels who dwell in the chestnut-trees,—too intimate, for almost every day in the summer he would bring in one, until he nearly discouraged them. He was, indeed, a superb hunter, and would have been a devastating one, if his bump of destructiveness had not been offset by a bump of moderation. There was very little of the brutality of the lower animals about him; I don't think he enjoyed rats for themselves, but he knew his business, and for the first few months of his residence with us he waged an awful campaign against the horde, and after that his simple presence was sufficient to deter them from coming on the premises. Mice amused him, but he usually considered them too small game to be taken seriously; I have seen him play for an hour with a mouse, and then let him go with a royal condescension. In this whole matter of "getting a living," Calvin was a great contrast to the rapacity of the age in which he lived.

I hesitate a little to speak of his capacity for friendship and the affectionateness of his nature, for I know from his own reserve that he would not care to have it much talked about. We understood each other perfectly but we never made any fuss about it; when I spoke his name and snapped my fingers, he came to me; when I returned home at night, he was pretty sure to be waiting for me near the gate, and would rise and saunter along the walk, as if his being there were purely accidental,—so shy was he commonly of showing feeling; and when I opened the door he never rushed in, like a cat, but loitered, and lounged, as if he had had no intention of going in, but would condescend to. And yet, the fact was, he

French Cat. Artist unknown.

knew dinner was ready, and he was bound to be there. He kept the run of dinner-time. It happened sometimes, during our absence in the summer, that dinner would be early, and Calvin, walking about the grounds, missed it and came in late. But he never made a mistake the second day. There was one thing he never did,—he never rushed through an open doorway. He never forgot his dignity. If he had asked to have the door opened, and was eager to go out, he always went deliberately; I can see him now, standing on the sill, looking about at the sky as if he was thinking whether it were worth while to take an umbrella, until he was near having his tail shut in.

His friendship was rather constant than demonstrative. When we returned from an absence of nearly two years, Calvin welcomed us with evident pleasure, but showed his satisfaction rather by tranquil happiness than by fuming about. He had the faculty of making us glad to get home. It was his constancy that was so attractive. He liked companionship, but he wouldn't be petted, or fussed over, or sit in anyone's lap a moment; he always extricated himself from such familiarity with dignity and with no show of temper. If there was any petting to be done, however, he chose to do it. Often he would sit looking at me, and then, moved by a delicate affection, come and pull at my coat and sleeve until he could touch my face with his nose, and then go away contented. He had a habit of coming to my study in the morning, sitting quietly by my side or on the table for hours, watching the pen run over the paper, occasionally swinging his tail round for a blotter, and then going to sleep among the papers by the inkstand. Or, more rarely, he would watch the writing from a perch on my shoulder. Writing always interested him, and, until he understood it, he wanted to hold the pen.

He always held himself in a kind of reserve with his friend, as if he had said, "Let us respect our personality, and not make a 'mess' of friendship." He saw, with Emerson, the risk of degrading it to trivial conveniency. "Why insist on rash personal relations with your friend?" "Leave this touching and clawing." Yet I would not give an unfair notion of his aloofness, his fine sense of the sacredness of the me and the not-me. And, at the risk of not being believed, I will relate an incident, which was often repeated. Calvin had the practice of passing a portion of the night in the contemplation of its beauties, and would come into our chamber over the roof of the conservatory through the open window, summer and winter, and go to sleep on the foot of my bed. He would do this always exactly in this way; he never was content to stay in the chamber if we compelled him to go upstairs and through the door. He had the obstinacy of General Grant. But this is by the way. In the morning, he performed his toilet and went down to breakfast with the rest of the family. Now, when the mistress was absent from home, and at no other time, Calvin would come in the morning, when the bell rang, to the head of the bed, put up his feet and look into my face, follow me about when I rose, "assist" at the dressing, and in many purring ways show his fondness, as if he had plainly said, "I know that she has gone away, but I am here." Such was Calvin in rare moments.

He had his limitations. Whatever passion he had for nature, he had no conception of art. There was sent to him once a fine and very expressive cat's head in bronze, by Frémiet. I placed it on the floor. He regarded it intently, approached it cautiously and crouchingly, touched it with his nose, perceived the fraud, turned away abruptly, and never would notice it afterward. On the whole, his life was not only a successful one, but a happy one. He never had but one fear, so far as I know: he had a mortal and a reasonable terror of plumbers. He would never stay in the house when they were here. No coaxing could quiet him. Of course he didn't share our fear about their charges, but he must have had some dreadful experience with them in that portion of his life which is unknown to us. A plumber was to him the devil, and I have no doubt that, in his scheme, plumbers were foreordained to do him mischief.

In speaking of his worth, it has never occurred to me to estimate Calvin by the worldly standard. I know that it is customary now, when anyone dies, to ask how much he was worth, and that no obituary in the newspapers is considered complete without such an estimate. The plumbers in our house were one day overheard to say that, "They say that *she* says that *he* says that he wouldn't take a hundred dollars for him." It is unnecessary to say that I never made such a remark, and that, so far as Calvin was concerned, there was no purchase in money.

As I look back upon it, Calvin's life seems to me a fortunate one, for it was natural and unforced. He ate when he was hungry, slept when he was sleepy, and enjoyed existence to the very tip of his toes and the end of his expressive and slow-moving tail. He delighted to roam about the garden, and stroll among the trees, and to lie on the green grass and luxuriate in all the sweet influences of summer. You could never accuse him of idleness, and yet he knew the secret of repose. The poet who wrote so prettily of him that his little life was rounded with a sleep understated his felicity; it was rounded with a good many. His conscience never seemed to interfere with his slumbers. In fact, he had good habits and a contented mind. I can see him now walk in at the study door, sit down by my chair, bring his tail artistically about his feet, and look up at me with unspeakable happiness in his handsome face. I often thought that he felt the dumb limitation which denied him the power of language. But since he was denied speech, he scorned the inarticulate mouthings of the lower animals. The vulgar mewing and yowling of the cat species was beneath him; he sometimes uttered a sort of articulate and well-bred ejaculation, when he wished to call attention to something that he considered remarkable, or to some want of his, but he never went whining about. He would sit for hours at a closed window, when he desired to enter, without a murmur, and when it was opened he never admitted that he had been impatient by "bolting" in. Though speech he had not, and the unpleasant kind of utterance given to his race he would not use, he had a mighty power of purr to express his measureless content with congenial society. There was in him a musical organ with stops of varied power and expression, upon which I have no doubt he could have performed Scarlatti's celebrated cat's-fugue.

Whether Calvin died of old age, or was carried off by one of the diseases incident to youth, it is impossible to say; for his departure was as quiet as his advent was mysterious. I only know that he appeared to us in this world in his perfect stature and beauty, and that after a time, like Lohengrin, he withdrew. In his illness there was nothing more to be regretted than in all his blameless life. I suppose there never was an illness that had more of dignity and sweetness and resignation in it. It came on gradually, in a kind of listlessness and want of appetite. An alarming symptom was his preference for the warmth of a furnace-register to the lively sparkle of the open wood-fire. Whatever pain he suffered, he bore it in silence, and seemed only anxious not to obtrude his malady. We tempted him with the delicacies of the season, but it soon became impossible for him to eat, and for two weeks he ate or drank scarcely anything. Sometimes he made the effort to take something, but it was evident that he made the effort to please us. The neighbors—and I am convinced that the advice of neighbors is never good for anything—suggested catnip. He wouldn't even smell it. We had the attendance of an amateur practitioner of medicine, whose real office was the cure of souls, but nothing touched his case. He took what was offered, but it was with the air of one to whom the time for pellets was passed. He sat or lay day after day almost motionless, never once making a display of those vulgar convulsions or contortions of pain which are so disagreeable to society. His favorite place was on the brightest spot of a Smyrna rug by the conservatory, where the sunlight fell and he could hear the fountain play. If we went to him and exhibited our interest in his condition, he always purred in recognition of our sympathy. And when I spoke his name, he looked up with an expression that said, "I understand it, old fellow, but it's no use." He was to all who came to visit him a model of calmness and patience in affliction.

I was absent from home at the last, but heard by daily postalcard of his failing condition; and never again saw him alive. One sunny morning, he rose from his rug, went into the conservatory (he was very thin then), walked around it deliberately, looking at all the plants he knew, and then went to the bay-window in the dining room, and stood a long time looking out upon the little field, now brown and sere, and toward the garden, where perhaps the happiest hours of his life had been spent. It was a last look. He turned and walked away, laid himself down upon the bright spot in the rug, and quietly died.

It is not too much to say that a little shock went through the neighborhood when it was known that Calvin was dead, so marked was his individuality; and his friends, one after another, came to see him. There was no sentimental nonsense about his obsequies; it was felt that any parade would have been distasteful to him. John, who acted as undertaker, prepared a candlebox for him, and I believe assumed a professional decorum; but there may have been the usual levity underneath, for I heard that he remarked in the kitchen that it was the "dryest wake he ever attended." Everybody, however, felt a fondness for Calvin, and regarded him with a certain respect. Between him and Bertha there existed a great friendship, and she apprehended his nature; she used to say that sometimes she was afraid of him, he looked at her so intelligently; she was never certain that he was what he appeared to be.

When I returned, they had laid Calvin on a table in an upper chamber by an open window. It was February. He reposed in a candle-box, lined about the edge with evergreen, and at his head stood a little wine-glass with flowers. He lay with his head tucked down in his arms—a favorite position of his before the fire,—as if asleep in the comfort of his soft and exquisite fur. It was the involuntary exclamation of those who saw him, "How natural he looks!" As for myself, I said nothing. John buried him under the twin hawthorn-trees,—one white and the other pink,—in a spot where Calvin was fond of lying and listening to the hum of summer insects and the twitter of birds.

Perhaps I have failed to make appear the individuality of character that was so evident to those who knew him. At any rate, I have set down nothing concerning him but the literal truth. He was always a mystery. I do not know whence he came; I do not know whither he has gone. I would not weave one spray of falsehood in the wreath I lay upon his grave.

THE CAT IN THE LIFEBOAT

James Thurber

Cats named William, and there are many, have a distinction about them. Perhaps they simply confuse themselves with other Williams of their acquaintances, two-footed Williams that walk the world. They always have (and we know this from our own experience) a greater sense of fantasy than many other cats. For example, Dickens had a cat called William who answered happily to that name until she kindled kittens.

James Thurber's William is a contemporary corker.

A feline named William got a job as copy cat on a daily paper and was surprised to learn that every other cat on the paper was named Tom, Dick, or Harry. He soon found out that he was the only cat named William in town. The fact of his singularity went to his head, and he began confusing it with distinction. It got so that whenever he saw or heard the name William, he thought it referred to him. His fantasies grew wilder and wilder, and he came to believe that he was the Will of Last Will and Testament, and the Willy of Willy Nilly, and the cat who put the cat in catnip. He finally became convinced that Cadillacs were Catillacs because of him.

William became so lost in his daydreams that he no longer heard the editor of the paper when he shouted, "Copy cat!" and he became not only a ne'er-do-well, but a ne'er-do-anything. "You're fired," the editor told him one morning when he showed up for dreams.

"God will provide," said William jauntily.

"God has his eye on the sparrow," said the editor.

"So've I," said William smugly.

William went to live with a cat-crazy woman who had nineteen other cats, but they could not stand William's egotism or the tall tales of his mythical exploits, honors, blue ribbons, silver cups, and medals, and so they all left the woman's house and went to live happily in huts and hovels. The cat-crazy woman changed her will and made William her sole heir, which seemed only natural to him, since he believed that all wills were drawn in his favor. "I am eight feet tall," William told her one day, and she smiled and said, "I should say you are, and I am going to take you on a trip around the world and show you off to everybody."

William and his mistress sailed one bitter March day on the S.S. *Forlorna*, which ran into heavy weather, high seas, and hurricane. At midnight the cargo shifted in the towering seas, the ship listed menacingly, SOS calls were frantically sent out, rockets were fired into the sky, and the officers began running up and down companion-ways and corridors shouting, "Abandon ship!" And then another shout arose, which seemed only natural to the egotistical cat. It was,

Vashti, the Persian Princess. Artist unknown.

141

his vain ears told him, the loud repetition of "William and children first!" Since William figured no lifeboat would be launched until he was safe and sound, he dressed leisurely, putting on white tie and tails, and then sauntered out on deck. He leaped lightly into a lifeboat that was being lowered, and found himself in the company of a little boy named Johnny Green and another little boy named Tommy Trout, and their mothers, and other children and their mothers. "Toss that cat overboard!" cried the sailor in charge of the lifeboat, and Johnny Green threw him overboard, but Tommy Trout pulled him back in.

"Let *me* have that tomcat," said the sailor, and he took William in his big right hand and threw him, like a long incompleted forward pass, about forty yards from the tossing lifeboat.

When William came to in the icy water, he had gone down for the twenty-fourth time, and had thus lost eight of his lives, so he only had one left. With his remaining life and strength he swam and swam until at last he reached the sullen shore of a sombre island inhabited by surly tigers, lions, and other great cats. As William lay drenched and panting on the shore, a jaguar and a lynx walked up to him and asked him who he was and where he came from. Alas, William's dreadful experience in the lifeboat and the sea had produced traumatic amnesia, and he could not remember who he was or where he came from.

"We'll call him Nobody," said the jaguar.

"Nobody from Nowhere," said the lynx.

And so William lived among the great cats on the island until he lost his ninth life in a barroom brawl with a young panther who had asked him what his name was and where he came from and got what he considered an uncivil answer.

The great cats buried William in an unmarked grave because, as the jaguar said, "What's the good of putting up a stone reading 'Here lies Nobody from Nowhere'?"

MORAL: *O why should the spirit of mortal be proud, in this little voyage from swaddle to shroud?*

"MIDSHIPMAN," THE CAT

John Coleman Adams

We know from our own experience that a Marblehead cat is very beguiling. We once docked in Marblehead and allowed our cat to go ashore; he immediately mingled with some beautiful Marblehead cats. He had a Marblehead afternoon, and returned unwillingly to the boat at night.

This charming story of a very charming cat implies that all cats are welcome aboard, and that often they are made ship's mascots. This is untrue. Some cats, like some people, should never be aboard ship, and sailors from the beginning of history have been aware of this. The cat was more often tolerated than appreciated, and many felt that a cat certainly did not bring good luck.

One redeeming attribute of a cat at sea, however, is that he or she is a great indicator of the weather. If a cat cries at night, there will soon be a tempest. If she plays along with a string, she'll be provoking a storm, but if she appears to be smelling, take heed. She is smelling the wind.

This is a true story about a real cat who, for aught I know, is still alive and following the sea for a living. I hope to be excused if I use the pronouns "who" and "he" instead of "which" and "it," in speaking of this particular cat; because although I know very well that the grammars all tell us that "he" and "who" apply to persons, while "it" and "which" apply to things, yet this cat of mine always seemed to us who knew him to be so much like a human being, that I find it unsatisfactory to speak of him in any other way. There are some animals of whom you prefer to say "he," just as there are persons whom you sometimes feel like calling "it."

The way we met this cat was after this fashion: It was back somewhere in the seventies, and a party of us were cruising east from Boston in the little schooner-yacht "Eyvor." We had dropped into Marblehead for a day and a night, and some of the boys had gone ashore in the tender. As they landed on the wharf, they found a group of small boys running sticks into a woodpile, evidently on a hunt for something inside.

"What have you in there?" asked one of the yachtsmen.

"Nothin' but a cat," said the boys.

"Well, what are you doing to him?"

"Oh, pokin' him up! When he comes out we 'll rock him," was the answer, in good Marblehead dialect.

"Well, don't do it any more. What's the use of tormenting a poor cat? Why don't you take somebody of your size?"

The boys slowly moved off, a little ashamed and a little afraid of the big yachtsman who spoke; and when they were well out of sight the yachtsmen went on, too, and thought no more about the cat they had befriended. But when they had wandered about the tangled streets of the town for a little while, and paid the visits which all good yachtsmen pay, to the grocery and the post-office and the apothecary's soda-fountain, they returned to the wharf and found their boat. And behold, there in the stern-sheets sat the little gray-and-white cat of the woodpile! He had crawled out of his retreat and made straight for the boat of his champions. He seemed in no wise disturbed or disposed to move when they jumped on board, nor did he show anything but pleasure when they stroked and patted him. But when one of the boys started to put him ashore, the plucky little fellow showed his claws; and no sooner was he set on his feet at the edge of the wharf than he turned about and jumped straight back into the boat.

"He wants to go yachting," said one of the party, whom we called "The Bos'n."

"Ye might as wal take the cat," said a grizzly old fisherman standing on the wharf; "he doesn't belong to anybody, and ef he stays here the boys 'll worry him t' death."

"Let's take him aboard," said the yachtsmen. "It's good luck to have a cat on board ship."

Whether it was good luck to the ship or not, it was very clear that pussy saw it meant good luck to him, and curled himself down in the bottom of the boat, with a look that meant business. Evidently he had thought the matter all over and made up his mind that this was the sort of people he wanted to live with; and, being a Marblehead cat, it made no difference to him whether they lived afloat or ashore; he was going where they went, whether they wanted him or not. He had heard the conversation from his place in the woodpile, and had decided to show his gratitude by going to sea with these protectors of his. By casting in his lot with theirs he was paying them the highest compliment of which a cat is capable. It would have been the height of impoliteness not to recognize his distinguished appreciation. So he was allowed to remain in the boat, and was taken off to the yacht.

Upon his arrival there, a council was held, and it was unanimously decided that the cat should be received as a member of the crew; and as we were a company of amateur sailors, sailing our own boat, each man having his particular duties, it was decided that the cat should be appointed midshipman, and should be named after his position. So he was at once and ever after known as "Middy." Everybody took a great interest in him, and he took an impartial interest in everybody—though there were two people on board to whom he made himself particularly agreeable. One was the quiet, kindly professor, the captain of the Eyvor; the other was Charlie, our cook and only hired hand. Middy, you see, had a seaman's true instinct as to the official persons with whom it was his interest to stand well.

145

"Being a Marblehead cat it made no difference to him whether he lived afloat or ashore." Pictures drawn by W. H. Drake for the August 1892 issue of St. Nicholas.

It was surprising to see how quickly Middy made himself at home. He acted as if he had always been at sea. He was never seasick, no matter how rough it was or how uncomfortable any of the rest of us were. He roamed wherever he wanted to, all over the boat. At meal-times he came to the table with the rest, sat up on a valise and lapped his milk and took what bits of food were given him, as if he had eaten that way all his life. When the sails were hoisted it was his especial joke to jump upon the main-gaff and be hoisted with it; and once he stayed on his perch till the sail was at the mast-head. One of us had to go aloft and bring him down. When we had come to anchor and everything was snug for the night, he would come on deck and scamper out on the mainboom, and race from there to the bowsprit end as fast as he could gallop, then climb, monkey-fashion, half-way up the masts, and drop back to the deck or dive down into the cabin and run riot among the berths.

One day, as we were jogging along, under a pleasant southwest wind, and everybody was lounging and dozing after dinner, we heard the Bos'n call out, "Stop that, you fellows!" and a moment after, "I tell you, quit!—or I'll come up and make you!"

We opened our lazy eyes to see what was the matter, and there sat the Bos'n, down in the cabin, close to the companionway, the tassel of his knitted cap coming nearly up to the combings of the hatch; and on the deck outside sat Middy, digging his claws into the tempting yarn, and occasionally going deep enough to scratch the Bos'n's scalp.

When night came and we were all settled down in bed, it was Middy's almost invariable custom to go the rounds of all the berths, to see if we were properly tucked in, and to end his inspection by jumping into the captain's bed, treading himself a comfortable nest there among the blankets, and curling himself down to sleep. It was his own idea to select the captain's berth as the only proper place in which to turn in.

But the most interesting trait in Middy's character did not appear until he had been a week or so on board. Then he gave us a surprise. It was when we were lying in Camden harbor. Everybody

147

was going ashore to take a tramp among the hills, and Charlie, the cook, was coming too, to row the boat back to the yacht.

Middy discovered that he was somehow "getting left." Being a prompt and very decided cat, it did not take him long to make up his mind what to do. He ran to the low rail of the yacht, put his forepaws on it, and gave us a long, anxious look. Then as the boat was shoved off he raised his voice in a plaintive mew. We waved him a good-by, chaffed him pleasantly, and told him to mind the anchor, and have dinner ready when we got back.

That was too much for his temper. As quick as a flash he had dived overboard, and was swimming like a water-spaniel, after the dinghy!

That was the strangest thing we had ever seen in all our lives! We were quite used to elephants that could play at see-saw, and horses that could fire cannon, to learned pigs and to educated dogs; but a cat that of his own accord would take to the water like a full-blooded Newfoundland was a little beyond anything we had ever heard of. Of course the boat was stopped, and Middy was taken aboard drenched and shivering, but perfectly happy to be once more with the crew. He had been ignored and slighted; but he had insisted on his rights, and as soon as they were recognized he was quite contented.

Of course, after that we were quite prepared for anything that Middy might do. And yet he always managed to surprise us by his bold and independent behavior. Perhaps his most brilliant performance was a visit he paid a few days after his swim in Camden harbor.

We were lying becalmed in a lull of the wind off the entrance to Southwest Harbor. Near us, perhaps a cable's-length away, lay another small yacht, a schooner hailing from Lynn. As we drifted along on the tide, we noticed that Middy was growing very restless; and presently we found him running along the rail and looking eagerly toward the other yacht. What did he see—or smell—over there which interested him? It could not be the dinner, for they were not then cooking. Did he recognize any of his old chums from

148

Marblehead? Perhaps there were some cat friends of his on the other craft. Ah, that was it! There they were on the deck, playing and frisking together,—two kittens! Middy had spied them, and was longing to take a nearer look. He ran up and down the deck, mewing and snuffing the air. He stood up in his favorite position when on lookout, with his forepaws on the rail. Then, before we realized what he was doing, he had plunged overboard again, and was making for the other boat as fast as he could swim! He had attracted the attention of her company, and no sooner did he come up alongside than they prepared to welcome him. A fender was lowered, and when Middy saw it he swam toward it, caught it with his forepaws, clambered along it to the gunwale, and in a twinkling was over the side and on the deck scraping acquaintance with the strange kittens.

How they received him I hardly know, for by that time our boat was alongside to claim the runaway. And we were quite of the mind of the skipper of the "Winnie L.," who said, as he handed our bold midshipman over the side, "Well, that beats all *my* going a-fishing!"

Only a day or two later Middy was very disobedient when we were washing decks one morning. He trotted about in the wet till his feet were drenched, and then retired to dry them on the white spreads of the berths below. That was quite too much for the captain's patience. Middy was summoned aft, and, after a sound rating, was hustled into the dinghy which was moored astern, and shoved off to the full length of her painter. The punishment was a severe one for Middy, who could bear anything better than exile from his beloved shipmates. So of course he began to exercise his ingenious little brain to see how he could escape. Well under the overhang of the yacht he spied, just about four inches out of water, a little shoulder of the rudder. That was enough for him. He did not stop to think whether he would be any better off there. It was a part of the yacht, and that was home. So overboard he went, swam for the rudder, scrambled on to it, and began howling piteously to be taken on deck again; and, being a spoiled and much-indulged

149

cat, he was soon rescued from his uncomfortable roosting-place and restored to favor.

I suppose I shall tax your powers of belief if I tell you many more of Middy's doings. But truly he was a strange cat, and you may as well be patient, for you will not soon hear of his equal. The captain was much given to rifle-practice, and used to love to go ashore and shoot at a mark. On one of his trips he allowed Middy to accompany him, for the simple reason, I suppose, that Middy decided to go, and got on board the dinghy when the captain did. Once ashore, the marksman selected a fine large rock as a rest for his rifle, and opened fire upon his target. At the first shot or two Middy seemed a little surprised, but showed no disposition to run away. After the first few rounds, however, he seemed to have made up his mind that since the captain was making all that racket it must be entirely right and proper, and nothing about which a cat need bother his head in the least. So, as if to show how entirely he confided in the captain's judgment and good intentions, that imperturbable cat calmly lay down, curled up, and went to sleep in the shade of the rock over which the captain's rifle was blazing and cracking about once in two minutes. If anybody was ever acquainted with a cooler or more self-possessed cat I should be pleased to hear the particulars.

I wish that this chronicle could be confined to nothing but our shipmate's feats of daring and nerve. But, unfortunately, he was not always blameless in his conduct. When he got hungry he was apt to forget his position as midshipman, and to behave just like any cat with an empty stomach. Or perhaps he may have done just what any hungry midshipman would under the circumstances; I do not quite know what a midshipman does under all circumstances and so I can not say. But here is one of this cat midshipman's exploits. One afternoon, on our way home, we were working along with a head wind and sea toward Wood Island, a haven for many of the small yachts between Portland and the Shoals. The wind was light and we were a little late in making port. But as we were all agreed that it would be pleasanter to postpone our dinner till we were at anchor,

150

the cook was told to keep things warm and wait till we were inside the port before he set the table. Now, his main dish that day was to be a fine piece of baked fish; and, unfortunately, it was nearly done when we gave orders to hold back the dinner. So he had closed the drafts of his little stove, left the door of the oven open, and turned into his bunk for a quiet doze,—a thing which every good sailor does on all possible occasions; for a seafaring life is very uncertain in the matter of sleep, and one never quite knows when he will lose some, nor how much he will lose. So it is well to lay in a good stock of it whenever you can.

It seems that Middy was on watch, and when he saw Charlie fast asleep he undertook to secure a little early dinner for himself. He evidently reasoned with himself that it was very uncertain when we should have dinner and he'd better get his while he could. He quietly slipped down to the stove, walked coolly up to the oven, and began to help himself to baked haddock.

He must have missed his aim or made some mistake in his management of the business, and, by some lucky chance for the rest of us, waked the cook. For, the first we knew, Middy came flying up the cabin companionway, followed by a volley of shoes and spoons and pieces of coal, while we could hear Charlie, who was rather given to unseemly language when he was excited, using the strongest words in his dictionary about "that thief of a cat!"

"What's the matter?" we all shouted at once.

"Matter enough, sir!" growled Charlie, "That little cat's eaten up half the fish! It's a chance if you get any dinner to-night, sir."

You may be very sure that Middy got a sound wigging for that trick, but I am afraid the captain forgot to deprive him of his rations as he threatened. He was much too kindhearted.

The very next evening Middy startled us again by a most remarkable display of coolness and courage. After a weary thrash to windward all day, under a provokingly light breeze, we found ourselves under the lee of the little promontory at Cape Neddick, where we cast anchor for the night. Our supply of water had run very low, and so, just after sunset, two of the party rowed ashore in

151

the tender to replenish our water-keg, and by special permission Middy went with them.

It took some time to find a well, and by the time the jugs were filled it had grown quite dark. In launching the boat for the return to the yacht, by some ill-luck a breaker caught her and threw her back upon the beach. There she capsized and spilled out the boys, together with their precious cargo. In the confusion of the moment, and the hurry of setting matters to rights, Middy was entirely forgotten, and when the boat again was launched, nobody thought to look for the cat. This time everything went well, and in a few minutes the yacht was sighted through the dusk. Then somebody happened to think of Middy! He was nowhere to be seen. Neither man remembered anything about him after the capsize. There was consternation in the hearts of those unlucky wights. To lose Middy was almost like losing one of the crew.

But it was too late and too dark to go back and risk another landing on the beach. There was nothing to be done but to leave poor Middy to his fate, or at least to wait until morning before searching for him.

But just as the prow of the boat bumped against the fender on the yacht's quarter, out from under the stern-sheets came a wet, bedraggled, shivering cat, who leaped on board the yacht and hurried below into the warm cabin. In that moist adventure in the surf, Middy had taken care of himself, rescued himself from a watery grave, got on board the boat as soon as she was ready, and sheltered himself in the warmest corner. All this he had done without the least outcry, and without asking any help whatever. His self-reliance and courage were extraordinary.

Well, the pleasant month of cruising drew to a close, and it became a question what should be done with Middy. We could not think of turning him adrift in the cold world, although we had no fears but that so bright and plucky a cat would make a living anywhere. But we wanted to watch over his fortunes, and perhaps take him on the next cruise with us when he should have become a more settled and dignified Thomas. Finally, it was decided that he should be boarded for the winter with an artist, Miss Susan H——, a friend of one of our party. She wanted a studio-cat, and would be particularly pleased to receive so accomplished and traveled a character as Middy. So when the yacht was moored to the little wharf at Annisquam, where she always ended her cruises, and we were packed and ready for our journey to Boston, Middy was tucked into a basket and taken to the train. He bore the confinement with the same good sense which had marked all his life with us, though I think his feelings were hurt at the lack of confidence we showed in him. And, in truth, we were a little ashamed of it ourselves, and when once we were on the cars somebody suggested that he be released from his prison just to see how he would behave. We might have known he would do himself credit. For when he had looked over his surroundings, peeped above the back of the seat at the passengers, taken a good look at the conductor, and counted the rest of the party to see that none of us was missing, Middy snuggled down upon the seat, laid his head upon the captain's knee and slept all the way to Boston.

That was the last time I ever saw Middy. He was taken to his new boarding-place in Boylston Street, where he lived very pleasantly for a few months, and made many friends by his pleasing manners and unruffled temper. But I suppose he found it a little dull in Boston. He was not quite at home in his esthetic surroundings. I have always believed he sighed for the freedom of a sailor's life. He loved to sit by the open window when the wind was east, and seemed to be dreaming of far-away scenes. One day he disappeared. No trace of him was ever found. A great many things may have happened to him. But I never could get rid of the feeling that he went down to the wharves and the ships and the sailors, trying to find his old friends, looking everywhere for the stanch little Eyvor; and, not finding her, I am convinced that he shipped on some East Indiaman and is now a sailor cat on the high seas.

SPOONER

Eleanor Farjeon

In the London of Eleanor Farjeon's childhood, the backyard gardens were always filled with visiting cats that gave great delight to the children.

Beverley Nichols once said that such cats ignored all yells. "Boo, damn, shish," meant nothing; "Shish, hell, boo, blah," wouldn't move them at all.

Eleanor Farjeon, the perfect Londoner, adored cats. She started to write when she was about eight years old, and her long, productive career contained some charming ghost stories. "Spooner" is about a very special cat indeed.

My cousin, William Saunders, died suddenly and tragically in a road accident in London. He had a 1915 bullet in his leg, and hobbled. As children, and as boy and girl in our teens, we had been like brother and sister to each other. We were both only children, lived in adjacent roads in South Hampstead, and spent much of our free time together. It was from Bill I caught fire about cricket. I did not shape well in our back-garden games, but Bill drilled the science into me theoretically, taught me how to score, and companioned me to Lords as often as he could scrape up the time and the pocket-money. I learned to love the game as a saga, even the dull patches which were an essential part of it. Tennis is lyrical; but cricket is epic. No epic remains at inspiration point from start to finish. You live through a cricket-match, as you live through much of life, on expectation. To the critic who slated his longer poems for their dull patches, Byron replied: "The night cannot be all stars." The stars show up all the brighter for the night.

Of course we chose our teams, or rather, were chosen by them. I couldn't say by what inevitable process I became Lancashire and Bill Yorkshire. Every summer the rivalry waxed fierce between us two young Londoners who had never been to Lancaster or York. The rivalry of sport is an indisseverable bond. We honoured each other's hierarchies, but swore by our own. When I, in our schoolroom strife, shouted, "Maclaren!", Bill hurled back "Jackson!" like a thunderbolt. Just before the first World War we began to see less of each other, and after it we never met at all. He settled down with his war-wound in a little house he bought in St. John's Wood; I had drifted by circumstance up north, and was earning my living in a large industrial town. Even kinship did not save us from one of those almost complete separations which happen to childhood friends, the mere thought of which, in the first decade of the century, would have seemed laughable to us. There was no estrangement of any sort. We were not letter-writers. We exchanged notes at Christmas, and once a year, on our birthdays, something else. The two days fell in the same week in June, and I never let Bill's pass without posting him a red rose. A few days later he responded with a white one. It was the postscript to our cricket rivalry.

I did not even know that Bill had died when I heard from a solicitor that he had left me the little house in Selina Place, just as it stood, lock, stock and barrel. I was on the eve of retiring on a pension which was not much more than a pleasant competence, so Bill's legacy came as a Godsend. The house, which stood detached in a quarter of an acre of garden, was furnished, I was told,

155

from top to toe, and all it contained was mine, free of legacy duty. I instantly abandoned the tentative plans I had been considering for my retirement, blessed my old Bill from a grateful heart, packed my modest possessions, strapped Spooner into his basket, and travelled to London with as little delay as possible.

Spooner was my red tabby. When I say he had the most exquisite stance, and, running, carried his tail with enchanting style, anyone whose cricket-memories extend back to the turn of the century will know why I gave him that name. I had never ceased to worship the gods of my youth; and if Maclaren was the Zeus, Spooner was the Apollo at whose shrine I had poured my most ardent libations. Many a time he had been a feather in my red-rosed cap, when Yorkshire lost a match, and Bill could hardly wish me a civil good night.

We arrived in time for late tea, on Midsummer Eve. Midsummer Day was Bill's birthday; he would have been sixty-one. On June the twenty-seventh I was to become sixty-three. But the Bill who had just hobbled to his death with his years upon him was still to me the lithe young man I had seen racing balls to the boundary from long-on (Bill insisted on keen fielding). And Mary Shearn, the elderly woman to whom he had bequeathed his house behind Lords Cricket-ground, to him no doubt was still little pigtailed Molly, biting the end of her pencil as she worked out a bowling average. In winter we played elaborate paper-cricket, assisted by a pack of cards and a dice-box. So as the front door was opened to me by a nice Mrs. Meadows, who had looked after Bill and was prepared to look after me, I had the strange feeling of four or five decades slipping away behind me, and almost expected that in another minute I should encounter Bill himself, towelling his shoulders after a sweating innings, and teasing me because my unaccustomed hairpins were falling out. The very look of the house made it easy to think so; the oddly-shaped rooms, furnished simply and shabbily with the kindly furniture of his boyhood, the maple frames of the pictures, the old-fashioned french windows opening on to a low balcony with three iron-work steps down to the sunny-shady garden: all had re-

156

Friends. Nineteenth-century illustration from Chatterbox.

tained the air of our adolescence. I stood still, feeling and smelling rather than seeing it.

"I've laid your tea under the weeping ash, Miss Shearn. Poor Mr. Saunders liked it best there; he could hear the appeals, he said."

"The appeals, Mrs. Meadows?"

"From the cricket-ground. I can't say I ever hear them myself, but then my ears aren't so quick, I expect."

No, I expect not, I thought. Sitting in his garden, within range of the lordly pitch, Bill's ears were sharpened on the hone of half a century.

"Did he go often to the matches, Mrs. Meadows?"

"Oh yes, very often, when he was at his best. What a dear little puss. Shall you let her out in the garden?"

"Him, Mrs. Meadows. I won't unstrap him till there's some thing for him to eat. What is there in the house?"

"I was doing you some fried fillets for supper."

"That will do beautifully. Bring me one with the tea, please, and some margarine."

"To butter his feet, yes, miss. What do you call him?"

"Spooner."

"Spooner—Spooner—Spooner!" Mrs. Meadows let out the high call peculiar to women who call in their cats at night. Spooner opened a wary eye, but made no sign. Mrs. Meadows departed. I would have much to ask her later on, I know; but not to-day. I did not want the present imposed on this delicious sense of the past in which I was swimming as on a summer sea: the sort of sea children dream of before and after their holidays. Mrs. Meadows returned with the teapot (a table was ready-laid under the tree), a tin plate of fish, an extra saucer, and a pat of margarine.

"Thank you, Mrs. Meadows. Perhaps you'd better leave us before I undo him."

"Very well, miss. He'll soon get used to me. They know who's fond of them, don't you, pretty? Meadows is more one for dogs. It near broke his heart when Mr. Saunders—" Mrs. Meadows gulped

158

and wiped her eyes on her apron. I respected her grief, but her unfinished sentence left me faintly puzzled. "Meadows has taken your boxes up to your room. Mr. Bill's room it is. One of the cupboards isn't quite cleared out. Shall I unpack for you?"

"No, thank you. I'd better settle everything myself, and get my bearings. I haven't brought very much, but I'll clear the cupboard if I need more room."

"I'll leave the key in it then, miss."

"Did Bill—did Mr. Saunders keep it locked?"

"He didn't like me ever to touch what was in it. I often thought perhaps he kept some savings there, but when the valuers came they found nothing of any account."

Mrs. Meadows left me, and I unstrapped the basket with endearing sounds and caresses. I caught Spooner on the stretch, buttered his protesting paws, and put the plate of fish under his nose. He turned his head away and roamed leisurely round my deck-chair, stopping here and there to lick his white pads. Then he came round to the fish, discovered it for himself, fell to, devoured half of it heartily, eyed the remainder with loathing, stood before me with milk-demanding eyes, refused it out of his own saucer, drank it lavishly from mine, and begun to prowl the garden with great caution. He nosed lions and jackals in every rosebush.

Roses! Suddenly I was overwhelmed with the scent of them. I turned my head and found myself looking at a small rosebed of great beauty. Eleven exquisite white standard trees dominated it, below them sprawled a mat of red rose-bushes: eleven more. I burst out laughing.

"Bill!—you *rotter!*"

I recognised the white roses at once. From these standards my rival had plucked his annual trophy, never hinting that the white rose had dominated the red. In a single moment I heard some thirty-five years of chuckles, as Bill snipped from the upper-team the most perfect specimen he could find to rout me with. I even imagined him apostrophizing it by name . . .

Of course! I jumped to my feet. I knew in a flash he had done

159

what I would have done. Yes, each bush and each standard had its tag. The upright Frau Karl Druschkis were labelled: "Hobbs"—"Hirst"—"Sutcliffe". The crawling Hugh Dicksons: "A. C. Maclaren"—"Tyldesley"—"R. H. Spooner".

"I'll Spooner you!" I cried. "Here! Spooner, Spooner!"

A low growl answered me, the jungle growl that the gentlest cat can emit when you touch his kill. Spooner was crouched in the grass, hairs bristling, eyes glittering. It always gives me a shiver when I see a cat seeing what I can't see. Spooner was seeing—what?

He made ready to spring; then suddenly dashed in frantic haste up the ash, and stood with steeply-arched spine, glaring down. At such moments his electric eyes change from honey to tomato-red.

I did my best to coax him to come down. He would not. Only when Mr. Meadows arrived with a ladder was Spooner restored to my arms, trembling, I thought, with equal fear and fury. I carried him at once into the house, where he ate the rest of his fish avidly, drank copious water, and followed me to my bedroom. Here he fell asleep very suddenly on my bed, coiled round on himself like a golden ammonite.

It did not take me long to settle my things. There was no wardrobe, but the fireplace was flanked, in the Victorian fashion, by painted cupboards fixed against the wallpaper, not reaching quite to the ceiling. One would have shelves, the other hanging-space. There were two chests of drawers, an old one of mahogany with drop-handles, and a light yellow one with china knobs. I remembered this cheap chest as being part of Bill's boyish outfit; the varnish was worn off, and I had some difficulty in opening a drawer from which a knob had gone. An insufficient doily stood on the top; the surface it left exposed was scored with Bill's penknife: "B. S." cut several times, and in one place, with particular care, "F. S." I tried to recall to what Saunders the F belonged, and remembered that his father, with whom he did not get on very well, was called Francis. My heart warmed to Bill cherishing the furniture of his youth; it was this heterogeneousness, this loving tastelessness, that gave the rooms in his house their wistful quality. I found I did not want to alter anything, and hoped I need not shift what Bill kept in his cupboard. Luckily for me, the empty cupboard was the hanging one. A modern rail had been fitted, which took my dress-hangers. When my wardrobe was arranged I examined the one with shelves in it. The first thing I took out was a cricket-bat.

Then I knew. I knew what it was the valuers did not value. Everything on the shelves had to do with Bill's passion. It delved deep back to his seventh or eighth year. Small bats, growing bigger and bigger, pads the same, balls broken at the seams, a split bail marked in red ink "T. Richardson", photographs, picture-postcards and newspaper prints, of batsmen, bowlers, umpires: newspaper cuttings, too, of hundreds of games, Wisdens galore, Snaith's "Willow the King" read to saturation point; cardboard shoe-boxes crammed with letters and autographs: Townsend's among them. I recalled how at one match when the small boys broke loose, Bill had chased Townsend almost to the Pavilion, pestering him for his signature; and how Townsend had muttered, "Oh, I *can't!*" and fled. Bill had returned to me red-faced with shame, and eyes suspiciously moist. So you did get him after all, Bill. I'm so glad!— And among the shoe-boxes a larger one, containing old copybooks with marbled covers in which Bill had kept the scores of our paper-games. An incomplete, very dirty pack of cards. And a scribbled sheet that seemed strangely familiar—yes! a bowling-score, the dots very black from Molly's well-sucked pencil, and the maiden M's marked scrupulously from corner to corner. Oh Bill, dear Bill! I won't disturb your boyhood's treasure-house. All my old junk shall be scrapped ere one scrap of yours.

I shut the door gently, everything replaced, and as gently pushed Spooner away with my foot, for I felt him trying to shove his way into the cupboard.

"This is not the place for puss-cats," I admonished him, stooping to soften the admonition with a caress—and found that there was nothing to caress; for Spooner was still coiled up, sound asleep, on my quilt.

* * *

I kicked off my slippers, had a bath in the old-fashioned bath with a mahogany surround, dressed in something fresh, and went down to dinner. It was simple and nicely-cooked, and I began to feel that I and Spooner were batting on a good wicket. Mrs. Meadows brought the dishes in and out, and I had an impression that Meadows was helping her, for I caught a glimpse of him in the passage when the door was ajar, saw rather than heard him whisper something, and Mrs. Meadows shake her head at him. "I wouldn't, not to-night," I heard her say; and then she came in and put the summer pudding before me.

I decided to ask no questions; for the moment I was the visiting team on the Meadows' home ground. I did not yet belong, things must come about in their own way. So I merely said, "I shall go to bed early to-night. We'll have plenty to talk about in the next few days."

"Yes, miss. Where did you want Spooner to sleep?"

"He sleeps with me. He usually tucks down, but he may be restless to-night, especially as there's a moon. I shall only open my window at the top."

"We'll have to keep an eye on him," agreed Mrs. Meadows. "Goodness knows, we don't want no more accidents."

I couldn't think of an adequate answer to this. I helped myself again to the pudding, saying, "This is delicious, Mrs. Meadows. By the way—or really, not at all by the way, of course—I'm sure you know that to-morrow is Mr. Bill's birthday."

"Oh yes indeed, miss! But he won't be here to play his cricket-match."

"His cricket-match, Mrs. Meadows?"

"It was just a bit of play-acting, of course, but on his birthday he always made Meadows buckle on his pads for him, and he'd put on his gloves, and take his bat (he always kept it oiled), and Meadows had to bowl to him in the garden. He couldn't run, of course; but he scored by where his hits went, so many for the ash, so many for the conservatory end, a boundary for the fig-tree on the far wall, and so on. He was no end bucked one year when he broke a pane in the top of the conservatory. 'What price Jessop?' he said. It was you, miss, wasn't it, always sent him that red rose?"

"Yes, Mrs. Meadows. We'll put one in the vase in front of his picture to-morrow."

"I don't think he was ever merrier than when he went out to cut you your white one. 'The return match, Mrs. Meadows,' he used to say, 'ba goom, this'll dish her, so much for Spooner!' he'd say—Spooner!" ejaculated Mrs. Meadows. "Well I never! Did he know about your little cat, miss?"

"No, I'm sure he didn't. We didn't really write to each other, you know. But I did call my cat Spooner because of an old joke between us when we were little. And he was thinking of it when he cut the rose."

"It's what you might call a coincidence, mightn't you, miss."

"Perhaps, Mrs. Meadows." And perhaps not, Mrs. Meadows.

When I went up to bed the room was not as I had left it. I had been careful not quite to close the knobless drawer in the yellow chest, till I got it mended. It had been dragged still further out, and the contents were messed up, and some of them were on the floor. Among these my best pair of gloves, the left one badly chewed; and my second-best pair in a corner, torn to shreds; and in the fireplace the string gloves a friend had knitted, restored to their original string. Whose doing? Spooner's? He had long given up his masticating kittenhood, and his elegant limbs and delicate little head could not have pushed and jammed the drawer as I now found it. But where *was* Spooner? He seemed to have disappeared.

I spied him on the top of the hanging-cupboard. He was in a strange state, and for the second time that day refused to come down. When I stood on a chair and reached for him, he snarled. But not, I thought, at me. I could not blame him for being perturbed; I was rather perturbed myself, the difference being that I did not know what was perturbing me; and I was quite sure Spooner did know.

"Is it a Poltergeist?" I asked him. "What is it, Spooner?"

He tried to struggle out of my arms to the cupboard again; I soothed him, and presently he quietened down, and paraded the carpet gingerly, sniffing at my damaged finery, until I had tidied it up and put it away. I decided to shut the knobless drawer for the night; I didn't want anything rummaging while I slept.

But though I was puzzled, I wasn't really afraid. I felt no malice in the air, no antagonism, only the agitation of something itself perturbed, but in no sense dangerous. Should I consult Mrs. Meadows? Better not. I would investigate the mystery in the daylight. I got into bed, and Spooner, after his fashion, lay on my pillow with one pad on my cheek.

I woke in moonlight to the baying of a dog. Spooner was sitting upright by my ear. I sat up too. The baying sounded like a call, a challenge. Spooner made a mad rush at the window, clawed at the frame, at the sashes, at the glass. I had carried out my plan of shutting the lower half, leaving only a little opening at the top. To my horror, Spooner scrambled up the curtain like a monkey, and pressed his way through the crack. Cats are more fluid than solid, they can pour themselves through any sluice like water. I saw my red cat tremble half-in half-out, and disappear like a meteor into the garden. I flung up the sash, called him sternly by name, and without waiting for the answer I did not expect, ran down as I was, hoping to be in time to stop him from leaping a wall. The moonlight was warm, the garden seemed scarcely to breathe, the rose-scent was intolerably strong. I did not know roses smelt so strong at night. Drawn to the bed, with its teams of red and white, I saw Spooner standing almost erect against one of the standards. He was beautifully poised, and perfectly calm. Once more he was looking at what I could not see, and seemed to be listening too. After a few moments he dropped on all-fours, stood sniffing as he might a fellow-cat, turned tail, and walked with composure into the house. I followed meekly. Whatever was toward, Spooner now had it in charge. As he led me up the stairs his tail was erect; so I knew that there was nothing to worry about.

Back in the bedroom Spooner proceeded to the cupboard with the shelves. There he planted himself, looking at me expectantly.

164

I hesitated, like the crass human I am; but I have never yet known a cat who could not make its commands imperative, even if not explicable. Spooner stood on his hind legs, stretched himself like elastic as high as the keyhole, and laid a paw on either side of the key. I turned it, and opened the cupboard.

What would Spooner do next? He did nothing at all, but merely waited with his eyes on the door of the room. Again, I saw nothing; then the door silently opened a little further, and Nothing entered. Nor could I hear anything; but Anything was there. A disturbance now began inside the cupboard; on one of the shelves the objects became dislodged, a ball rolled out, a box of papers scattered itself at my feet, bit by bit the shelf was cleared of its litter—until, among other things, the ancient batting glove dropped on the floor. It did not remain there. It appeared to drag itself across the carpet, and into the passage. I heard it flopping down from stair to stair.

I looked at Spooner. He was cleaning his white pads with particular care. In the moonlight they gleamed as though they were freshly pipe-clayed. As soon as they were done to his satisfaction, he strolled back to my pillow and went to sleep.

"Did you hear a dog bay in the night, Mrs. Meadows?" I asked.

She hesitated in the act of clearing my breakfast away. "Yes, miss, I fancied I did. It sounded for all the world like poor old Jack."

"Jack?"

"Mr. Bill's Yorkshire terrier, miss."

"I never knew my cousin had a dog." (But why should I, Bill? You never knew I had dog's rival, cat.)

"Oh yes, he was all the world to Mr. Bill. Of course, that's how it happened."

"How what happened?"

"The dreadful accident. Surely you knew about it?"

"I know nothing, Mrs. Meadows. I didn't even know my cousin had died till I heard from his lawyer. Do you mind telling me?"

Mrs. Meadows began to sob uncontrollably. As though he had

165

been waiting for his cue, Mr. Meadows appeared in the doorway.

"Now Mother, doan't take on. You go to t' kitchen an' recover yersel'. *Ah'll* tell Miss Shearn." The burly red-faced little man stood before me, twisting his cap in his hands. "Middlesex were playin' Yarksheer, ye see. Mr. Bill never missed a Yarksheer match if he could help it. Ah were goin' to arm him there, as Ah allus did, but he thought he'd be late, an' got ahead o' me. The tyke dashed after him, out into t'road. Mr. Bill cried summat like *'Save it!'* because one o' them big house-movin' vans were coming. It got the tyke an' knocked the maister flat. We brought 'em home together, tyke in t' maister's arms, dead as a doornail. Maister he died before t' ambulance come."

"And that was the end," I whispered. (Bill—giving his life to save Yorkshire.)

"No, miss, not quite. It's summat Ah've got to speak to you about, if you doan't mind."

"Go on, Meadows."

"When he wur lyin' there, gaspin' to fetch his breath, he sez to me, 'Bury Jack in t'garden under t' fig, an' put a wood cross wi' his name on it same as it is on his collar. *In Lovin' Memory,* doan't forget,' he sez. In a little while he fetched his breath agen. 'When you lay Jack to rest, lay wi' him my bat, and see it's oiled, an' my pads an' my gloves, an' the new ball. Jack an' me'll want 'em on Midsummer Day."

"That's to-day, Meadows."

"It's t' day he allus played his match, d'ye see. The tyke played too. He allus fielded t' ball. He fielded under t' fig-tree at long-on. Jack were a gradely fielder."

"Did you do what he asked, Meadows?"

"Ah did, miss. But t' missus thought the sight of the cross might upset you, if you saw it sudden, not knowin' nawthen about it; so Ah hid it yesterday afore you come, an' thought to tell you about it to-day. Which now Ah've done."

Little Mr. Meadows wiped his arm across his brow.

"Come along," I said. "We'll put Jack's cross up together." We

166

went into the garden, where the wooden cross was concealed in the fig-tree corner.

"On'y one thing troubles me," he said as we went. "Ah found t' maister's bat, an' t' new ball he allus bought in March, an' t' right-'and battin'-glove. But *could* Ah find that left-'and glove? Ah could not. Ah'm afraid if t' ball rises," said Mr. Meadows with a watery smile, "t' maister 'll get grazed bad upon t' knuckles."

"I don't think you need worry, Meadows," I said. "I think Jack will see to it that he's all right."

"Ba goom, Ah 'ope so. Now then, Tommy, 'oo do you think you are?" Spooner was sitting on the dog's little grave, still cleaning his white forelegs meticulously. Meadows gave him a not too gentle shove with his thick boot. "Get off t' pitch, son." But Spooner had taken centre and seemed set for a century. He moved only just enough aside to leg to allow Meadows to set up the wooden cross, on which was inscribed:

IN LOVING MEMORY OF F. S. JACKSON

Cat and Mouse, by C. Barnes.

THE STRANGE CAT

John Oxenford

John Oxenford and the magnificent artist George Cruikshank once combined their talents to explore "strange frights."

When fear has once taken possession of us, as Oxenford said, experience does not always make folks wise, but strange frights often lead to some delicious laughter. This memorable drawing has never been published since it appeared a century and a quarter ago.

How vividly, among the events of our boyish days, do we remember the "strange cat" that got into the lumber-room at the top of the house! Our elder brother and "the boy" had endeavored to dislodge the animal, which figured in their description as a thing of intense blackness and monstrous dimensions, with great frightful staring green eyes, horrid long claws, and such a tail! Not "frightened of cats" were we, for we had a favorite one of our own; but *this*—it trebled in magnitude and horror the wildest and most savage inhabitants of the then Exeter 'Change. Their own fears had magnified the "strange cat" into a monster; and then they wilfully enlarged the picture to terrify *us*—a feat, in which they succeeded, as we dared not go to the upper rooms alone. For two or three days this "reign of terror" lasted, when, a favorable opportunity being watched for, the "young master" and the "young man" marched up, broom and brush in hand, to hunt out this strange secreted intruder—this black tiger of the upper wilderness. As for our tiny self, we had ventured part of the way up-stairs to witness the result, imagining that the enemy would make its exit by an attic window. Oh, horror! A loud knocking was heard above; a tremendous shouting next arose, succeeded instantly by an appalling cry of "Here it comes!" This was, shall we say, *enough?* it was too much; we turned and *flew* down stairs— the last "flight" of stairs being, with the aid of the handrail, but one leap. The street door! No, we could not open it. Against it, then, we set our back, in an agony of fear, and uttered a cry that would have terrified a whole legion of cats. The hunters were in full cry. Down came the wild animal, followed by brooms and brushes, bounding and rattling over the stairs—a clatter that rent the roof. What saw we then? Not a poor, half-starved, *frightened* animal leaping over the banisters to get out of *our* way, and to escape through the garden door; no, of this piteous, this actual spectacle, we saw nothing; but, in its place—*This*

*The Strange Cat,
by George Cruikshank
(1792–1878),
English caricaturist
and illustrator.*

This little "tail piece" expanded to the dimensions of a full-sized Newfoundland dog, surrounded by a blaze of fire, will convey some idea of what, in the extremity of misapprehension, we actually did see.

169

THE CAT AND THE CORNFIELD

Bryan MacMahon

Pangur Bán, or the white cat, has a special niche in the literature of animals in Ireland. Long before the Middle Ages, when the rest of the world was going through the Dark Ages, Ireland had a group of scholarly monks who retired to live in the forests and devote themselves to the sharp observation of the world around them. They read, wrote, and illuminated books. One such unknown hermit wrote a poem to his only companion, his Pangur Bán or white cat, and to this day that aristocratic name is honored.

In Ireland, all you need to make a story is two men with completed characters—say, a parish priest and his sexton. There at once you have conflict. When, as a foil for the sexton, you throw in a mature tinker girl, wild and lissom, love interest is added to conflict. And when, finally, you supply a snow-white cat, a cornfield, and a shrewish woman who asks three questions, the parts if properly put together should at least provide a moderate tale.

The scene is laid in a village asleep on a summer hill: the hour of the day is mid-morning. The village is made up of a church that

170

The White Cat, by Meredith Nugent.

lacks a steeple, a pair of pubs—one thatched and the other slated—
with maybe a dozen higgledy-piggledy houses divided equally as between thatch and slate. The gaps between the houses yield glimpses
of well-foliaged trees beyond which the countryside falls away into
loamy fields.

On the morning of our story, the sexton, a small grumpy fellow
of middle age with irregular red features, by name Denny Furey,
had just finished sweeping out the brown flagstones of the church

porch. He then took up the wire mat at the door and tried irritably but vainly to shake three pebbles out of it.

At the sound of the rattling pebbles, the sexton's white cat which was sitting on the sunny wall of the church beside his master's cabin, looked up and mewed soundlessly.

Denny glanced sourly at the cat. "Pangur Bán," he said, "if you didn't sleep in my breeches and so have 'em warm before my shanks on frosty mornings, I'd have you drowned long 'go!" The cat—he had pale green eyes and a blotch on his nose—silently mewed his misunderstanding.

Suddenly there came a sound of harness bells. A tinker's spring-cart, painted bright green and blue, with a shaggy piebald cob between the shafts, drew slowly past the church gate. Sitting on the near wing of the cart was a tinker girl wearing a tartan dress and a bright shoulder-shawl. Eighteen, perhaps; more likely, nineteen. She had wild fair hair and a nut-brown complexion. Spying the sexton struggling with the mat, her eyes gleamed with puckish pleasure.

Meeting her gaze, Denny grimaced ill-temperedly and then half-turned his back on her. As on a thought he swung around to scowl her a reminder of her duty. Slowly the girl cut the sign of the Cross on herself.

Just beyond the church gateway, the cob's lazy motion came to a halt. The girl continued to stare at the sexton. Angrily Denny dropped the mat. Swiftly he raised his right hand as if he had been taken with a desire to shout: "Shoo! Be off with yourself at once!" The words refused to come.

Pangur Bán raised himself on shuddering legs, arched his back and sent a gracious but soundless mew of welcome in the girl's direction.

"That you may be lucky, master!" the tinker girl said. Then: "Your wife—have she e'er an old pair of shoes?"

"Wife! Wife! I've no wife!" Denny turned sharply away and snatched up his brush.

The girl watched as the sexton's movements of sweeping became indefinably jaunty. Then her smiling eyes roved and rested for a moment on the thatched cabin at the left of the church gate.

Without turning round, Denny shouted: "Nothing for you today!"

The girl was slow in replying. Her eyes still fast on the cabin, she said: "I know you've nothin' for me, master!" She did not draw upon the reins.

Denny stopped brushing. His stance indicated that again he was struggling to say: "Be off!" Instead of speaking, he set his brush against the church wall, turned his head without moving his shoulders and looked fully at the girl. She answered his eyes with frankness. They kept looking at one another for a long time. At last, his altering gaze still locked in hers, Denny turned his body around.

As if caught in drowse Denny set aside his brush. He donned his hat, then walked slowly toward the church gate. Lost rosaries clinked as the white-painted iron yielded to his fingers. Denny looked to left and to right. Up to this their eyes had been bound fast to one another.

The sunlit village was asleep. Pangur Bán lay curled and still on the warm wall.

A strange tenderness glossed Denny's voice. "Where are you headin' for?" he asked. The gate latched shut behind him.

"Wherever the cob carries me!"

Again the girl's gaze swiveled to the cabin. "Is that your house?" she asked, and then, as she glanced again at the wall: "Is that your cat?"

"Ay! . . . Ay!"

For a long while the girl kept looking at the little house with its small deeply recessed windows. She noted well the dark-green half-door above which shone a latch of polished brass.

"Do you never tire of the road?" Denny asked.

"Do you never tire of being fettered?" the girl flashed. She had turned to look at him directly.

Both sighed fully and deeply. Under the black hat Denny's eyes had begun to smoulder.

Secretly the girl dragged on the rein. As the cob shifted from one leg to another, she uttered a small exclamation of annoyance. Her

173

red and green skirt made a wheel as she leaped from the vehicle and advanced to make an obscure adjustment to the harness. This done she prepared to lead her animal away.

Denny glanced desperately around. Uproad stood a hissing gander with his flock of geese serried behind him.

"I'll convey you apass the gander!" he blurted.

The tinker girl glanced at the gander; her mouthcorners twitched in a smile. She made a great to-do about gathering up the reins and adjusting her shawl. As she led the animal away, Denny moved to the far side of the road and kept pace with her as she went. Walking thus, apart yet together, they left the village and stepped downhill. Once the sexton glanced fearfully over his shoulder; the village was not so much asleep as stone-dead.

As the white road twisted, the village on the hillock was unseen. The cob—a hairy, bony animal—moved swiftly on the declivity so that Denny had to hurry to keep up with the girl and her animal.

The splendor of the summer accompanied them. The gauds of the harness were winking in the bright light. The countryside was a silver shield inclining to gold. Their footfalls were muted in the limestone road dust. Muted also were the noise of the horse's un-shod hooves and the ringing of the harness bells. At last they came to the foot of the hillock. Here the road ran between level fields. Denny looked over his shoulder and saw Pangur Bán fifty yards behind him walking stealthily on the road margin.

"Be off!" the sexton shouted.

Pangur Bán paused to utter his soundless mew.

The girl smiled. They walked on for a space. Again Denny turned. "Be off, you Judas!" he shouted. He snatched up a stone and flung it at the cat.

The instant the stone left the sexton's hand, Pangur judged that it was going to miss him. He remained utterly without movement. When the stone had gone singing away into stillness, the cat went over and smelled at a piece of road metal the bounding stone had disturbed. Pangur mewed his mystification into the sky; then spurted faithfully on.

The road again twisted. Now it was commanded by the entrance to the village on the hillock.

Here in a cornfield at the left-hand side of the road, the ripening corn was on the swing from green to gold. The field was a house of brightness open to the southern sky. Directly beside their boots a gap offered descent to the sown ground. The cob stopped dead and began to crop the roadside grass.

"Let us sit in the sun," the sexton ventured. He indicated the remote corner of the cornfield.

The girl smiled in dreamy agreement. With slow movements she tied her cob to the butt of a whitethorn bush. The pair walked along by the edge of the corn and sat down on the grassy edge of the farthest headland. Here the corn screened them from the view of a person passing on the road. The fierceness and lushness of growth in this sun-trap had made the hedge behind them impenetrable. Denny set his hat back on his poll. Then he took the girl's hand in his and began to fondle it. Points of sweat appeared on his agitated face.

Twice already, from the top of the grassy fence, Pangur Bán had stretched out a paw in an attempt to descend into the cornfield. On each occasion thistles and thorns tipping his pads had dissuaded him from leaping. Through slim upended ovals of dark pupil the cat ruefully eyed the cropping horse, then turned to mew his upbraidings in the direction of his master. Tiring of this, he settled himself patiently to wait.

Pangur Bán sat with his tail curled around his front paws. His eyes were reluctant to open in the sunlight. His ears began to sift the natural sounds of the day.

Reading his Office, the huge old priest walked the village. Glancing up from his breviary, he noticed the brush idle against the church wall: he also spied the wire mat that lay almost concealed on the lawn grass. The impudence of the gander the priest punished with a wave of his blackthorn stick. Standing on the road in front of the sexton's cabin, he sang out: "Denny! Denny Furey!" There was no reply.

The priest shuffled to the church door and in a lowered voice again called for his sexton. At last, with an angry shrug of his shoulders, he again turned his attention to his breviary. Still reading, he sauntered downhill and out into the open country.

After a while he raised his eyes. First he saw the brown and white pony, then he spied the flame that was the cat burning white beside the olive cornfield.

The old man's face crinkled. He grunted. Imprisoning his stick in his left armpit, he began to slouch in the direction of Pangur Bán. From time to time his eyes strayed over the gilt edging and the colored markers of his book.

Denny glanced up from his sober love-making.

"Divine God!" he exclaimed.

The girl was leaning back on the grass: her posture tautened a swath of green hay to silver. She was smiling up at the sky as she spaced her clean teeth along a grass stem.

Reaching the cat, the priest halted. "Pangur Bán," he wheedled in a low voice. His eyes were roving over the cornfield. The cat tilted his back against the lower may leaves, set his four paws together and drooped as if for a bout of languid gaiety.

For a moment or two the priest tricked with the cat. Then he threw back his shoulders. "To think that I don't see you, Denny Furey!" he clarioned.

Denny and the girl were silent and without movement. About them the minute living world asserted itself in the snip of grasshoppers.

Again the priest thundered: "Nice example for a sexton!"

The sweat beaded above Denny's eyebrows. His thighs began to shiver in the breeches his cat slept in. The girl peered at the priest through the altering lattice of the corn-heads. Her expression was quizzical as she glanced at Denny.

From the roadway came again the dreaded voice: "If it's the last thing I do, Denny Furey, I'll strip you of your black coat!"

At this moment a shrewish woman, wearing a black and green

176

shawl, thrust around the bend of the road. She was resolutely headed for the village.

Seeing the woman approach, the priest quickly turned his face away from the cornfield and resumed his pacing along the road. His lips grew busy with the Latin psalms.

Peeping out and recognizing the newcomer, Denny Furey at first swore softly, then he began to moan. "The parish will be ringin' with the news before dark!" he sniffled.

The woman blessed the priest so as to break him from his Office: then in a tone of voice that expressed thin concern: "Did I hear your voice raised, Father?"

The priest lowered his shaggy eyebrows. "Sermons don't sprout on bushes, my good woman!"

"Ah! Practisin' you were!"

Her crafty eyes alighted on the white cat. "Would it be bird-chasin' the sexton's cat is?"

"It could be, now that you mention it!"

There was a pause. The conversation of the wheat spars was only one step above silence. Flicking the cornfield and the cart with a single glance, the woman said, in a half whisper: "People say that tinker girls'd pick the eye out of your head!"

"Did you never hear tell of the virtue of charity, woman?" the priest growled.

The woman made her crumbled excuses. It suited the priest not to accept them. Hurriedly she walked away. Resentment was implicit in the puffs of road-dust that spouted from beneath her toe-caps. Before the village swallowed her up, she looked over her shoulder. The priest was standing in mid-road waiting to parry this backward glance.

Again the priest turned his attention to the cornfield. With a sound half-grunt, half-chuckle, he untied the cob, and leading it by the head, turned away in the direction of the village.

The instant the harness bells began to ring, the tinker girl sprang to her feet and raced wildly but surefootedly along the edge of the cornfield. "Father!" she cried out. "Father!"

The priest came to a halt. Well out of the range of his stick, the girl stopped. "So I've drawn you, my vixen!" the priest said.

Breathlessly, the girl bobbed a half-curtsy.

"What're you goin' to do with my animal, Father?"

"Impounding him I am—unless you get that sexton o' mine out of the cornfield at once."

The girl leaped on to the low fence: "Come out o' the cornfield," she shouted, "I want to recover my cob!"

There was a pause. Then Denny shuffled to his feet. The cat stood up and mewed loyal greetings to his lord.

The priest stood at the horse's head. The angry girl was on the fence; her arms akimbo. Shambling dismally, Denny drew nearer. When he had reached the roadway, the tinker girl cried out: "I was goin' my road, Father, when he coaxed me into the cornfield!"

Denny opened his mouth, but no words came. He began to blink his moist eyes. His mouth closed fast. He kept his distance from the priest's stick. As Pangur Bán began rubbing himself against the end of the beloved breeches, the sexton gave the cat the side of his long boot and sent him careening into the bushes.

"*A chait*, ou'r that!" he said.

"Aha, you scoundrel!" the priest reproved, "Can you do no better than abuse a dumb animal?"

Turning to the girl: "Take your cob! And if I catch you in this village again, by the Holy Man, I'll give you the length and breadth of my blackthorn!"

"He said he'd convey me apass the gander, Father!"

Three times she lunged forward. Three times her buttocks winced away. At last she mustered courage enough to grasp the winkers. Clutching the ring of the mouthpiece, she swung the pony down-road. When she had gained a few yards she leaped lightly on to the broad board on the side of the cart and slashed at the cob's rump with the free dangle of the reins. The animal leaped forward.

The priest, the sexton, the cat. The sunlit, rustling cornfield.

"Come on, me bucko!" the priest said grimly.

He began to lead the way home. The sexton trailed a miserable yard or two behind. Glory was gone out of his life. The wonderful day seemed to mock him. The future was a known road stretching before his leaden legs. What he had thought would prove a pleasant bauble had turned to a crown of thorns. In the past, whenever he had chafed against the drab nature of his existence, he had consoled himself thus: "One day, perhaps today, I'll run and buy me a hoop of bright colors."

Denny began to compare his soul to a pebble trapped in a wire mat of despair.

Gradually the priest became infected with Denny's moroseness. Side by side, the priest and his sexton continued to move homewards. In the faraway, the sound of the harness bells was a recessional song of adventure.

Behind the pair and at a discreet distance, Pangur Bán traveled quietly. Now and again he paused to mew his loyalty into the sunny world.

The White Cat,
by Meredith Nugent.

THE YELLOW CAT

Michael Joseph

When Michael Joseph was asked by Who's Who to describe his hobbies, one word sufficed: "Cats." Earlier in this book, Sir Michael wrote of his personal encounters with cats. Here is a rare fictional contribution, new to America, that explores the supernatural aspect of cats.

It all began when Grey was followed home, inexplicably enough, by the strange, famished yellow cat. The cat was thin with large, intense eyes which gleamed amber in the forlorn light of the lamp on the street corner. It was standing there as Grey passed, whistling dejectedly, for he had had a depressing run of luck at Grannie's tables, and it made a slight piteous noise as it looked up at him. Then it followed at his heels, creeping along as though it expected to be kicked unceremoniously out of the way.

Grey did, indeed, make a sort of half-threatening gesture when, looking over his shoulder, he saw the yellow cat behind.

"If you were a black cat," he muttered, "I'd welcome you—but get out!"

Eighteenth-century engraving depicting a macabre cat.
Artist unknown.

The cat's melancholy amber eyes gleamed up at him, but it made no sign and continued to follow. This would have annoyed Grey in his already impatient humour, but he seemed to find a kind of savage satisfaction in the fact that he was denied even the trifling consolation of a good omen. Like all gamblers, he was intensely superstitious, although he had had experience in full measure of the futility of all supposedly luck-bringing mascots. He carried a monkey's claw sewn in the lining of his waistcoat pocket, not having the courage to throw it away. But this wretched yellow cat that ought to have been black did not irritate him as might have been expected.

He laughed softly; the restrained, unpleasant laugh of a man fighting against misfortune.

"Come on, then, you yellow devil; we'll sup together."

He took his gloveless hand from his coat pocket and beckoned to the animal at his heels; but it took as little notice of his gesture of invitation as it had of his menacing foot a moment before. It just slid along the greasy pavement, covering the ground noiselessly, not deviating in the slightest from the invisible path it followed, without hesitation.

It was a bitterly cold, misty night, raw and damp. Grey shivered as he thrust his hand back into the shelter of his pocket and hunched his shoulders together underneath the thin coat that afforded but little protection against the cold.

With a shudder of relief he turned into the shelter of the court-yard which lay between the icy street and the flight of stairs which led to his room. As he stumbled numbly over the rough cobblestones of the yard he suddenly noticed that the yellow cat had disappeared.

He was not surprised and gave no thought whatever to the incident until, a few minutes later, at the top of the ramshackle stairs, the feeble light of a hurricane lamp revealed the creature sitting, or rather lying, across the threshold of his door.

He took an uncertain step backward. He said to himself: "That's odd." The cat looked up at him impassively with brooding, sullen

This haunted cat by Robert Seymour (1800?–1836) illustrated Shakespeare's King Lear. *Seymour, English book illustrator and caricaturist, was the first to produce plates for Dickens'* Pickwick Papers.

182

eyes. He opened the door, stretching over the animal to turn the crazy handle.

Silently the yellow cat rose and entered the shadowy room. There was something uncanny, almost sinister in its smooth, noiseless movements. With fingers that shook slightly, Grey fumbled for matches, struck a light and, closing the door behind him, lit the solitary candle.

He lived in this one room, over a mews which had become almost fashionable since various poverty-stricken people, whose names still carried some weight with the bourgeois tradesmen of this Mayfair backwater, had triumphantly installed themselves; and Grey turned it skillfully to account when he spoke with casual indifference of "the flat" he occupied, "next to Lady Susan Tyrrell's."

Grey, although he would never have admitted it, was a card-sharper and professional gambler. But even a cardsharper needs a little ordinary luck. Night after night he watched money pass into the hands of "the pigeons," ignorant, reckless youngsters, and foolish old women who, having money to burn, ought by all the rules of the game to have lost. Yet when playing with him, Grey, a man respected even among the shabby fraternity of those who live by their wits, they won. He had turned to roulette, but even with a surreptitious percentage interest in the bank he had lost. His credit was exhausted. Grannie herself had told him he was a regular Jonah. He was cold, hungry and desperate. Presently his clothes, the last possession, would betray him, and no longer would he be able to borrow the casual trifle that started him nightly in his desperate bout with fortune.

His room contained a wooden bed and a chair. A rickety table separated them. The chair served Grey as a wardrobe; on the table stood a candle with a few used matches which he used to light the cheap cigarettes he smoked in bed; the grease had a habit of ad-hering to the tobacco when the candle was used, and Grey was fastidious. The walls were bare save for a cupboard, a pinned-up *Sporting Life* Racing Calendar and two cheap reproductions of Kirchner's midinettes. There was no carpet on the floor. A piece of linoleum stretched from the empty grate to the side of the bed.

At first Grey could not see the cat, but the candle, gathering strength, outlined its shadow grotesquely against the wall. It was crouched on the end of the bed.

He lighted one of the used matches and lit the small gas-ring which was the room's sole luxury. Gas was included in the few shillings he paid weekly for rent; consequently Grey used it for warmth. He seldom used it to cook anything, as neither whisky (which he got by arrangement with one of Grannie's waiters), bread nor cheese, which formed his usual diet, require much cooking.

The cat moved and, jumping noiselessly on to the floor, cautiously approached the gas-ring, by the side of which it stretched its lean yellowish body. Very softly but plaintively it began to mew.

Grey cursed it. Then he turned to the cupboard and took out a cracked jug. He moved the bread on to his own plate and poured out the little milk it contained in the shallow bread-plate.

The cat drank, not greedily but with fierce rapidity which betokens hunger and thirst. Grey watched it idly as he poured whisky into a cup. He drank, and refilled the cup. He then began to undress, carefully, in order to prolong the life of his worn dinner-jacket.

A Starving Cat. Artist unknown.

The cat looked up. Grey, taking off his shirt, beneath which, having no vest, he wore another woollen shirt, became uncomfortably aware of its staring yellow eyes. Seized with a crazy impulse, he poured the whisky from his cup into the remainder of the milk in the plate.

"Share and share alike," he cried. "Drink, you——"

Then the yellow cat snarled at him; the vilest, loathesome sound; and Grey for a moment was afraid. Then he laughed, as if at himself for allowing control to slip, and finished undressing, folding the garments carefully, and hanging them on the chair.

The cat went back to its place at the foot of the bed, its eyes gleaming warily in Grey's direction. He restrained his impulse to throw it out of the room and clambered between the rough blankets without molesting it.

By daylight the cat was an ugly misshapen creature. It had not moved from the bed. Grey regarded it with amused contempt.

Usually the morning found him profoundly depressed and irritable. For some unaccountable reason he felt now almost light-hearted.

He dressed, counted his money and decided to permit himself the luxury of some meagre shopping in the adjacent Warwick Market, which supplied the most expensive restaurant proprietors with the cheapest food. Nevertheless, it was an accommodating spot for knowledgeable individuals like Grey

The cat, still crouching on the bed, made no attempt to follow him, and he closed the door as softly as its erratic hinges would allow, aware that the cat's eyes still gazed steadily in his direction.

In the market, he obeyed an impulse to buy food for the cat, and at the cost of a few pence added a portion of raw fish to his purchases. On the way home he cursed himself for a fool, and would have thrown the fish away, the clumsy paper wrapping having become sodden with moisture, when he was hailed by a voice he had almost forgotten.

"Grey! Just the man I want to see!"

Grey greeted him with a fair show of amiability, although, if appearance were any indication, the other was even less prosperous than himself. He, too, had been an *habitué* of Grannie's in the old

185

days, but had long since drifted out on the sea of misfortune. Despite his shabby appearance, he turned to Grey and said:

"You'll have a drink?" Then, noting Grey's dubious glance, he laughed and added: "It's on me all right. I've just touched lucky."

A little later Grey emerged from the public-house on the corner the richer by five pounds, which the other had insisted on lending him in return for past favours. What exactly the past favours had been, Grey was too dazed to inquire; as far as he could recollect he had always treated the man with scant courtesy. He did not even remember his name.

He was still trying to remember who the man was when he climbed the stairs. He knew him well enough, for Grey was the type who never forgets a face. It was when his eyes alighted on the yellow cat that he suddenly remembered.

The man was Felix Mortimer. And Felix Mortimer had shot himself during the summer!

At first Grey tried to assure himself that he had made a mistake. Against his better judgment he tried to convince himself that the man merely bore a strong resemblance to Felix Mortimer. But at at the back of his mind *he knew*.

Anyway, the five-pound note was real enough.

He methodically placed the fish in a saucepan and lit the gas-ring.

Presently the cat was eating, in that curious, deliberate way it had drunk the milk the night before. Its emaciated appearance plainly revealed that it was starving; yet it devoured the fish methodically, as though now assured of a regular supply.

Grey, turning the five-pound note in his hand, wondered whether the cat had after all changed his luck. But his thoughts kept reverting to Felix Mortimer. . . .

The next few days left him in no doubt. At Grannie's that night fortune's pendulum swung back unmistakably. He won steadily. From roulette he turned to *chemin de fer*, elated to find that his luck held good.

"Your luck's changed—with a vengeance!" said one of the "regulars" of the shabby genteel saloon.

"With a vengeance," echoed Grey, and paused; wondering with

the superstition of the born gambler if there were significance in the phrase.

He left Grannie's the richer by two hundred odd pounds.

His success was the prelude to the biggest slice of luck, to use his own phrase, that he had ever known. He gambled scientifically, not losing his head, methodically banking a proportion of his gains each morning; planning, scheming, striving to reach that high-water mark at which, so he told himself with the gambler's time-worn futility, he would stop and never gamble again.

Somehow he could not make up his mind to leave the poverty-stricken room in the fashionable mews. He was terribly afraid it would spell a change of luck. He tried to improve it, increase its comfort, but it was significant that he bought first a basket and a cushion for the yellow cat.

For there was no doubt in his mind that the cat was the cause of his sudden transition from poverty to prosperity. In his queer, intensely superstitious mind, the yellow cat was firmly established as his mascot.

He fed it regularly, waiting on it himself as though he were its willing servant. He made a spasmodic attempt to caress it, but the cat snarled savagely at him and, frightened, he left it alone. If the cat ever moved from the room he never saw it go; whenever he went in or came out the cat was there, watching him with its gleaming amber eyes.

He accepted the situation philosophically enough. He would talk to the cat of himself, his plans for the future, the new people he met—for money had speedily unlocked more exalted doors than Grannie's—all this in the eloquence derived from wine and solitude, he would pour out into the unmoved ears of the cat, crouching at the foot of the bed. And then, without daring to speak of it, he would think of Felix Mortimer and the gift that had proved the turning-point of his fortunes.

The creature watched him impassively, contemptuously indifferent to his raving or his silence. But the weird *ménage* continued, and Grey's luck held good.

The days passed and he became ambitious. He was now within

reach of that figure which he fondly imagined would enable him to forsake his precarious existence. He told himself that he was now, to all intents and purposes, safe. And he decided to move into more civilised and appropriate surroundings.

Nevertheless, he himself procured an expensive wicker contraption to convey the yellow cat from the garret to his newly acquired and, by contrast, luxurious maisonnette. It was furnished in abominable taste, but the reaction from sheer poverty had its effect. And then he had begun to drink more than was good for a man who required a cool head and a steady nerve for at least part of a day which was really night.

One day he had cause to congratulate himself on his new home. For he met, for the first time in his thirty odd years of life, a woman. Now, Grey divided women into two classes. There were "the regulars"—soulless creatures with the gambler's fever and crook's alphabet—and "pigeons," foolish women, some young, most of them old, who flourished their silly but valuable plumage to be plucked by such as he.

But Elise Dyer was different. She stirred his pulses with a strange, exquisite sensation. Her incredibly fair hair, flaxen as waving corn, her fair skin, her deep violet eyes and her delicate carmine mouth provoked him into a state of unaccustomed bewilderment.

They talked one night of mascots. Grey, who had never mentioned the yellow cat to a soul, whispered that he would, if she cared, show her the mascot that had brought him his now proverbial good luck. The girl agreed, with eager enthusiasm, to his diffident suggestion to go with him to his flat; and he, in his strange simplicity, stammered that she would do him honour. He had forgotten that Elise Dyer knew him for a rich man.

Elated by his triumph, he paid her losses and called for champagne. The girl plied him skilfully with wine, and presently he was more drunk than he had been since the beginning of his era of prosperity.

They took a cab to the flat. Grey felt that he had reached the

The Scratch. Nineteenth-century engraving by unknown artist.

pinnacle of triumph. Life was wonderful, glorious! What did anything matter now?

He switched on the light and the girl crossed his threshold. The room which they entered was lavishly illuminated, the lights shaded into moderation by costly fabrics. The room, ornate and over-furnished, reflected money. The girl gave a gasp of delight.

For the first time the cat seemed aware of something unusual. It stretched itself slowly and stood up, regarding them with a fierce light in its eyes.

The girl screamed.

"For God's sake take it away!" she cried. "I can't bear it! I can't be near it. Take that damned cat away!" And she began to sob wildly, piteously, retreating towards the door.

At this Grey lost all control and, cursing wildly, shouting bestial things at the oncoming animal, seized it by the throat.

"Don't—don't cry, dearie," panted Grey, holding the cat; "I'll settle this swine soon enough. Wait for me!" And he staggered through the open door.

Grey ran through the deserted streets. The cat had subsided under the clutch of his fingers and lay inert, its yellowish fur throbbing. He scarcely knew where he was going. All he realised was an overwhelming desire to be rid of the tyranny of this wretched creature he held by the throat.

At last he knew where he was going. Not far from Grey's new establishment ran the Prince's canal, that dark, sluggish stream that threads its way across the fashionable residential district of the outlying west. To the canal he ran; and without hesitation he threw the yellow cat into the water.

The next day he realised what he had done. At first he was afraid, half hoping that the superstitious spasm of fear would pass. But a vivid picture swam before his eyes, the broken surface of a sluggish dream. . . .

"You're a coward," she taunted him. "Why don't you act like a man? Go to the tables and see for yourself that you can still win in spite of your crazy cat notions!"

At first he refused, vehemently; but it gradually dawned on him that therein lay his chance of salvation. Once let him throw down the gauntlet *and win* and his peace of mind would be assured.

That night he received a vociferous welcome on his return to the Green Baize Club.

It was as he feared. He lost steadily.

Then suddenly an idea came to him. Supposing the cat were still alive? Why hadn't he thought of that before? Why, there was a saying that every cat had nine lives! For all he knew it might have swum safely to the bank and got away.

His feverish impulse crystallised into action. He hurriedly left the club and beckoned urgently to a passing taxicab.

After what seemed interminable delay he reached the spot where he had madly flung the cat away from him. The stillness of the water brought home to him the futility of searching for the animal here. This was not the way to set to work.

The thing preyed on his mind in the days that followed. Exhaustive inquiries failed to discover the least trace of the yellow cat.

Night after night he went to the tables, lured there by the maddening thought that if only he could win he would drug the torment and be at peace. But he lost . . .

And then a strange thing happened.

One night, returning home across a deserted stretch of the park, he experienced a queer, irresistible impulse to lift his feet from the grass and make for the gravel path. He resented the impulse, fought against it; he was cold and worn out, and by cutting across the grass he would save many minutes of weary tramping. But the thing—like a mysterious blind instinct—persisted, and in the end he found himself running, treading gingerly on the sodden grass.

He did not understand why this had happened to him.

The next day Grey did not get out of his bed until late in the afternoon.

He crossed the room in search of his dressing-gown and caught sight of himself in the glass of his wardrobe. Only then did he realise that he was clambering over the floor with his head near the

191

carpet, his hands outstretched in front of him. He stood upright with difficulty and reached a shaking hand for brandy.

It took him two hours to struggle into his clothes, and by the time he was ready to go out it was nearly dark. He crept along the street. The shops were closing. He saw nothing of them until he reached the corner where he halted abruptly, with a queer sensation of intense hunger. On the cold marble before him lay unappetising slabs of raw fish. His body began to quiver with suppressed desire. Another moment and nothing could have prevented him seizing the fish in his bare hands, when the shutters of the shop dropped noisily across the front of the sloping marble surface.

Grey knew that something had happened, that he was very ill. Now that he could not see the vision of the yellow cat, his mind was a blank. Somehow he retraced his footsteps and got back to his room.

The bottle of brandy stood where he had left it. He had not turned on the light, but he could see it plainly. He dragged it to his lips.

With a crash it went to the floor, while Grey leapt into the air, savage with nausea. He felt that he was choking. With an effort he pulled himself together, to find that it was beyond his power to stop the ghastly whining sound that issued from his lips. He tried to lift himself on to the bed, but in sheer exhaustion collapsed on the floor, where he lay still in an attitude not human.

The room lightened with the dawn and a new day passed before the thing on the floor moved. Something of the clarity of vision which comes to starving men now possessed him. He stared at his hands.

The fingers seemed to have withered; the nails had almost disappeared, leaving a narrow streak of hornish substance forming in their place. He tore himself frantically towards the window. In the fading light he saw that the backs of his hands were covered with a thin, almost invisible surface of coarse, yellowish fur.

Unimaginable horrors seized him. He knew now that the scarlet thread of his brain was being stretched to breakingpoint. Presently it would snap. . . .

Unless—unless. The yellow cat alone could save him. To this last human thought he clung, in an agony of terror.

Unconscious of movement, he crept swiftly into the street, his shapeless eyes peering in the darkness which surrounded him. He groped his way stealthily towards the one place which the last remnant of his brain told him might yield the secret of his agony.

Down the silent bank he scrambled headlong, towards the still water. The dawn's pale radiance threw his shadow into a grotesque pattern. On the edge of the canal he halted, his hands embedded in the sticky crumbling earth, his head shaking, his eyes searching in agonised appeal, into the depths of the motionless water.

There he crouched, searching, searching. . . .

And there in the water he saw the yellow cat.

He stretched out the things that were his arms, while the yellow cat stretched out its claws to enfold him in the broken mirror of the water.

A DISCOURSE ON CATS

Bill Nye

Bill Nye, a friend of Mark Twain's, walked the floor at night as did Twain, putting together "feeble, puling, colicky, journalistic children" that were the newspapers of the last century. Twain and Nye knew about cats because from the very beginning cats were an editor's comfort and a printer's pride.

I am not fond of cats as a general rule. I never yearned to have one around the house. My idea always was that I could have trouble enough in a legitimate way without adding a cat to my woes. With a belligerent cook and a communistic laundress, it seems to me most anybody ought to be unhappy enough without a cat.

I never owned one until a tramp cat came to our house one day during the present autumn—and tearfully asked to be loved. He didn't have anything in his make-up that was calculated to win anybody's love, but he seemed contented with a little affection—one ear was gone, and his tail was bald for six inches at the end, and he was otherwise well calculated to win confidence and sympathy. Though we could not be madly in love with him, we decided to be friends, and give him a chance to win the general respect.

Nineteenth-century drawing by an unknown artist.

Everything would have turned out all right if the bobtail waif had not been a little given to investigation. He wanted to know more about the great world in which he lived, so he began by inspecting my house. He got into the storeroom closet, and found a place where the carpenter had not completed his job. This is a feature of the Laramie artisan's style. He leaves little places in unobserved corners generally, so that he can come back someday and finish it at an additional cost of fifty dollars. This cat observed that he could enter at this point and go all over the imposing structure between the flooring and the ceiling. He proceeded to do so.

We will now suppose that a period of two days has passed. The wide halls and spacious façades of the Nye mansion are still. The lights in the banquet-hall are extinguished, and the ice-cream freezer is hushed to rest in the woodshed. A soft and tearful yowl, deepened into a regular ring-tail-peeler, splits the solemn night in twain. Nobody seemed to know where it came from. I rose softly and went to where the sound had seemed to well up from. It was not there.

I stood on a piece of cracker in the dining-room a moment, waiting for it to come again. This time it came from the boudoir of our French artist in soup-bone symphonies and pie—Mademoiselle Bridget O'Dooley. I went there and opened the door softly, so as to let the cat out without disturbing the giant mind that had worn itself out during the day in the kitchen, bestowing a dry shampoo to the china.

Then I changed my mind and came out. Several articles of *vertu*, beside Bridget, followed me with some degree of vigor.

The next time the tramp cat yowled he seemed to be in the recesses of the bathroom. I went downstairs and investigated. In doing so I drove my superior toe into my foot, out of sight, with a door that I encountered. My wife joined me in the search. She could not do much, but she aided me a thousand times by her counsel. If it had not been for her mature advice I might have lost much of the invigorating exercise of that memorable night.

Toward morning we discovered that the cat was between the floor of the children's play-room and the ceiling of the dining-room. We tried till daylight to persuade the cat to come out and get acquainted, but he would not.

At last we decided that the quickest way to get the poor little thing out was to let him die in there, and then we could tear up that portion of the house and get him out. While he lived we couldn't keep him still long enough to tear a hole in the house and get at him.

It was a little unpleasant for a day or two waiting for death to

196

come to his relief, for he seemed to die hard, but at last the unearthly midnight yowl was still. The plaintive little voice ceased to vibrate on the still and pulseless air. Later, we found, however, that he was not dead. In a lucid interval he had discovered the hole in the store-room where he entered, and, as we found afterward a gallon of coal-oil spilled in a barrel of cut-loaf sugar, we concluded that he had escaped by that route.

That was the only time that I ever kept a cat, and I didn't do it then because I was suffering for something to fondle. I've got a good deal of surplus affection, I know, but I don't have to spread it out over a stump-tail orphan cat.

Nineteenth-century engraving by an unknown artist.

CATS OF THE NEW YORK SUN

Charles Dana

*Nobody quite knows why Newspaper Row has always been filled
with delightful cats. (One of the most famous of all such cats,
Mehitabel, liked the peculiar sound of typewriters.) Such newspaper cats disport themselves with ease in the presence of newspaper men and women. Perhaps all of them are highly individualistic.*

One of the greatest of all United States newspapers was the Sun.
*A very special newspaper had to have a very special cat, and a very
special editor to describe him. The* Sun's *famous editor, Charles
Dana, responded to a request from Helen M. Winslow with the following description of the* Sun's *family of cats. "I can only vouch for
its veracity," she said, "by quoting the famous phrase, 'If you see it in
the* Sun, *it is so.'"*

Sun office cat *(Felis Domestica; var. Journalistica).* This is a variation of the common domestic cat, of which but one family is known
to science. The habitat of the species is in Newspaper Row; its
lair is in the *Sun* building, its habits are nocturnal, and it feeds on
discarded copy and anything else of a pseudo-literary nature upon
which it can pounce. In dull times it can subsist upon a meagre

198

Educated Cats, by David Ericson.

diet of telegraphic brevities, police court paragraphs, and city jot-
tings; but when the universe is agog with news, it will exhibit the
insatiable appetite which is its chief distinguishing mark of difference from the common *felis domestica.* A single member of this
family has been known, on a "rush" night, to devour three and a
half columns of presidential possibilities, seven columns of general
politics, pretty much all but the head of a large and able-bodied
railroad accident, and a full page of miscellaneous news, and then
claw the nether garments of the managing editor, and call attention
to an appetite still in good working order.

The progenitrix of the family arrived in the *Sun* office many
years ago, and installed herself in a comfortable corner, and within
a few short months she had noticeably raised the literary tone of the
paper, as well as a large and vociferous family of kittens. These

199

kittens were weaned on reports from country correspondents, and the sight of the six children and the mother cat sitting in a semi-circle was one which attracted visitors from all parts of the nation. Just before her death—immediately before, in fact—the mother cat developed a literary taste of her own and drank the contents of an ink-bottle. She was buried with literary honors, and one of her progeny was advanced to the duties and honors of office cat. From this time the line came down, each cat taking the "laurel greener from the brows of him that uttered nothing base," upon the death of his predecessor. There is but one blot upon the escutcheon of the family, put there by a recent incumbent who developed a mania at once cannibalistic and infanticidal, and set about making a free lunch of her offspring, in direct violation of the Raines law and the maternal instinct. She died of an overdose of chloroform, and her place was taken by one of the rescued kittens.

It is the son of this kitten who is the present proud incumbent of the office. Grown to cat-hood, he is a creditable specimen of his family, with beryl eyes, beautiful striped fur, showing fine mot-tlings of mucilage and ink, a graceful and aspiring tail, an appetite for copy unsurpassed in the annals of his race, and a power and perseverance in vocality, chiefly exercised in the small hours of the morning, that, together with the appetite referred to, have earned for him the name of the Mutilator. Up to the age of one year the Mutilator made its lair in the inside office with the Snake Editor, until a tragic ending came to their friendship. During a fortnight's absence of the office cat upon important business, the Snake Editor cultivated the friendship of three cockroaches, whom he debauched by teaching them to drink beer spilled upon his desk for that purpose. On the night of the cat's return, the three bugs had become disgracefully intoxicated, and were reeling around the desk beating time with their legs to a rollicking catch sung by the Snake Editor. Before the muddled insects could crawl into a crack, the Mutilator was upon them, and had bolted every one. Then with a look of reproach at the Snake Editor, he drew three perpendicular red lines across that gentleman's features with his claws and departed in high scorn, nor could he ever thereafter be lured into the inner office where the serpent-sharp was laying for him with a space measure. Since that time he has lived in the room occupied by the reporters and news editors.

Many hundreds of stories, some of them slanderous, have been told about the various *Sun* office cats, but we have admitted here none of these false tales. The short sketch given here is beyond suspicion in all its details, as can be vouched for by many men of high position who ought to know better.

Card Players, by Joseph G. Francis.

201

HE WROTE TO THE RATS

Julian Ralph

It takes a staunch cat to face a rat, and even then he may be out-faced because, curiously enough, when Mr. Cat meets Mr. Rat they are two aristocrats of the world, trying to downface each other. The following story is based on a very real folklore practice. It dates back to medieval times when people attempted to drive away un-wanted animals with writs of rejection—letters to the animals them-selves suggesting that they leave the premises.

As late as the end of the nineteenth century a man in Baltimore County, Maryland, wrote such a letter to the rats in which he told them to "go past the stone house and then keep on until you come to the large white house up on the right and turn in there." Evi-dently, the rats did take up their abode in the new spot; the large white house probably belonged to an unpopular neighbor.

Our suspicions were first aroused by the disappearance of a whole beefsteak. Before that we did not know we were entertaining any rats in our cellar. When we made the discovery, we were at a loss to know how to act; but one day there came to the house a poor old

HE WROTE TO THE RATS.

Illustrations by W. H. Drake for St. Nicholas in 1889.

woman who lives mysteriously by offering needles, and thread, and pencils, and candy of sizes and kinds that nobody likes and nobody buys. At our house she gets a cup of tea and ten cents, and, to ease her conscience, she leaves a peppermint stick for the little ones. The kitchen-girl told her of the loss of the steak.

"Well," said the mysterious old woman, "I would write a letter to the rats and they will go away. That is what we used to do when I lived at home in Germany."

Fancy the surprise of the kitchen-maid! She thought the old woman had lost her mind.

The rats became an intolerable nuisance, and the news of what the old woman had recommended was brought to me. The children were anxious to have the experiment tried.

"It can do no harm," I said, and at once drew up the following letter:

> To THE Boss RAT: Get out of our cellar at once. We hired this house for ourselves, and you have no business to make yourselves at home, living here and stealing our provisions. If you do not heed this warning we will keep a terrier and make it very lively for you.
>
> Yours angrily,
> THE PEOPLE OF THIS HOUSE.

I quite prided myself on this missive. I thought it was at once logical in its argument, firm in tone, and very generous, inasmuch as the rats could see that we might have hired a terrier first and written the letter afterward. I at first put the letter in an envelope; but we all agreed afterward that even if rats could read they might not know anything about envelopes, and so I tore the cover off and laid the letter on the cellar floor with its written side up.

We then waited to see what effect it would have. Alas! the rats behaved worse than ever and robbed us of everything that suited their tastes. Then the poor old German woman came again on her rounds, and the children saw her and informed her of the failure.

"Read the letter to me," said she.

It was read to her.

"Oh, dear, dear, dear!" she exclaimed. "What an impudent letter to send to the rats! It is a mercy they haven't attacked some of the people in the house and bitten them in their beds. I could not sleep a wink in a house where such a letter had been sent to the rats."

She spoke very gravely and with evident alarm. I inquired very particularly about her manner afterward and was told that it seemed far from a mere pretence of being vexed.

"Why!" she exclaimed. "Rats are *kings,* in their way. At least they are in Germany. They must be treated very politely. Tell your parents to write another letter at once and let it be soft and gentle and very respectful. Call them, 'Dear rats' or 'Dear friends,' and find no fault with what they do—only be sure to recommend some other place for them to go to, for it is a rule that rats will never leave a home unless they are told of a better place close by, to which they can go. Oh, dear, dear, dear!—I wonder you are not afraid to stay in the house after such a letter."

When I reached home I thought, as before, that there could be no harm in doing as the old woman said; and I confess I felt guilty of some stupidity in not having known, as every one ought to know, that politeness is always better than rudeness. There is a wealth of wisdom in the homely saying, "More flies are caught with syrup than with vinegar." It costs nothing to be kind and courteous, and as we know that more can be done among men and women by gentleness than by anger, why might not the same be true with regard to rats? Thus I reflected, and therefore I wrote this letter:

> DEAR RATS: We have discovered signs of your presence in our cellar. Perhaps you mean to honor us and pay us a compliment in coming to this particular cellar in a city where there are a hundred thousand such resorts. It may be news to you that there lives not far away a French family, much given to rich gravies, sweetmeats, delightful pastries, rare and high-scented imported cheese, and various other luxuries of which we know you to be fond. If you should go there, you would fare better than in our cellar. Of course, we should miss you,— but we feel certain we could bear it.
>
> Believing, from what we see of your activity and appetites, that you are all very well and happy and that you have been benefited by our having the plumbing attended to the other day, we beg the right to sign ourselves,
>
> Yours politely,
THE PEOPLE OF THIS HOUSE.

That touch about the plumbing was my own; but the phrase, "yours politely," was dictated by the children, who assured me that the word "polite" must be somewhere in the letter, in some form or other. It really took me a long while to make up my mind where to tell the rats to go, and I felt no little ashamed when at last the thought of the rich gravies and pastries led me to recommend my neighbors, the French folks. To be sure, I do not know them, and no one will ever tell them what I did; but I must confess I never would have been guilty of such an unneighborly act had I really believed the rats would have paid any attention to the letter.

They did not. They grew more and more at home, and even became so noisy that the ladies more than once thought that burglars had broken in downstairs. "Master Fitz," our Tom-cat, was sent into the cellar to drive them out; but after the first encounter he bounded back into the kitchen, bleeding on one cheek and one leg; and if ever a cat said anything, he plainly spoke, and very indignantly, too. "I am a tremendous mouser," was what he meant to convey, "but when it comes to eating up rats that are bigger than I am, I must beg to be excused!"

We all waited for the old woman, and when she came the children eagerly informed her of the failure of even the most polite letter-writing where rats are concerned.

She is a shrewd old woman. She did not like to admit she was wrong, so she said she was sure that if we hadn't written that very rude first letter the rats would have gone.

"I know they would if they were German rats," she said; "but I never wrote to American rats, and perhaps they are different."

The four-footed robbers are still at home in our cellar, and not even the children believe it worth while to write to them again.

THE BLACK CAT

William Wintle

"The Black Cat" by Edgar Allan Poe does not appear in this book because it has been so often reprinted. That story, however, was dynamite as far as the development of the supernatural story was concerned.

William Wintle, a famous booklore collector, had the pleasant habit of writing stories, particularly for his young relatives, as Christmas gifts, in the long and miserable English winters. This tale enlarges upon that strange disease that has afflicted so many people, the hatred of cats—a fear that toyed with Napoleon's nerves, and triggered panic in Adolf Hitler.

If there was one animal that Sydney disliked more than another it was a cat. Not that he was not fond of animals in a general way—for he had a distinct affection for an aged retriever that had formerly been his—but somehow a cat seemed to arouse all that was worst in him. It always appeared to him that if he had passed through some previous stage of existence, he must have been a mouse or a bird and thus have inherited—so to speak—an instinctive dread and hatred for the enemy of his earlier days.

The presence of a cat affected him in a very curious fashion. There was first of all a kind of repulsion. The idea of the eyes of the animal being fixed on him; the thought of listening for a soundless tread; and the imagined touch of the smooth fur; all this made him shudder and shrink back. But this feeling quickly gave place to a still stranger fascination. He felt drawn to the creature that he feared—much as a bird is supposed, but quite erroneously, to be charmed by a snake. He wanted to stroke the animal and to feel its head rubbing against his hand: and yet at the same time the idea of the animal doing so filled him with a dread passing description. It was something like that morbid state in which a person finds actual physical pleasure in inflicting pain on himself. And then there was sheer undisguised fear. Pretend as he might, Sydney was in deadly fear when a cat was in the room. He had tried and tried, time and again, to overcome it; but without success. He had argued from the well-known friendliness of the domestic cat; from its notorious timidity; and from its actual inability to do any very serious harm to a strong and active man. But it was all of no use. He was afraid of cats; and it was useless to deny it.

At the same time, Sydney was no enemy to cats. He was the last man in the world to hurt one. No matter how much his slumber might be disturbed by the vocal efforts of a love-sick marauder on the roof in the small hours of the morning, he would never think of hurling a missile at the offender. The sight of a half-starved cat left behind when its owner was away in the holiday season filled him with a pity near akin to pain. He was a generous subscriber to the Home for Lost Cats. In fact, his whole attitude was inconsistent and contradictory. But there was no escape from the truth—he disliked and feared cats.

Probably this obsession was to some extent fostered by the fact that Sydney was a man of leisure. With more urgent matters to occupy his thoughts, he might have outgrown these fancies with the advance of middle age. But the possession of ample means, an inherited dislike for any kind of work calling for energy, and two or three interesting hobbies which filled up his time in an easy and soothing fashion, left him free to indulge his fancies. And fancies, when indulged, are apt to become one's masters in the end; and so it proved with Sydney.

He was engaged in writing a book on some phase of Egyptian life in the olden days, which involved considerable study of the collections in the British Museum and elsewhere, as well as much search for rare books among the antiquarian bookshops. When not out on these pursuits, he occupied an old house which like most old and rambling places of its kind was the subject of various queer stories among the gossips of the neighbourhood. Some tragedy was supposed to have happened there at some date not defined, and in consequence something was supposed to haunt the place and to do something from time to time. Among local gossips there was much value in that nebulous term "something," for it covered a multitude of inaccurate recollections and of foggy traditions. Probably Sydney had never heard the reputation of his house, for he led a retired life and had little to do with his neighbours. But if the tales had reached his ears, he gave no sign; nor was he likely to do so. Apart from the cat obsession, he was a man of eminently balanced mind. He was about the last person to imagine things or to be influenced by any but proved facts.

The mystery which surrounded his untimely end came therefore as a great surprise to his friends: and the horror that hung over his later days was only brought to partial light by the discovery of a diary and other papers which have provided the material for this history. Much still remains obscure, and cannot now be cleared up; for the only man who could perhaps throw further light on it is no longer with us. So we have to be content with such fragmentary records as are available.

It appears that some months before the end, Sydney was at home reading in the garden, when his eyes happened to rest upon a small heap of earth that the gardener had left beside the path. There was nothing remarkable about this; but somehow the heap seemed to fascinate him. He resumed his reading; but the heap of earth was insistent in demanding his attention. He could not keep his thoughts off it, and it was hard to keep his eyes off it as well. Sydney was not the man to give way to mental dissipation of this kind, and he resolutely kept his eyes fixed on his book. But it was a struggle; and in the end he gave in. He looked again at the heap; and this time with some curiosity as to the cause of so absurd an attraction.

Apparently there was no cause; and he smiled at the absurdity of the thing. Then he started up suddenly, for he saw the reason of it. The heap of earth was exactly like a black cat! And the cat was crouching as if to spring at him. The resemblance was really absurd, for there were a couple of yellow pebbles just where the eyes should have been. For the moment, Sydney felt all the repulsion and fear that the presence of an actual cat would have caused him. Then he rose from his chair, and kicked the heap out of any resemblance to his feline aversion. He sat down again and laughed at the absurdity of the affair—and yet it somehow left a sense of disquiet and of vague fear behind. He did not altogether like it.

It must have been about a fortnight later when he was inspecting some Egyptian antiquities that had recently reached the hands of a London dealer. Most of them were of the usual types and did not interest him. But a few were better worth attention; and he sat down to examine them carefully. He was specially attracted by some ivory tablets, on which he thought he could faintly trace the remains of handwriting. If so, this was a distinct find, for private memoranda of this sort are very rare and should throw light on some of the more intimate details of private life of the period, which are not usually recorded on the monuments. Absorbed in this study, a sense of undefined horror slowly grew upon him and he found himself in a kind of daydream presenting many of the uncanny qualities of nightmare. He thought himself stroking an immense black cat which grew and grew until it assumed gigantic proportions. Its soft fur thickened around his hands and entwined itself around his fingers like a mass of silky, living snakes; and his skin tingled with multitudinous tiny bites from fangs which were venomous; while the purring of the creature grew until it became a very roar like that of a cataract and overwhelmed his senses. He was mentally drowning in a sea of impending catastrophe, when, by an expiring effort, he wrenched himself free from the obsession and sprang up. Then he discovered that his hand had been mechanically stroking a small unopened animal mummy, which proved on closer examination to be that of a cat.

The next incident that he seems to have thought worth recording happened a few nights later. He had retired to rest in his usual health and slept soundly. But towards morning his slumbers were disturbed by a dream that recalled the kind of nocturnal fear that is common in childhood. Two distant stars began to grow in size and brilliancy until he saw that they were advancing through space towards him with incredible speed. In a few moments they must overwhelm him in a sea of fire and flame. Onwards they came, bulging and unfolding like great flaming flowers, growing more dazzling and blinding at every moment; and then, just as they were upon him, they suddenly turned into two enormous cat's eyes, flaming green and yellow. He sprang up in bed with a cry, and found himself at once wide awake. And there on the window-sill lay a great black cat, glowering at him with lambent yellow eyes. A moment later the cat disappeared.

But the mysterious thing of it was that the window-sill was not accessible to anything that had not wings. There was no means by which a cat could have climbed to it. Nor was there any sign of a cat in the garden below.

The date of the next thing that happened is not clear, for it does not appear to have been recorded at the time. But it would seem to have been within a few days of the curious dream. Sydney had occasion to go to a cupboard which was kept locked. It contained manuscripts and other papers of value; and the key never left his possession. To his knowledge the cupboard had not been opened for at least a month past. He now had occasion to refer to a collection of notes in connection with his favourite study. On opening the cupboard, he was at once struck by a curious odour. It was not exactly musky, but could only be described as an animal odour; slightly suggestive of that of a cat. But what at once arrested Sydney's notice

211

and caused him extreme annoyance was the fact that the papers had been disturbed. The loose papers contained in some pigeon-holes at the back had been drawn forwards into a loose heap on the shelf. They looked for all the world like a nest, for they had been loosely arranged in a round heap with a depression in the middle. It looked as if some animal had coiled itself up to sleep there; and the size of the depression was just such as would be made by a cat.

Sydney was too much annoyed by the disturbance of his papers to be greatly impressed at the moment by their curious arrangement; but it came home to him as a shock when he began to gather the papers together and set them in order. Some of them seemed to be slightly soiled, and on closer examination he found that they were besprinkled with short black hairs like those of a cat.

About a week afterwards he returned later in the evening than usual, after attending a meeting of a scientific society to which he belonged. He was taking his latch key from his pocket to open the door when he thought that something rubbed against his leg. Looking down, he saw nothing; but immediately afterwards he felt it again, and this time he thought he saw a black shadow beside his right foot. On looking more closely, nothing was to be seen; but as he went into the house he distinctly felt something soft brush against his leg. As he paused in the hall to remove his overcoat, he saw a faint shadow which seemed to go up the stairs. It was certainly only a shadow and nothing solid, for the light was good and he saw it clearly. But there was nothing in motion to account for the passing shadow. And the way the shadow moved was curiously suggestive of a cat.

The next notes in the book that Sydney seems to have devoted to this curious subject appear to be a series of mere coincidences: and the fact that he thought them worth recording shows only too clearly to what an extent his mind was now obsessed. He had taken the numerical value of the letters C, A, T, in the alphabet, 3, 1, and 20 respectively, and by adding them together had arrived at the total 24. He then proceeded to note the many ways in which this number had played its part in the events of his life. He was born on the 24th of the month, at a house whose number was 24; and his mother was 24 years old at the time. He was 24 years old when his father died and left him the master of a considerable fortune. That was just 24 years ago. The last time he had balanced his affairs, he found that he was worth in invested funds—apart from land and house—just about 24 thousand pounds. At three different periods, and in different towns, he had chanced to live at houses numbered 24; and that was also the number of his present abode. Moreover the number of his ticket for the British Museum Reading Room ended with 24, and both his doctor and his solicitor were housed under that same persistent number. Several more of these coincidences had been noted by him; but they were rather far-fetched and are not worth recording here. But the memoranda concluded with the ominous question, "Will it all end on the 24th?"

Soon after these notes were written, a much more serious affair had to be placed on record. Sydney was coming downstairs one evening, when he noticed in a badly lighted corner of the staircase something that he took to be a cat. He shrank back with his natural dislike for the animal; but on looking more closely he saw that it was nothing more than a shadow cast by some carving on the stair-head. He turned away with a laugh; but, as he turned, it certainly seemed that the shadow moved! As he went down the stairs he twice stumbled in trying to save himself from what he thought was a cat in danger of being trodden upon; and a moment later he seemed to tread on something soft that gave way and threw him down. He fell heavily and shook himself badly.

On picking himself up with the aid of his servant he limped into his library, and there found that his trousers were torn from a little above the ankle. But the curious thing was that there were three parallel vertical tears—just such as might be caused by the claws of a cat. A sharp smarting led to further investigation; and he then found that there were three deep scratches on the side of his leg, exactly corresponding with the tears in the trousers.

In the margin of the page on which he recorded this accident, he has added the words, "This cat means mischief." And the whole

213

tone of the remaining entries and of the few letters that date from this time shows only too clearly that his mental outlook was more or less tinged and obscured by gloomy forebodings.

It would seem to have been on the following day that another disturbing trifle occurred. Sydney's leg still pained him, and he spent the day on a couch with one or two favourite books. Soon after two o'clock in the afternoon, he heard a soft thud, such as might be caused by a cat leaping down from a moderate height. He looked up, and there on the window-sill crouched a black cat with gleaming eyes; and a moment later it sprang into the room. But it never reached the floor—or, if it did, it must have passed through it! He saw it spring; he saw it for the moment in mid-air; he saw it about to alight on the floor; and then—it was not there!

He would have liked to believe that it was a mere optical delusion; but against that theory stood the awkward fact that the cat in springing down from the window knocked over a flower-pot; and there lay the broken pieces in evidence of the fact.

He was now seriously scared. It was bad enough to find himself seeing things that had no objective reality; but it was far worse to be faced by happenings that were certainly real, but not to be accounted for by the ordinary laws of nature. In this case the broken flower-pot showed that if the black cat was merely what we call a ghost for lack of any more convenient term, it was a ghost that was capable of producing physical effects. If it could knock a flower-pot over, it could presumably scratch and bite—and the prospect of being attacked by a cat from some other plane of existence will hardly bear being thought of.

Certainly it seemed that Sydney had now real ground for alarm. The spectre cat—or whatever one likes to call it—was in some way gaining power and was now able to manifest its presence and hostility in more open and practical fashion. That same night saw a proof of this. Sydney dreamed that he was visiting the Zoological Gardens when a black leopard of ferocious aspect escaped from its cage and sprang upon him. He was thrown backwards to the ground and pinned down by the heavy animal. He was half crushed by its weight; its claws were at his throat; its fierce yellow eyes were staring into

214

his face; when the horror of the thing brought the dream to a sudden end and he awoke. As consciousness returned he was aware of an actual weight on his chest; and on opening his eyes he looked straight into the depths of two lambent yellow flames set in a face of velvet black. The cat sprang off the bed and leaped through the window. But the window was closed and there was no sound of breaking glass.

Sydney did not sleep much more that night. But a further shock awaited him on rising. He found some small blood stains on his pillow; and an inspection before the looking glass showed the presence of two groups of tiny wounds on his neck. They were little more than pin-pricks; but they were arranged in two semi-circular groups, one on either side of the neck and just such as might be

Deadly Nightshade.
Early nineteenth-century wood engraving. Artist unknown.

caused by a cat trying to grasp the neck between its two forepaws.

This was the last incident recorded in Sydney's diary; and the serious view that he took of the situation is shown by certain letters that he wrote during the day, giving final instructions to his executors and settling various details of business—evidently in view of his approaching end.

What happened in the course of the final scene of the tragedy we can only guess from the traces left behind: but there is sufficient evidence to show that the horror was an appalling one.

The housekeeper seems to have been awakened once during the night by a strange noise which she could only describe as being like an angry cat snarling; while the parlour maid, whose room was immediately above that occupied by Sydney, says that she dreamt that she heard her master scream horribly once or twice.

In the morning, Sydney did not answer when called at his usual hour; and, as the door was found to be locked, the housekeeper presently procured assistance and had it broken open. He was found crouching on the floor and leaning against the wall opposite the window. The carpet was saturated with blood; and the cause was quickly evident. The unfortunate man's throat had been torn open on either side, both jugular veins being severed. So far as could be made out, he had retired to bed and had been attacked during sleep, for the sheets were bespattered with blood. He had apparently got out of bed in his struggles to overcome the Thing that had him fast in its fearful grip. The look of horror on his distorted face was said by the witnesses to be past description.

Both window and door were fastened, and there was nothing to show how the assailant entered. But there was something to show how it left. The bloodstains on the floor recorded the footprints of a gigantic cat. They led across the floor from the corpse to the opposite wall—and there they ceased. The cat never came back; but whether it passed through the solid wall or melted into thin air, no one knows. In some mysterious way it came and went; and in passing it did this deed of horror.

It was a curious coincidence that the tragedy took place on Christmas Eve—the 24th day of the month!

THE CONSCIENTIOUS CAT

Agnes A. Sandham

Here is a firsthand account of the mining scene in the Sierra Nevadas in California a hundred years ago. Although the world of the mines was almost exclusively run by men, many women reporters were around the mining camps writing down their experiences in a personal history of the Far West that we are grateful for today.

We now know that the cats are particularly sensitive to earth movements of any kind. They and many other animals can sense, for example, an earthquake, and obviously during the days of mining they were able to sense the slightest earth movements.

It was a curious place for a cat—the lonely "Hydraulic Mines," on the crest of the Sierra Nevada Mountains in California. Where she came from, no one could tell. My acquaintance with her was made in a singular and altogether startling manner. It was in this wise: I was visiting the mines, and, under the guidance of the superintendent, had just passed over the brow of a great hill crowned with a thick growth of magnificent sugar pines, when suddenly we came upon the Hydraulic Mines—so lonely, so dreary, so utterly uninviting in appearance and situation, that I could not help asking, "Could

217

anything but a gold-hunting man be induced to live in such a place?"

"Wait and see," replied the superintendent as he walked in the direction of a rough shanty used by the miners as a place of shelter.

Just then I was startled at seeing a white cat come dashing toward us at full speed, her tail puffed out to an enormous size, and apparently pursued by a number of men armed with picks and crow-bars.

Full of sympathy for the poor cat making such a wild race for her life, I glanced toward the shanty which must be her only refuge. As I did so a dog's head was thrust cautiously out—only the head —and then stopped. Round the corner of the hut dashed the flying cat, and, before the dog's head could be drawn in, there came a violent collision, and a perfect storm of howls and hisses which marked the meeting of the angry cat and the much astonished dog. In spite of my sympathy, I could not help laughing heartily at this ludicrous collision—and my laugh was echoed by the cruel men who, as I supposed, were chasing poor pussy with murderous designs. But my laughter was suddenly cut short as I saw what seemed to be the great mountain sliding directly upon me, and, following the example of the cat, I turned and fled for shelter to the hut, while the men redoubled their laughter.

"What under the sun is the matter?" I asked, perplexed alike by the cat, the rushing men, and the moving mountain.

And then, with many jokes and much laughter, the whole matter was explained.

It appears that one cold and stormy night, about a year before my visit to the mines, the men were startled by a pitiful mewing out-side the camp. One of the miners, following up the sound of distress, soon returned with a most forlorn and miserable-looking kitten, more dead than alive. How she came to that desolate camp and where she came from was a mystery, but the miners, naturally ten-der-hearted, and welcoming anything that brought a change in the monotony of their daily life, took pity on the foundling and at once adopted her. Perhaps, too, the sight of such a home-body as a cat, away off in that desolate spot, brought back memories of their boy-

Illustrations by Henry Sandham (1842–1910), Canadian painter and illustrator who had a studio in Boston from 1880 to 1901 and contributed to Century *magazine.*

hood and the old homes far to the east in Maine woods or on New Hampshire hills, and called up, for all of them, a picture of the happy childhood days before the fever of adventure had led them so far from the dear old home in the mad race for gold.

Well, whatever their thoughts, they adopted the cat and made her so warm and comfortable, with plenty of milk to drink and a warm fire to curl before, that pussy was soon purring away as contentedly as if she had never been a homeless wanderer.

There is no such thing as stopping work in the mines. Day and night the work goes on, and the men are divided into day and night gangs, each of which works for a certain length of time, relieving the other at regular intervals. So it happened that pussy, dozing before the fire, was aroused by a stir in the room, and glancing up saw the miner who had rescued and cared for her preparing to go out to his work. Determined not to lose sight of her preserver, she jumped up and followed him. When the men arrived at their destination, pussy at once took up her position near her friend and carefully watched the proceedings.

A hydraulic mine is one in which water is made to take the part of pick and shovel. A tremendous pressure forces the water through a great iron pipe three or four feet in diameter, and sends it in a torrent against the bank of dirt in which the gold is hidden. This mighty stream of water washes away the bank and brings it caving and tumbling down, while it separates the gold from the gravel, and with the occasional assistance of blasting powder does a vast amount of mining work.

It was at one of these hydraulic mines that the fugitive cat had found friends; and as after several visits she lay watching their operations, she seemed to reason it all out in her own mind that as soon as the great dirt-bank opposite her showed signs of giving way under the action of the water forced against it, the men would rush for shelter to the shanty near by, to which, of course, she too would scamper to escape the falling earth. So, reasoned pussy, if these kind friends of mine are always in danger from these tumbling-down banks, why cannot I, in return for their kindness, watch the dirt-banks and give them proper warning?

220

Now, as you all know, there is nothing a cat dislikes so much as
water; just watch your kitty shake her paws daintily when she steps
into a puddle, and see how disgusted she is if a drop of water falls
on her nose or back. But this Sierra Nevada pussy was a most conscientious cat. She felt that it was her duty to make some sacrifice
for her friends, and so, after thinking it all over, she took her place
right on top of the nozzle of the "monitor" (as the big iron pipe
through which the water is forced is called), and here, in spite of
occasional and most unwelcome shower-baths, she would watch for
the first movement of the falling bank, when away she would go like
a flash with all the miners at her heels until they all reached the
shelter of the hut. So faithfully did she perform her self-imposed task
that, in a little while, the men gave up their precaution of keeping

221

one eye on the dangerous slide and waited for puss to give the signal. As soon as they saw her spring down from the comfortable bed which the miners had made for her on the "monitor," they would all cry, "The cat; the cat!" and start on a run for the shanty. And it was at just such a moment that I came to the mine and encountered this most conscientious cat leading her friends to safety.

She soon learned also to distinguish between the various phases of hydraulic mining; and when the "monitor" was being used simply for washing the gold or for general "cleaning up" purposes, she knew that there was no danger, and would serenely close her eyes and take a comfortable nap on her cushion, regardless of what was going on around her, until by some strange instinct she knew that the "monitor" was turned upon the bank again, and was awake and watchful in an instant. Her very color, too, was a help to her friends, as, being a white cat, she served on dark nights as a guide to the men who came to relieve the gang to which pussy belonged, and which no consideration would induce her to desert.

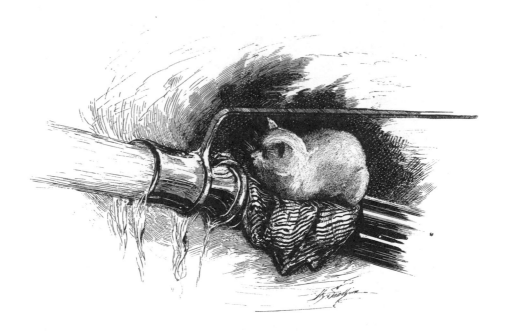

Now, it happened that about the time of pussy's appearance at the mine a very unprepossessing mongrel pup had been left at the camp, as not worth taking away, and so he too was adopted by the kind-hearted miners. But alas! the dog proved as great a coward as the cat was a heroine. His only thought was to look out for number one, and he did that so thoroughly that when he too had learned that a sudden move on the part of the men meant danger, he would scud into the hut in an agony of fear, and, like the dastardly dog he was, retreat into the farthest corner with his tail between his legs. Evidently, when I first made his acquaintance, he had not heard them rushing toward the hut and had thus been caught napping, and hence the collision I had witnessed. He was such a good-for-nothing that the men called him "Tailings"—which also means the refuse gravel and dirt out of which every speck of gold has been taken. And in such awe did he stand of Pussy that, though they took their meals together, "Tailings" always waited until pussy had finished before he presumed to take a bite, wagging his tail until the ground was swept clean, and whining meanwhile with hunger and impatience. Once, and once only, he endeavored to assert himself and take a bite before his betters. Pussy stopped eating, looked the culprit sternly in the eye, and then, slowly lifting her paw, brought it down with a sudden blow exactly in the center of the dog's nose. "Tailings" gave such a howl that the miners thought the whole mountain was caving in, and rushed out to see what was the matter. Pussy went on calmly finishing her dinner, and "Tailings" never again presumed to eat at the first table, to rebel against Pussy's rules.

YE MARVELLOUS LEGEND OF TOM CONNOR'S CAT

Samuel Lover

The Irish have always known that the cat has supernatural abilities, and these have been the subject of many traditional tales and legends. It took Samuel Lover, however, to give a particular, humorous twist to one such legend.

The Irish, like the Egyptians, believed there was special significance in the way the pupils of cats' eyes contract and dilate, which they interpreted as a mysterious representation of the moon's changes. Thus, being creatures of the moon, cats had to be propitiated.

"There was a man in these parts, sir, you must know, called Tom Connor, and he had a cat that was equal to any dozen of rat-traps, and he was proud of the baste, and with rayson; for she was worth her weight in goold to him in saving his sacks of meal from the thievery of the rats and mice; for Tom was an extensive dealer in corn, and influenced the rise and fall of that article in the market, to the extent of a full dozen of sacks at a time, which he either kept or sold, as the spirit of free trade or monopoly came over him. In-

224

deed, at one time, Tom had serious thoughts of applying to the government for a military force to protect his granary when there was a threatened famine in the country."

"Pooh! pooh! sir," said the matter-of-fact little man: "as if a dozen sacks could be of the smallest consequence in a whole country —pooh! pooh!"

"Well, sir," said Murtough, "I can't help you if you don't believe; but it's truth what I'm telling you, and pray don't interrupt me, though you may not believe; by the time the story's done you'll have heard more wonderful things than *that*—and besides, remember you're a stranger in these parts, and have no notion of the extra-ordinary things, physical, metaphysical, and magical, which constitute the idiosyncrasy of rural destiny."

The little man did not know the meaning of Murtough's last sentence—nor Murtough either; but, having stopped the little man's throat with big words, he proceeded:

"This cat, sir, you must know, was a great pet, and was so up to everything, that Tom swore she was a'most like a Christian, only she couldn't speak, and had so sensible a look in her eyes, that he was sartin sure the cat knew every word that was said to her. Well, she used to set by him at breakfast every morning, and the eloquent cock of her tail, as she used to rub against his leg, said: 'Give me some milk, Tom Connor,' as plain as print, and the plentitude of her purr afterwards spoke a gratitude beyond language. Well, one morning, Tom was going to the neighbouring town to market, and he had promised the wife to bring home shoes to the childre' out o' the price of the corn; and sure enough before he sat down to breakfast, there was Tom taking the measure of the children's feet, by cutting notches on a bit of stick; and the wife gave him so many cautions about getting a 'nate fit' for 'Billy's purty feet', that Tom, in his anxiety to nick the closest possible measure, cut off the child's toe. This disturbed the harmony of the party, and Tom was obliged to breakfast alone, while the mother was endeavouring to cure Billy; in short, trying to make a *heal* of his *toe*. Well, sir, all the time Tom was taking measure for the shoes, the cat was observing

The Jam Jar. Artist unknown. The cat appeared frequently as illustrative material in English and Irish magazines of the last century.

him with that luminous peculiarity of eye for which her tribe is remarkable; and when Tom sat down to breakfast the cat rubbed up against him more vigorously than usual; but Tom being bewildered, between his expected gain in corn and the positive loss of his child's toe, kept never minding her, until the cat, with a sort of caterwauling growl, gave Tom a dab of her claws, that went clean through his leathers, and a little further. 'Wow!' says Tom, with a jump, clapping his hand on the part, and rubbing it, 'by this and that, you drew the blood out o' me,' says Tom; 'you wicked divil—tish!—go along!' says he, making a kick at her. With that the cat gave a reproachful look at him, and her eyes glared just like a pair of mail-coach lamps in a fog. With that, sir, the cat, with a mysterious '*mi-ow*', fixed a most penetrating glance on Tom, and distinctly uttered his name.

"Tom felt every hair on his head as stiff as a pumphandle; and scarcely crediting his ears, he returned a searching look at the cat, who very quietly proceeded in a sort of nasal twang:

" 'Tom Connor,' says she.

" 'The Lord be good to me!' says Tom, 'if it isn't spakin' she is!'

" 'Tom Connor,' says she again.

" 'Yes, ma'am,' says Tom.

" 'Come here,' says she; 'whisper—I want to talk to you, Tom,' says she, 'the laste taste in private,' says she—rising on her hams and beckoning him with her paw out o' the door, with a wink and a toss o' the head aiqual to a milliner.

"Well, as you may suppose, Tom didn't know whether he was on his head or his heels, but he followed the cat, and off she went and squatted herself under the hedge of a little paddock at the back of Tom's house; and as he came round the corner, she held up her paw again, and laid it on her mouth, as much as to say 'Be cautious, Tom.' Well, divil a word Tom could say at all, with the fright, so up he goes to the cat, and says she:

" 'Tom,' says she, 'I have a great respect for you, and there's something I must tell you, because you're losing character with your neighbours,' says she, 'by your goin's on,' says she, 'and it's out o' the respect that I have for you, that I must tell you,' says she.

227

" 'Thank you ma'am,' says Tom.

" 'You're going off to the town,' says she, 'to buy shoes for the childre',' says she, 'and never thought o' getting me a pair.'

" 'You!' said Tom.

" 'Yis, me, Tom Connor,' says she, 'and the neighbours wondhers that a respectable man like you allows your cat to go about the counthry barefutted,' says she.

" 'Is it a cat to ware shoes?' says Tom.

" 'Why not?' says she; 'doesn't horses ware shoes?—and I have a prettier foot than a horse, I hope,' says she with a toss of her head.

" 'Faix, she spakes like a woman; so proud of her feet,' says Tom to himself, astonished, as you may suppose, but pretending never to think it remarkable all the time; and so he went on discoursin'; and says he: 'It's thrue for you, ma'am,' says he, 'that horses ware shoes—but that stands to rayson, ma'am, you see—seeing the hardship their feet has to go through on the hard roads.'

" 'And how do you know what hardship my feet has to go through?' says the cat, mighty sharp.

" 'But, ma'am,' says Tom, 'I don't well see how you could fasten a shoe on you,' says he.

" 'Lave that to me,' says the cat.

" 'Did anyone ever stick walnut shells on you, pussy?' says Tom, with a grin.

" 'Don't be disrespectful, Tom Connor,' says the cat, with a frown.

" 'I ax your pard'n ma'am,' said he, 'but as for the horses you wor spakin' about warin' shoes, you know their shoes is fastened on with nails, and how would your shoes be fastened on?'

" 'Ah, you stupid thief!' says she, 'haven't I illigant nails o' my own?' and with that she gave him a dab of her claw, that made him roar.

" 'Ow! murdher!' says he.

" 'Now no more of your palaver, Misther Connor,' says the cat; 'just be off and get me the shoes.'

" 'Tare and ouns!' says Tom, 'what'll become o' me if I'm to get shoes for my cats?' says he, 'for you increase your family four times a year, and you have six or seven every time,' says he; 'and then you must all have two pair apiece—wirra! wirra!—I'll be ruined in shoe-leather,' says Tom.

" 'No more o' your stuff,' says the cat; 'don't be standin' here undher the hedge talkin' or we'll lose our karacthers—for I've re-marked your wife is jealous, Tom.'

" 'Pon my sowl, that's thrue,' says Tom, with a smirk.

" 'More fool she,' says the cat, 'for 'pon my conscience, Tom, you're as ugly as if you wor bespoke.'

"Off ran the cat with these words, leaving Tom in amazement. He said nothing to the family, for fear of fright'ning them, and off he went to the *town*, as he *pretended*—for he saw the cat watching him through a hole in the hedge; but when he came to a turn at the end of the road, the dickings a mind he minded the market, good or bad, but went off to Squire Botherum's, the magisthrit, to sware examinations agen the cat."

"Pooh! pooh!—nonsense!" broke in the little man, who had listened thus far to Murtough with an expression of mingled wonder and contempt, while the rest of the party willingly gave up the reins to nonsense, and enjoyed Murtough's legend and their com-panion's more absurd common sense.

"Don't interrupt him, Coggins," said Mister Wiggins.

"How can you listen to such nonsense!" returned Coggins. "Swear examinations against a cat, indeed! pooh! pooh!"

"My dear sir," said Murtough, "remember this is a fairy story, and that the country all round here is full of enchantment. As I was telling you, Tom went off to swear examinations."

"Ay, ay!" shouted all but Coggins; "go on with the story."

"And when Tom was asked to relate the events of the morning, which brought him before Squire Botherum, his brain was so be-wildered between his corn, and his cat, and his child's toe, that he made a very confused account of it.

" 'Begin your story from the beginning,' said the magistrate to Tom.

" 'Well, your honour,' says Tom, 'I was goin' to market this mor-

229

nin', to sell the child's corn—I beg your pard'n—my own toes, I mane, sir.'

" 'Sell your toes!' said the Squire.

" 'No, sir, takin' the cat to market, I mane——'

" 'Take a cat to market!' said the Squire. 'You're drunk, man.'

" 'No, your honour, only confused a little; for when the toes began to spake to me—the cat, I mane—I was bothered clane——'

" 'The cat speak to you!' said the Squire. 'Phew! worse than before—you're drunk, Tom.'

" 'No, your honour; it's on the strength of the cat I come to spake to you——'

" 'I think it's on the strength of a pint of whisky, Tom——'

" 'By the vartue o' my oath, your honour, it's nothin' but the cat.' And so Tom then told him all about the affair, and the Squire was regularly astonished. Just then the bishop of the diocese and the priest of the parish happened to call in, and heard the story; and the bishop and the priest had a tough argument for two hours on the subject: the former swearing she must be a witch; but the priest denying *that*, and maintaining she was *only* enchanted, and that part of the argument was afterwards referred to the primate, and subsequently to the conclave at Rome; but the Pope declined interfering about cats, saying he had quite enough to do minding his own bulls.

" 'In the meantime, what are we to do with the cat?' says Botherum.

" 'Burn her,' says the bishop, 'she's a witch.'

" '*Only* enchanted,' said the priest, 'and the ecclesiastical court maintains that——'

" 'Bother the ecclesiastical court!' said the magistrate; 'I can only proceed on the statutes'; and with that he pulled down all the lawbooks in his library, and hunted the laws from Queen Elizabeth down, and he found that they made laws against everything in Ireland, *except a cat*. The divil a thing escaped them but a cat, which did *not* come within the meaning of any Act of Parliament—*the cats only had escaped.*

" 'There's the alien act, to be sure,' said the magistrate, 'and perhaps she's a French spy in disguise.'

" 'She spakes like a French spy, sure enough,' says Tom: 'and she was missin', I remember, all last Spy-Wednesday.'

" 'That's suspicious,' says the Squire, 'but conviction might be difficult; and I have a fresh idea,' says Botherum.

" 'Faith, it won't keep fresh long, this hot weather,' says Tom, 'so your honour had betther make use of it at wanst.'

" 'Right,' says Botherum, 'we'll make her a subject to the game laws; we'll hunt her,' says he.

" 'Ow!—elegant!' says Tom; 'we'll have a brave run out of her.'

" 'Meet me at the cross roads,' says the Squire, 'in the morning, and I'll have the hounds ready.'

"Well, off Tom went home; and he was racking his brain what excuse he could make to the cat for not bringing the shoes; and at last he hit one off, just as he saw her cantering up to him, half a mile before he got home.

" 'Where's the shoes, Tom?' says she.

" 'I have not got them to-day, ma'am,' says he.

" 'Is that the way you keep your promise, Tom?' says she; 'I'll tell you what it is, Tom—I'll tare the eyes out o' the childre' if you don't get me those shoes.'

" 'Whist, whist!' says Tom, frightened out his life for his children's eyes. 'Don't be in a passion, pussy. The shoemaker said he had not a shoe in his shop, nor a last that would make one to fit you; and he says I must bring you into the town for him to take your measure.'

" 'And when am I to go?' says the cat, looking savage.

" 'To-morrow,' says Tom.

" 'It's well you said that, Tom,' said the cat, 'or the devil an eye I'd leave in your family this night,' and off she hopped.

"Tom thrimbled at the wicked look she gave.

" 'Remember!' says she, over the hedge, with a bitter caterwaul.

" 'Never fear,' says Tom.

"Well, sure enough, the next mornin' there was the cat at cock-crow, licking herself as nate as a new pin, to go into the town, and out came Tom with a bag undher his arm and the cat after him.

" 'Now git into this, and I'll carry you into the town,' says Tom, opening the bag.

" 'Sure, I can walk with you,' says the cat.

" 'Oh, that wouldn't do,' says Tom; 'the people in the town is curious and slandherous people, and sure it would rise ugly remarks if I was seen with a cat afther me—a dog is a man's companion by nature, but cats does not stand to rayson.'

"Well, the cat, seeing there was no use in argument, got into the bag, and off Tom set to the crossroads with the bag over his shoulder, and he came up, *quite innocent-like*, to the corner, where the Squire, and his huntsman, and the hounds, and a pack of people were waitin'. Out came the Squire on a sudden, just as if it was all by accident.

" 'God save you, Tom,' says he.

" 'God save you kindly, sir,' says Tom.

" 'What's that bag you have at your back?' says the Squire.

" 'Oh, nothin' at all, sir,' says Tom, makin' a face all the time, as much as to say, I have her safe.

" 'Oh, there's something in that bag, I think,' says the Squire; 'you must let me see it.'

" 'If you bethray me, Tom Connor,' says the cat, in a low voice, 'by this and that I'll never spake to you again!'

" ''Pon my honour, sir,' says Tom, with a wink and a twitch of his thumb towards the bag, 'I haven't anything in it.'

" 'I have been missing my praties of late,' says the Squire; 'and I'd just like to examine that bag,' says he.

" 'Is it doubting my charackther you'd be sir?' says Tom, pretending to be in a passion.

" 'Tom, your sowl!' says the voice in the sack, '*if you let the cat out of the bag*, I'll murther you.'

" 'An honest man would make no objection to be sarched,' said the Squire, 'and I insist on it,' says he, laying hold o' the bag, and Tom purtending to fight all the time; but, my jewel! before two minutes, they shook the cat out o' the bag, sure enough, and off she went, with her tail as big as a sweeping brush, and the Squire, with a thundering view halloo after her, clapt the dogs at her heels, and away they went for the bare life. Never was there seen such running as that day—the cat made for a shaking bog, the loneliest place in the whole country, and there the riders were all thrown out, barrin' the huntsman, who had a web-footed horse on purpose for soft places, and the priest, whose horse could go anywhere by reason of the priest's blessing; and, sure enough, the huntsman and his riverence stuck to the hunt like wax; and just as the cat got on the border of the bog, they saw her give a twist as the foremost dog closed with her, for he gave her a nip in the flank. Still she went on, however, and headed them well, towards an old mud cabin in the middle of the bog, and there they saw her jump in at the window, and up came the dogs the next minit, and gathered round the house, with the most horrid howling ever was heard. The huntsman alighted, and went into the house to turn the cat out again, when what should he see but an old hag lying in bed in the corner!

" 'Did you see a cat come in here?' says he.

" 'Oh, no—o—o—o!' squealed the old hag in a trembling voice; 'there's no cat here,' says she.

" 'Yelp, yelp, yelp!' went the dogs outside.

" 'Oh, keep the dogs out of this,' says the old hag—'oh—o—o—o!' and the hunstman saw her eyes glare under the blanket, just like a cat's.

" 'Hillo!" says the huntsman, pulling down the blanket—and what should he see but the old hag's flank all in a gore of blood.

" 'Ow, ow! you old divil—is it you? you old cat!' says he, opening the door.

"In rushed the dogs—up jumped the old hag, and changing into a cat before their eyes, out she darted through the window again, and made another run for it; but she couldn't escape, and the dogs gobbled her while you could say 'Jack Robinson'. But the most remarkable part of this extraordinary story, gentlemen, is that the pack was ruined from that day out; for after having eaten the enchanted cat, *the devil a thing they would ever hunt afterwards but mice.*"

THE "CENTURY" CAT

Mary F. Honeyman

The Century Company with its Century *magazine had truly an open door to quality writing at the end of the nineteenth century—but it had more than the usual welcome extended by clever editors, both women and men. It had a very special office cat whose fame was deservedly widespread.*

His experiences have been somewhat different from those of cats in general. In the first place, he began life very high up in the world; that is to say, in the seventh story of the building which is the home of the *St. Nicholas* magazine. At an early age he went into business, not as an office boy, but as an office cat; for mice were plenty in the great building, and their sharp little white teeth did much mischief in nibbling the backs off the magazines for the morsel of paste that secures the cover. And these mice, perhaps knowing more than most mice, having been familiar with good literature all their days, just laughed at mouse-traps, no matter how temptingly baited with toasted cheese, and refused to be caught in them on any terms. At length it was decided to get a cat to put an end to their depredations;

The Century Cat drawn from life by J. C. Beard.

and what cat could be better than the gray one who lived on the top floor with the janitor, and was then some three years old? So it came about that he was installed as The Century Cat; and what could be more fitting than that he should receive the name "Century"? A good friend of his at once gave him a fine collar with his name engraved upon it, and very soon he came to know his name.

His duties were so faithfully performed that in a short time no mice were to be seen about the premises; but how or when they were disposed of no one knew, though there was a general impression that the cat and the mice arranged their affairs at night when they had the building to themselves. Certainly, during the day Century devoted most of his time to sleeping, sometimes curled up into a huge furry ball, as like as not on top of a tall heap of magazines, his head resting on one of his soft gray paws.

235

He evidently believed that a cat must live, and was inclined to be a trifle particular as to both the quality and the quantity of the beef or mutton, and milk that were daily brought from a restaurant for his delectation. In this way, although he could not be said to draw a salary, yet his name was upon the pay-roll, and his weekly account was audited with the general business of the magazines.

Century was not unmindful of his social duties, and during some portion of every day he gave his friends an opportunity of showing him those little attentions of which all cats are so fond. He walked about the entire office on the tops of the desks, stepping carefully over the books, letters, papers, etc., with which they were covered, never displacing anything, and strange to say, never upsetting the ink. Once, though, he did get a paw into a large inkstand accidentally, and then walking over one of the large wrappers in which the magazines are mailed, the perfect impression of the paw was left upon the paper, many times repeated, in violet ink. This was preserved as a specimen of the office cat's handwriting.

In some particularly cozy corner or near some chosen friend he would lie down and take his afternoon nap; and very amusing it was to see what trouble people would take so that the cat might not be disturbed. Sometimes he would station himself on the counter and make friends with the persons who came in, very few of whom failed to pat and speak to the beautiful creature. These courtesies were generally received with dignified condescension. Occasionally, however, he seemed to throw dignity to the winds; and then with ears laid back and tail erect, he would scamper down the corridor, just a city block from the front to the rear of the building, and back again as fast as he could go.

In summer, when the windows were open, he liked to lie far out on the sill, stretched at full length. And if any one, fearful that he might fall from his lofty perch, tried to persuade him to take a safer position, he would scold and resume the outermost ledge as soon as possible. One thing here disturbed his peace of mind, and that was when the sparrows would alight on the telegraph wires, not far from the windows, and there chirp and twitter in the most exasperating manner. Long, sly looks he took at them, and if they came nearer than usual he would show his teeth and "talk" in what seemed to be a very disagreeable way.

If Century were telling this story himself, I suppose he would say that his most dreadful experience was on the night when the building took fire. It was some time before the poor fellow could be found, thoroughly frightened and very wet but not at all burned. He never seemed to recover entirely from the scare, however, and this fact may have led to the suggestion, when the question of office vacations came up last summer, that Century should take a vacation, too. Why not? He must find it very trying to be shut up alone from noon on Saturday till the following Monday morning, all summer long, to say nothing of every night. So it was arranged that the cat should have a vacation, and should spend it in one of the pretty villages of New Jersey.

After a little, the spirit of investigation seemed to take possession of our cat. Every tree, every shrub, the flowers, and the grass he must sniff and rub against in the peculiar fashion in which cats make acquaintance; this not once, but again and again. The trees impressed him greatly, and it was not long before he attempted to run up one—rather shyly at the start, and not very far, but gradually he lost all fear and climbed as nimbly as any cat need. Insects were curiosities to this town-bred creature, and he would perk his head on one side and look at a grasshopper or a cricket with a comically critical air. Of course he knew no better than to play with bees. Having pinned one to the wall, he proceeded to examine it closely; and, when stung, he shook his head vigorously and seemed much surprised that the smart could not be dislodged in that way. Toads afforded him endless diversion. He would keep one in sight for hours, giving it an occasional pat, or chasing it if he felt inclined to frolic. As to birds, their number and variety evidently filled him with amazement, not to mention the entire unconcern with which they would alight close to him to pick up a crumb or a seed.

He was disposed to be very neighborly at first; in fact he seemed to think that one country house was quite as good as another—an opinion that usually led to his hostess's going about the neighborhood at nightfall inquiring for a large Maltese cat. When found he invariably made forcible protest against being carried home.

Fears that he might not be able to defend himself against other cats and dogs proved to be quite groundless. He took his stand from the very first morning that he lay dozing in the porch and waited for an intrusive terrier to come up barking noisily. Then Century flew at that dog, taking care not to let him escape from the premises until a sound thrashing had been administered, when he was allowed to depart wailing down the street, a wiser dog, for he has passed daily ever since without vouchsafing so much as a growl. Dogs much larger than Century are admonished to depart without ceremony; and as to cats, all and sundry, a warning "S-p-t-z-f-f, s-p-t-t-t!" is the only salutation that the boldest waits for.

Century dearly loves to get into the dining room at dinner, when he will steal from chair to chair, softly purring; and having attracted attention by gently touching one's elbow with his paw, or rubbing his head against one's arm, he will sit up on his haunches, very straight, drop those soft gray paws forward close together on his breast, and so wait for whatever choice morsel he may have. Cheese he likes exceedingly, and will do his most irresistible "begging" when his keen scent apprises him that cheese is upon the table.

He is still in the country, nowise anxious to return to the city and to business, apparently; and I know not where you will find a sleeker, happier, more comfortable cat. He is affectionate and grateful to a degree, though people who do not like cats will tell you that they are never the one nor the other.

A long vacation, did you say? Century does not think it too long, I am sure; and when did you ever find that fault with one of your vacations?

238

JUNO

Harriet Beecher Stowe

Harriet Beecher Stowe, the creator of Uncle Tom's Cabin, *lived, during the reign of Juno, in a cottage in Hartford, Connecticut. The rear of her property adjoined Mark Twain's, and Juno had free and easy access to the camaraderie of Mark Twain's remarkable cats. Juno was also a friend of that most admirable of cats, Charles Dudley Warner's Calvin.*

The most beautiful and best trained cat I ever knew was named Juno, and was brought up by a lady who was so wise in all that related to the care and management of animals, that she might be quoted as authority on all points of their nurture and breeding; and Juno, carefully trained by such a mistress, was a standing example of the virtues which may be formed in a cat by careful education.

Never was Juno known to be out of place, to take her nap elsewhere than on her own appointed cushion, to be absent at mealtimes, or, when the most tempting dainties were in her power, to anticipate the proper time by jumping on the table to help herself.

In all her personal habits Juno was of a neatness unparalleled in cat history. The parlor of her mistress was always of a waxen and spotless cleanness, and Juno would have died sooner than violate its sanctity by any impropriety. She was a skilful mouser, and her sleek, glossy sides were a sufficient refutation of the absurd notion that a cat must be starved into a display of her accomplishments. Every rat, mouse, or ground mole that she caught was brought in and laid at the feet of her mistress for approbation. But on one point her mind was dark. She could never be made to comprehend the great difference between fur and feathers, nor see why her mistress should gravely reprove her when she brought in a bird, and warmly commend when she captured a mouse.

After a while a little dog named Pero, with whom Juno had struck up a friendship, got into the habit of coming to her mistress's apartment at the hours when her modest meals were served, on which occasions Pero thought it would be a good idea to invite himself to make a third. He had a nice little trick of making himself amiable, by sitting up on his haunches, and making little begging gestures with his two fore-paws,—which so much pleased his hostess that sometimes he was fed before Juno. Juno observed this in silence for some time; but at last a bright idea struck her, and, gravely rearing up on her haunches, she imitated Pero's gestures with her fore-paws. Of course this carried the day, and secured her position.

Cats are often said to have no heart,—to be attached to places, but incapable of warm personal affection. It was reserved for Juno by her sad end to refute this slander on her race. Her mistress was obliged to leave her quiet home, and go to live in a neighboring city; so she gave Juno to the good lady who inhabited the other part of the house.

But no attentions or care on the part of her new mistress could banish from Juno's mind the friend she had lost. The neat little parlor where she had spent so many pleasant hours was dismantled and locked up, but Juno would go, day after day, and sit on the ledge of the window-seat, looking in and mewing dolefully. She refused food; and, when too weak to mount on the sill and look in, stretched herself on the ground beneath the window, where she died for love of her mistress, as truly as any lover in an old ballad.

The Christmas Cat. Nineteenth-century engraving by R. B. Birch.

You see by this story the moral that I wish to convey. It is, that watchfulness, kindness, and care will develop a nature in animals such as we little dream of. Love will beget love, regular care and attention will give regular habits, and thus domestic pets may be made agreeable and interesting.

Anyone who does not feel an inclination or capacity to take the amount of care and pains necessary for the well-being of an animal ought conscientiously to abstain from having one in charge. A carefully tended pet, whether dog or cat, is a pleasant addition to a family of young people; but a neglected, ill-brought-up, ill-kept one is only an annoyance.

Arthur Rackham illustration
from St. Nicholas, *1913.*

242

MY FATHER'S CAT

William Rossetti

Many literary families of the nineteenth century rejoiced in cats. There was the faithful cat of those four wonderful children in York-shire, Anne, Emily, Charlotte, and Branwell Brontë, whose love for animals was deep and wide. And there were those equally fascinating Rossetti children in London; not having the freedom of the moors, they had to be satisfied with a tabby cat. But they knew well that it was never their cat—it was their father's cat.

So do cats choose, and once a choice has been made, all the over-tures in the world from other people will not change their basic loyalty.

In all my earlier years I used frequently to see my father come home in the dusk, rather fagged with his round of teaching; and, after dining, he would lie down flat on the hearth-rug, close by the fire, snoring vigorously. Beside him would stand up our old familiar tabby cat, poised on her haunches, and holding on by her fore-claws inserted into the fender-wires, warming her furry front. Her atti-tude (I have never seen any feline imitation of it) was peculiar—

243

somewhat in the shape of a capital Y. "The cat making the Y" was
my father's phrase for this performance. She was the mother of a
numerous progeny. One of her daughters—also long an inmate of
our house—was a black and white cat named Zoe by my elder sister
Maria, who had a fancy for anything Greekish; but Zoe never made
a Y.

Kittens, by W. A. Rogers.

244

MY FATHER, THE CAT

Henry Slesar

Currently writers undertake bright, charming stories of cats, or give us rewarding insights and encounters with this wonderful animal. There was a time, however, when the poor cat was nothing but the witch's friend, an ally to the prince of the power of darkness, an imp of wickedness. Even in Western Europe, it was not until the time of Louis XIV that a cat began to creep into the court and heart of human life after the dark ages.

Henry Slesar's story of a cat's remarkable lineage has crept into the classics of fantasy.

My mother was a lovely, delicate woman from the coast of Brittany, who was miserable sleeping on less than three mattresses, and who, it is said, was once injured by a falling leaf in her garden. My grandfather, a descendant of the French nobility whose family had ridden the tumbrils of the Revolution, tended her fragile body and spirit with the same loving care given rare, brief-blooming flowers. You may imagine from this his attitude concerning marriage. He lived in terror of the vulgar, heavy-handed man who would one day win my mother's heart, and at last, this persistent dread killed him. His concern was unnecessary, however, for my mother chose a suitor who was as free of mundane brutality as a husband could be. Her choice was Dauphin, a remarkable white cat which strayed onto the estate shortly after his death.

Dauphin was an unusually large Angora, and his ability to speak in cultured French, English, and Italian was sufficient to cause my mother to adopt him as a household pet. It did not take long for her to realize that Dauphin deserved a higher status, and he became her friend, protector, and confidante. He never spoke of his origin, nor where he had acquired the classical education which made him such an entertaining companion. After two years, it was easy for my mother, an unworldly woman at best, to forget the dissimilarity in their species. In fact, she was convinced that Dauphin was an enchanted prince, and Dauphin, in consideration of her illusions, never dissuaded her. At last, they were married by an understanding clergyman of the locale, who solemnly filled in the marriage application with the name of M. Edwarde Dauphin.

I, Etienne Dauphin, am their son.

To be candid, I am a handsome youth, not unlike my mother in the delicacy of my features. My father's heritage is evident in my large, feline eyes, and in my slight body and quick movements. My mother's death, when I was four, left me in the charge of my father and his coterie of loyal servants, and I could not have wished for a finer upbringing. It is to my father's patient tutoring that I owe whatever graces I now possess. It was my father, the cat, whose gentle paws guided me to the treasure houses of literature, art, and music, whose whiskers bristled with pleasure at a goose well cooked, at a meal well served, at a wine well chosen. How many happy hours we shared! He knew more of life and the humanities, my father, the cat, than any human I have met in all my twenty-three years.

Until the age of eighteen, my education was his personal challenge. Then, it was his desire to send me into the world outside the gates. He chose for me a university in America, for he was deeply fond of what he called "that great raw country," where he believed

Puss in Boots illustration by Gustave Doré, French painter and illustrator (1833–1883).

my feline qualities might be tempered by the aggressiveness of the roughcoated barking dogs I would be sure to meet.

I must confess to a certain amount of unhappiness in my early American years, torn as I was from the comforts of the estate and the wisdom of my father, the cat. But I became adapted, and even upon my graduation from the university, sought and held employment in a metropolitan art museum. It was there I met Joanna, the young woman I intended to make my bride.

Joanna was a product of the great American southwest, the daughter of a cattle-raiser. There was a blooming vitality in her face and her body, a lustiness born of open skies and desert. Her hair was not the gold of antiquity; it was new gold, freshly mined from the black rock. Her eyes were not like old-world diamonds; their sparkle was that of sunlight on a cascading river. Her figure was bold, an open declaration of her sex.

She was, perhaps, an unusual choice for the son of a fairylike mother and an Angora cat. But from the first meeting of our eyes, I knew that I would someday bring Joanna to my father's estate to present her as my fiancée.

I approached that occasion with understandable trepidation. My father had been explicit in his advice before I departed for America, but on no point had he been more emphatic than secrecy concerning himself. He assured me that revelation of my paternity would bring ridicule and unhappiness upon me. The advice was sound, of course, and not even Joanna knew that our journey's end would bring us to the estate of a large, cultured, and conversing cat. I had deliberately fostered the impression that I was orphaned, believing that the proper place for revealing the truth was the atmosphere of my father's home in France. I was certain that Joanna would accept her father-in-law without distress. Indeed, hadn't nearly a score of human servants remained devoted to their feline master for almost a generation?

We had agreed to be wed on the first of June, and on May the fourth, emplaned in New York for Paris. We were met at Orly Field by François, my father's solemn manservant, who had been delegated not so much as escort as he was chaperone, my father having retained much of the old world properties. It was a long trip by automobile to our estate in Brittany, and I must admit to a brooding silence throughout the drive which frankly puzzled Joanna.

However, when the great stone fortress that was our home came within view, my fears and doubts were quickly dispelled. Joanna, like so many Americans, was thrilled at the aura of venerability and royal custom surrounding the estate. François placed her in charge of Madame Jolinet, who clapped her plump old hands with delight at the sight of her fresh blonde beauty, and chattered and clucked like a mother hen as she led Joanna to her room on the second floor. As for myself, I had one immediate wish: to see my father, the cat.

He greeted me in the library, where he had been anxiously awaiting our arrival, curled up in his favorite chair by the fireside, a wide-mouthed goblet of cognac by his side. As I entered the room, he lifted a paw formally, but then his reserve was dissolved by the emotion of our reunion, and he licked my face in unashamed joy.

François refreshed his glass, and poured another for me, and we toasted each other's well-being.

"To you, *mon purr*," I said, using the affectionate name of my childhood memory.

"To Joanna," my father said. He smacked his lips over the cognac, and wiped his whiskers gravely. "And where is this paragon?"

"With Madame Jolinet. She will be down shortly."

"And you have told her everything?"

I blushed. "No, *mon purr*, I have not. I thought it best to wait until we were home. She is a wonderful woman," I added impulsively. "She will not be—"

"Horrified?" my father said. "What makes you so certain, my son?"

"Because she is a woman of great heart," I said stoutly. "She was educated at a fine college for women in Eastern America. Her ancestors were rugged people, given to legend and folklore. She is a warm, human person—"

"Human," my father sighed, and his tail swished. "You are expecting too much of your beloved, Etienne. Even a woman of the finest character may be dismayed in this situation."

"But my mother—"

"Your mother was an exception, a changeling of the fairies. You must not look for your mother's soul in Joanna's eyes." He jumped from his chair, and came towards me, resting his paw upon my knee. "I am glad you have not spoken of me, Etienne. Now you must keep your silence forever."

249

I was shocked. I reached down and touched my father's silky fur, saddened by the look of his age in his gray, goldflecked eyes, and by the tinge of yellow in his white coat.

"No, *mon purr*," I said. "Joanna must know the truth. Joanna must know how proud I am to be the son of Edwarde Dauphin."

"Then you will lose her."

"Never! That cannot happen!"

My father walked stiffly to the fireplace, staring into the gray ashes. "Ring for François," he said. "Let him build the fire. I am cold, Etienne."

I walked to the cord and pulled it. My father turned to me and said: "You must wait, my son. At dinner this evening, perhaps. Do not speak of me until then."

"Very well, father."

When I left the library, I encountered Joanna at the head of the stairway, and she spoke to me excitedly.

"Oh, Etienne! What a *beautiful* old house. I know I will love it! May we see the rest?"

"Of course," I said.

"You look troubled. Is something wrong?"

"No, no. I was thinking how lovely you are."

We embraced, and her warm full body against mine confirmed my conviction that we should never be parted. She put her arm in mine, and we strolled through the great rooms of the house. She was ecstatic at their size and elegance, exclaiming over the carpeting, the gnarled furniture, the ancient silver and pewter, the gallery of family paintings. When she came upon an early portrait of my mother, her eyes misted.

"She was lovely," Joanna said. "Like a princess! And what of your father? Is there no portrait of him?"

"No," I said hurriedly. "No portrait." I had spoken my first lie to Joanna, for there was a painting, half-completed, which my mother had begun in the last year of her life. It was a whispering little watercolor, and Joanna discovered it to my consternation.

"What a magnificent cat!" she said. "Was it a pet?"

"It is Dauphin," I said nervously.

250

She laughed. "He has your eyes, Etienne."

"Joanna, I must tell you something—"

"And this ferocious gentleman with the moustaches? Who is he?"

"My grandfather. Joanna, you must listen—"

François, who had been following our inspection tour at shadow's-length, interrupted. I suspected that his timing was no mere coincidence.

"We will be serving dinner at seven-thirty," he said. "If the lady would care to dress—"

"Of course," Joanna said. "Will you excuse me, Etienne?"

I bowed to her, and she was gone.

At fifteen minutes to the appointed dining time, I was ready, and hastened below to talk once more with my father. He was in the dining room, instructing the servants as to the placement of the silver and accessories. My father was proud of the excellence of his table, and took all his meals in the splendid manner. His appreciation of food and wine was unsurpassed in my experience, and it had always been the greatest of pleasures for me to watch him at table, stalking across the damask and dipping delicately into the silver dishes prepared for him. He pretended to be too busy with his dinner preparations to engage me in conversation, but I insisted.

"I must talk to you," I said. "We must decide together how to do this."

"It will not be easy," he answered with a twinkle. "Consider Joanna's view. A cat as large and as old as myself is cause enough for comment. A cat that speaks is alarming. A cat that dines at table with the household is shocking. And a cat whom you must introduce as your—"

"Stop it!" I cried. "Joanna must know the truth. You must help me reveal it to her."

"Then you will not heed my advice?"

"In all things but this. Our marriage can never be happy unless she accepts you for what you are."

"And if there is no marriage?"

I would not admit to this possibility. Joanna was mine; nothing could alter that. The look of pain and bewilderment in my eyes

251

must have been evident to my father, for he touched my arm gently with his paw and said:

"I will help you, Etienne. You must give me your trust."

"Always!"

"Then come to dinner with Joanna and explain nothing. Wait for me to appear."

I grasped his paw and raised it to my lips. "Thank you, father!"

He turned to François, and snapped: "You have my instructions?"

"Yes, sir," the servant replied.

"Then all is ready. I shall return to my room now, Etienne. You may bring your fiancée to dine."

I hastened up the stairway and found Joanna ready, strikingly beautiful in shimmering white satin. Together, we descended the grand staircase and entered the room.

Her eyes shone at the magnificence of the service set upon the table, at the soldiery array of fine wines, some of them already poured into their proper glasses for my father's enjoyment: *Haut Médoc,* from *St. Estephe,* authentic *Chablis, Epernay Champagne,* and an American import from the Napa Valley of which he was fond. I waited expectantly for his appearance as we sipped our aperitif, while Joanna chatted about innocuous matters, with no idea of the tormented state I was in.

At eight o'clock, my father had not yet made his appearance, and I grew even more distraught as François signalled for the serving of the *bouillon au madère.* Had he changed his mind? Would I be left to explain my status without his help? I hadn't realized until this moment how difficult a task I had allotted for myself, and the fear of losing Joanna was terrible within me. The soup was flat and tasteless on my tongue, and the misery in my manner was too apparent for Joanna to miss.

"What is it, Etienne?" she said. "You've been so morose all day. Can't you tell me what's wrong?"

"No, it's nothing. It's just—" I let the impulse take possession of my speech. "Joanna, there's something I should tell you. About my mother, and my father—"

"Ahem," François said.

He turned to the doorway, and our glances followed his.

"Oh Etienne!" Joanna cried, in a voice ringing with delight.

It was my father, the cat, watching us with his gray, gold-flecked eyes. He approached the dining table, regarding Joanna with timidity and caution.

"It's the cat in the painting!" Joanna said. "You didn't tell me he was here, Etienne. He's beautiful!"

"Joanna, this is—"

"Dauphin! I would have known him anywhere. Here, Dauphin! Here, kitty, kitty, kitty!"

Slowly, my father approached her outstretched hand, and allowed her to scratch the thick fur on the back of his neck.

"Aren't you the pretty little pussy! Aren't you the sweetest little thing!"

"Joanna!"

She lifted my father by the haunches, and held him in her lap, stroking his fur and cooing the silly words that women address to their pets. The sight pained and confused me, and I sought to find an opening word that would allow me to explain, yet hoping all the time that my father would himself provide the answer.

Then my father spoke.

"Meow," he said.

"Are you hungry?" Joanna asked solicitously. "Is the little pussy hungry?"

"Meow," my father said, and I believed my heart broke then and there. He leaped from her lap and padded across the room. I watched him through blurred eyes as he followed François to the corner, where the servant had placed a shallow bowl of milk. He lapped at it eagerly, until the last white drop was gone. Then he yawned and stretched, and trotted back to the doorway, with one fleeting glance in my direction that spoke articulately of what I must do next.

"What a wonderful animal," Joanna said.

"Yes," I answered. "He was my mother's favorite."

MOQUO

Madame Michelet

*Madame Jules Michelet was the wife and collaborator of the famous
historian whose favorite fields included demonology and witchcraft.*

*She, however, liked the simple life of nature and had a particular
affection for cats. Cats in her time in France were not only pets, but
had to earn their keep. The large national printing office of France,
for example, had a staff of cats to guard the paper from rats and
mice. This was equally true in such sophisticated spots as Vienna,
which had its official cats. When they were too old for service, they
were placed, as well they should be, on the retired list.*

My father had a strong sympathy for cats. This was the result of early
experience. He and his brother, knocked pitilessly about in their
childhood between the harshness of home and the cruelty of school,
had, for solace and alleviation, two well-loved cats. Affection for
these animals became a family trait. When we were young, each of
us had a kitten. We gathered round the fire at night, and our sleek,
well-fed pets sat at our feet, basking in the grateful warmth.

There was one cat, however, that never joined the circle. He was

The Kitten and the Rooster. Nineteenth-century engraving
by unknown artist.

a poor ugly thing, and so conscious of his defects that he held aloof
with invincible shyness and reserve. He was the butt, the *souffre
douleur* of our little society; and the inborn malignity of our na-
tures found expression in the ridicule with which we pelted him.
His name was Moquo. He was thin and weak, his coat was scanty,
he needed the warm fireside more than the other cats; but the children frightened him, and his comrades, wrapped snugly in their
furry robes, disdained to take any notice of his presence. Only my
father would go to the dim, cold corner where he cowered, pick him

255

up, carry him to the hearth, and tuck him safely out of sight under a fold of his own coat. There, warm, safe, and unseen, poor Moquo would take courage, and softly purr his gratitude. Sometimes, however, we caught a glimpse of him, and then, in spite of my father's reproaches, we laughed and jeered at his melancholy aspect. I can still recall the shadowy creature shrinking away, and seeming to melt into the breast of his protector, closing his eyes as he crept backward, choosing to see and hear nothing.

There came a day when my father left us for a long journey and all the animals shared our grief at his departure. Time after time his dogs trotted a little way along the road he had taken to Paris, howling piteously for their master. The most desolate creature in the house was Moquo. He trusted no one; but, for a while, would steal to the hearth, looking wistfully and furtively at my father's vacant place. Then, losing hope, he fled to the woods, to resume the wild and wretched life of his infancy; and, though we tried, we never could entice him back to the home where he no longer had a friend.

An old print of Mather Byles (1706–1788), a Boston minister, and his cat. He called the cat his Mews (Muse). Engraving by Robert Seymour.

ARE CATS PEOPLE?

Oliver Herford

The delightful writer and artist Oliver Herford wrote about and drew cats with great pleasure. He is the author of a wonderful book published at the turn of the century called The Rubaiyat of a Persian Kitten, *which declaims:*

> *Myself when young, did eagerly frequent,*
> *The backyard fence and heard great argument,*
> *About it, and about, yet evermore,*
> *Came out with fewer fur than in I went.*

If a fool be sometimes an angel unawares, may not a foolish query be a momentous question in disguise? For example, the old riddle: "Why is a hen?" which is thought by many people to be the silliest question ever asked, is in reality the most profound. It is the riddle of existence. It has an answer, to be sure, but though all the wisest men and women in the world *and* Mr. H. G. Wells have tried to guess it, the riddle "Why is a hen?" has never been answered and never will be. So, too, the question: "Are cats people?" seemingly so trivial, may be, under certain conditions, a question of vital importance.

The Scare. Drawings by Joseph G. Francis.

Suppose, now, a rich man dies, leaving all his money to his eldest son, with the proviso that a certain portion of it shall be spent in the maintenance of his household as it then existed, all its members to remain under his roof, and receive the same comfort, attention, or remuneration they had received in his (the testator's) lifetime. Then suppose the son, on coming into his money, and being a hater of cats, made haste to rid himself of a feline pet that had lived in the family from early kittenhood, and had been an especial favorite of his father's.

Thereupon, the second son, being a lover of cats and no hater of money, sues for possession of the estate on the ground that his brother has failed to carry out the provisions of his father's will, in refusing to maintain the household cat.

The decision of the case depends entirely on the social status of the cat.

Shall the cat be considered as a member of the household? What constitutes a household anyway?

The definition of "household" in the Standard Dictionary is as follows: "*A number of persons living under the same roof.*"

If cats are people, then the cat in question is a person and a member of the household, and for failing to maintain her and provide her with the comfort and attention to which she has been used, the eldest son loses his inheritance. Having demonstrated that the question "Are cats people?" is anything but a trivial one, I now propose a court of inquiry, to settle once for all and forever, the social status of *felis domesticus*.

And I propose for the office of judge of that court—myself!

In seconding the proposal and appointing myself judge of the court, I have been careful to follow political precedent by taking no account whatever of any qualifications I may or may not have for the office.

For witnesses, I summon (from wherever they may be) two great shades, to wit: King Solomon, the wisest man of his day, and Noah Webster, the wordiest.

And I say to Mr. Webster, "Mr. Webster, what are the common

259

terms used to designate a domestic feline whose Christian name chances to be unknown to the speaker?" and Mr. Webster answers without a moment's hesitation:

"Cat, puss, pussy and pussy-cat."

"And what is the grammatical definition of the above terms?"

"They are called nouns."

"And what, Mr. Webster, is the accepted definition of a noun?"

"A noun is the name of a person, place or thing."

"Kindly define the word 'place'."

"A particular locality."

"And 'thing'."

"An inanimate object."

"That will do, Mr. Webster."

So, according to Mr. Noah Webster, the entity for which the noun cat stands, must, if not a person, be a locality or an inanimate object!

A cat is surely not a locality, and as for being an inanimate object, her chance of avoiding such a condition is nine times better even than a king's.

Then a cat *must* be a person.

Suppose we consult King Solomon.

In the Book of Proverbs, Chapter XXX, verse 26, Solomon says: "The coneys are but a feeble folk, yet they make their houses in the rocks."

A coney is a kind of rabbit; folk, according to Mr. Webster, only another word for people.

That settles it! If the rabbits are people, cats are people.

Long lives to the cat!

MY GRANDMOTHER'S CAT

Edna Dean Proctor

Somehow or other, grandmothers' cats have a wisdom that only grandmothers know. At least that is our experience. Perhaps simply because grandmothers have seen more and done more, they loom in childhood as models of wisdom, the greatest conveyors of comfort.

In this reminiscence, Edna Dean Proctor has caught the importance of a grandmother's cat when all such women were conductors of folklore. To the various cat weather omens which Miss Proctor describes, we might add the following from our own grandmother's animal wisdom. Yes, it is true that if a cat puts a tail up and its fur is electrified, a storm is indicated. But our grandmother knew very well that it also meant the approach of a dog, even if the dog was about half a mile away. And if you want further directions about the wind, you must watch the way a cat turns and washes its face after the rain. And finally, if you have ever seen some of the contorted positions cats take, you should remember that rhyme:

> *"When the cat lies on its brain,*
> *Then it's going to rain."*

Beauty was my grandmother's cat and the delight of my childhood. To this far-off day I remember her as distinctly as I do my aunt and cousins of that household, and even my dear grandmother herself. I know nothing of her ancestry and am not at all sure that she was royally bred, for she came, one chill night, a little wanderer to the door. But a shred of blue ribbon was clinging to her neck, and she was so pretty, and silky, and winsome that we children at once called her Beauty, and fancied she had strayed from some elegant home where she had been the pet of the household, lapping her milk from finest china and sleeping on a cushion of down. When we had warmed, and fed, and caressed her, we made her bed on a flannel-lined box among our dolls, and the next morning were up before the sun to see her, fearing her owners would appear and carry her away. But no one arrived to claim her, and she soon became an important member of the family, and grew handsomer, we thought, day by day. Her coat was gray with tiger markings, but paws and throat and nose were snowy white, and in spite of her excursions to barns and cellars her constant care kept them spotless—indeed, she was the very Venus of cats for daintiness and grace of pose and movement. To my grandmother her various attitudes had an undoubted meaning. If on a rainy day Beauty washed her face toward the west, her observant mistress would exclaim: "See, kitty is washing her face to the west. It will clear." Or, even when the sky was blue, if Beauty turned eastward for her toilet, the comment would be: "Kitty is washing her face to the east. The wind must be getting 'out' [from the sea], and a storm brewing." And when in the dusk of autumn or winter evenings Beauty ran about the room, chasing her tail or frolicking with her kittens instead of sleeping quietly by the fire as was her wont, my grandmother would look up and say: "Kitty is wild tonight. The wind will blow hard before morning." If I sometimes asked how she knew these things, the reply would be, "My mother told me when I was a little girl." Now her mother, my great-grandmother, was a distinguished personage in my eyes, having been the daughter of Captain Jonathan Prescott who commanded a company under Sir William Pepperell at the siege of Louisburg and lost his

The Hat, by J. L. Dolph. Dolph was one of the most important cat artists of the last century. A large household of cats and dogs served as models during his summers on Long Island.

life there; and I could not question the wisdom of colonial times. Indeed, to this hour I have a lingering belief that cats can foretell the weather.

And what a mouser she was! Before her time we often heard the rats and mice in the walls, but with her presence not one dared to peep, and cupboard and pantry were unmolested. Now and then she carried her forays to hedge and orchard, and I remember one sad summer twilight that saw her bring in a slender brown bird which my grandmother said was the cuckoo we had delighted to hear in the still morning among the alders by the river. She was scolded and had no milk that night, and we never knew her to catch a bird again.

Oh to see her with her kittens! She always hid them in the hay-mows, and hunting and finding them brought us no end of excitement and pleasure. Twice a day, at least, she would come to the house to be fed, and then how we watched her returning steps, stealing cautiously along the path and waiting behind stack or door the better to observe her—for pussy knew perfectly well that we were eager to see her darlings, and enjoyed misleading and piquing us, we imagined, by taking devious ways.

How well I recall that summer afternoon when, soft-footed and alone, I followed her to the floor of the barn. Just as she was about to spring to the mow she espied me, and, turning back, cunningly settled herself as if for a quiet nap in the sunny open door. Determined not to lose sight of her, I threw myself upon the fragrant hay; but in the stillness, the faint sighing of the wind, the far-off ripple of the river, the hazy outline of the hills, the wheeling swallows overhead, were blended at length in an indistinct dream, and I slept, oblivious of all. When I woke, pussy had disappeared, the sun was setting, the cows were coming from the pastures, and I could only return to the house discomfited. That particular family of kittens we never saw till a fortnight later, when the proud mother brought them in one by one, and laid them at my grandmother's feet.

What became of Beauty is as mysterious as the fate of the Dauphin. To our grief, she disappeared one November day, and we never saw her more. Sometimes we fancied she had been carried off by an admiring traveller; at others we tortured ourselves with the belief that the traditional wildcat of the north woods had devoured her. All we knew was that she had vanished; but when memory pictures that pleasant country home and the dear circle there, white-throated Beauty is always sleeping by the fire.

THE ATTIC

Algernon Blackwood

Algernon Blackwood kept many cats, and always enjoyed writing in their presence. They inspired, in part, that enormous gift for the supernatural that came so easily to him. He did not, however, allow them to sit on his shoulder. That was a liberty permitted to Henry James's cat; James considered it an appropriate resting place for his favorite feline. Could it have influenced his style?

The forest-girdled village upon the Jura slopes slept soundly, although it was not yet many minutes after ten o'clock. The clang of the *couvre-feu* had indeed just ceased, its notes swept far into the woods by a wind that shook the mountains. This wind now rushed down the deserted street. It howled about the old rambling building called La Citadelle, whose roof towered gaunt and humped above the smaller houses—Château left unfinished long ago by Lord Wemyss, the exiled Jacobite. The families who occupied the various apartments listened to the storm and felt the building tremble. "It's the mountain wind. It will bring the snow," the mother said, without looking up from her knitting. "And how sad it sounds."

Nineteenth-century engraving by an unknown artist.

But it was not the wind that brought sadness as we sat round the open fire of peat. It was the wind of memories. The lamplight slanted along the narrow room towards the table where breakfast things lay ready for the morning. The double windows were fastened. At the far end stood a door ajar, and on the other side of it the two elder children lay asleep in the big bed. But beside the window was a smaller unused bed, that had been empty now a year. And to-night was the anniversary. . . .

And so the wind brought sadness and long thoughts. The little chap that used to lie there was already twelve months gone, far, far beyond the Hole where the Winds came from, as he called it; yet it seemed only yesterday that I went to tell him a tuck-up story, to stroke Riquette, the old motherly cat that cuddled against his back and laid a paw beside his pillow like a human being, and to hear his funny little earnest whisper say, *"Oncle, tu sais, j'ai prié pour Petavel."* For La Citadelle had its unhappy ghost—of Petavel, the usurer, who had hanged himself in the attic a century gone by, and was known to walk its dreary corridors in search of peace—and this wise Irish mother, calming the boy's fears with wisdom, had told him, "If you pray for Petavel, you'll save his soul and make him happy, and he'll only love you." And, thereafter, this little imaginative boy had done so every night. With a passionate serious-ness he did it. He had wonderful, delicate ways like that. In all our hearts he made his fairy nests of wonder. In my own, I know, he lay closer than any joy imaginable, with his big blue eyes, his queer soft questionings, and his splendid child's unselfishness—a sun-kissed flower of innocence that, had he lived, might have sweetened half a world.

"Let's put more peat on," the mother said, as a handful of rain—like stones came flinging against the windows; "that must be hail." And she went on tiptoe to the inner room. "They're sleeping like two puddings," she whispered, coming presently back. But it struck me she had taken longer than to notice merely that; and her face wore an odd expression that made me uncomfortable. I thought she was somehow just about to laugh or cry. By the table a second she hesitated. I caught the flash of indecision as it passed. "Pan," she said suddenly—it was a nickname, stolen from my tuck-up stories, *he* had given me—"I wonder how Riquette got in." She looked hard at me. "It wasn't you, was it?" For we never let her come at night since he had gone. It was too poignant. The beastie always went cuddling and nestling into that empty bed. But this time it was not my doing, and I offered plausible explanations. "But—she's on the bed. Pan, *would* you be so kind——" She left the sentence un-finished, but I easily understood, for a lump had somehow risen in my own throat too, and I remembered now that she had come out from the inner room so quickly—with a kind of hurried rush al-most. I put "mère Riquette" out into the corridor. A lamp stood on the chair outside the door of another occupant further down, and I urged her gently towards it. She turned and looked at me—straight up into my face; but, instead of going down as I suggested, she went slowly in the opposite direction. She stepped softly towards a door in the wall that led up broken stairs into the attics. There she sat down and waited. And so I left her, and came back hastily to the peat fire and companionship. The wind rushed in behind me and slammed the door.

And we talked then somewhat busily of cheerful things; of the children's future, the excellence of the cheap Swiss schools, of Christmas presents, ski-ing, snow, tobogganing. I led the talk away from mournfulness; and when these subjects were exhausted I told stories of my own adventures in distant parts of the world. But "mother" listened the whole time—not to me. Her thoughts were all elsewhere. And her air of intently, secretly listening, bordered, I felt, upon the uncanny. For she often stopped her knitting and sat with her eyes fixed upon the air before her; she stared blankly at the wall, her head slightly on one side, her figure tense, attention strained—elsewhere. Or, when my talk positively demanded it, her nod was oddly mechanical and her eyes looked through and past me. The wind continued very loud and roaring; but the fire glowed, the room was warm and cosy. Yet she shivered, and when I drew attention to it, her reply, "I do feel cold, but I didn't know I shivered," was given as though she spoke across the air to some one else. But what impressed me even more uncomfortably were her repeated questions about Riquette. When a pause in my tales permitted, she would look up with "I wonder where Riquette went?" or, thinking of the inclement night, "I hope mère Riquette's not out of doors. Perhaps Madame Favre has taken her in?" I offered to go and see. Indeed I was already half-way across the room when there came the heavy bang at the door that rooted me to the ground where I stood. It was not wind. It was something alive that made it rattle. There was a second blow. A thud on the corridor boards followed, and then a high, odd voice that at first was as human as the cry of a child.

It is undeniable that we both started, and for myself I can answer truthfully that a chill ran down my spine; but what frightened me more than the sudden noise and the eerie cry was the way "mother" supplied the immediate explanation. For behind the words "It's only Riquette; she sometimes springs at the door like that; perhaps we'd better let her in," was a certain touch of uncanny quiet that made me feel she had known the cat would come, and knew also *why* she came. One cannot explain such impressions further. They leave their vital touch, then go their way. Into the little room, however, in that moment there came between us this uncomfortable sense that the night held other purposes than our own—and that my companion was aware of them. There was something going on far, far removed from the routine of life as we were accustomed to it. Moreover, our usual routine was the eddy, while this was the main stream. It felt big, I mean.

And so it was that the entrance of the familiar, friendly creature brought this thing both itself and "mother" *knew*, but whereof I as yet was ignorant. I held the door wide. The draught rushed through behind her, and sent a shower of sparks about the fireplace. The lamp flickered and gave a little gulp. And Riquette marched slowly past, with all the impressive dignity of her kind, towards the other door that stood ajar. Turning the corner like a shadow, she disappeared into the room where the two children slept. We heard the soft thud with which she leaped upon the bed. Then, in a lull of the wind, she came back again and sat on the oilcloth, staring into "mother's" face. She mewed and put a paw out, drawing the black dress softly with half-opened claws. And it was all so horribly suggestive and pathetic, it revived such poignant memories, that I got up impulsively—I think I had actually said the words, "We'd better put her out, mother, after all"—when my companion rose to her feet and forestalled me. She said another thing instead. It took my breath away to hear it. "She wants us to go with her. Pan, will you come too?" The surprise on my face must have asked the question, for I do not remember saying anything. "To the attic," she said quietly.

She stood there by the table, a tall, grave figure dressed in black, and her face above the lamp-shade caught the full glare of light. Its expression positively stiffened me. She seemed so secure in her singular purpose. And her familiar appearance had so oddly given place to something wholly strange to me. She looked like another person—almost with the unwelcome transformation of the sleep-walker about her. Cold came over me as I watched her, for I remembered suddenly her Irish second-sight, her story years ago of meeting a figure on the attic stairs, the figure of Petavel. And the idea of this motherly, sedate, and wholesome woman, absorbed day and night in prosaic domestic duties, and yet "seeing" things, touched the incongruous almost to the point of alarm. It was so distressingly convincing.

Yet she knew quite well that I would come. Indeed, following the excited animal, she was already by the door, and a moment later, still without answering or protesting, I was with them in the draughty corridor. There was something inevitable in her manner that made it impossible to refuse. She took the lamp from its nail on the wall, and following our four-footed guide, who ran with obvious pleasure just in front, she opened the door into the court-yard. The wind nearly put the lamp out, but a minute later we were safe inside the passage that led up flights of creaky wooden stairs towards the world of tenantless attics overhead.

And I shall never forget the way the excited Riquette first stood up and put her paws upon the various doors, trotted ahead, turned back to watch us coming, and then finally sat down and waited on the threshold of the empty, raftered space that occupied the entire length of the building underneath the roof. For her manner was more that of an intelligent dog than of a cat, and sometimes more like that of a human mind than either.

We had come up without a single word. The howling of the wind as we rose higher was like the roar of artillery. There were many broken stairs, and the narrow way was full of twists and turnings. It was a dreadful journey. I felt eyes watching us from all the yawning spaces of the darkness, and the noise of the storm smothered

270

footsteps everywhere. Troops of shadows kept us company. But it was on the threshold of this big, chief attic, when "mother" stopped abruptly to put down the lamp, that real fear took hold of me. For Riquette marched steadily forward into the middle of the dusty flooring, picking her way among the fallen tiles and mortar, as though she went towards—some one. She purred loudly and uttered little cries of excited pleasure. Her tail went up into the air, and she lowered her head with the unmistakable intention of being stroked. Her lips opened and shut. Her green eyes smiled. She *was* being stroked.

It was an unforgettable performance. I would rather have witnessed an execution or a murder than watch that mysterious creature twist and turn about in the way she did. Her magnified shadow was as large as a pony on the floor and rafters. I wanted to hide the whole thing by extinguishing the lamp. For, even before the mysterious action began, I experienced the sudden rush of conviction that others besides ourselves were in this attic—and standing very close to us indeed. And, although there was ice in my blood, there was also a strange swelling of the heart that only love and tenderness could bring.

But, whatever it was, my human companion, still silent, knew and understood. She *saw*. And her soft whisper that ran with the wind among the rafters, *"Il a prié pour Petavel et le bon Dieu l'a entendu,"* did not amaze me one quarter as much as the expression I then caught upon her radiant face. Tears ran down the cheeks, but they were tears of happiness. Her whole figure seemed lit up. She opened her arms—picture of great Motherhood, proud, blessed, and tender beyond words. I thought she was going to fall, for she took quick steps forward; but when I moved to catch her, she drew me aside instead with a sudden gesture that brought fear back in the place of wonder.

"Let them pass," she whispered grandly. "Pan, don't you see. . . . He's leading him into peace and safety . . . by the hand!" And her joy seemed to kill the shadows and fill the entire attic with white light. Then, almost simultaneously with her words, she swayed. I

271

was in time to catch her, but as I did so, across the very spot where we had just been standing—two figures, I swear, went past us like a flood of light.

There was a moment next of such confusion that I did not see what happened to Riquette, for the sight of my companion kneeling on the dusty boards and praying with a curious sort of passionate happiness, while tears pressed between her covering fingers—the strange wonder of this made me utterly oblivious to minor details. . . .

We were sitting round the peat fire again, and "mother" was saying to me in the gentlest, tenderest whisper I ever heard from human lips—"Pan, I think perhaps that's why God took him. . . ."

And when a little later we went in to make Riquette cosy in the empty bed, ever since kept sacred to her use, the mournfulness had lifted; and in the place of resignation was proud peace and joy that knew no longer sad or selfish questionings.

Child with Kitten.
Engraving by unknown artist
of the last century.

SYLVIA THE FIRST

Compton MacKenzie

Sir Compton MacKenzie, the author of that marvelous motion pic-
ture Tight Little Island, *as well as many books, first became ac-*
quainted with the wiseness of cats when he was two years old.

The first words that he remembered saying was when two very
small dogs jumped up at him. "Go down, baby bow-wows," he
managed. Mr. Barnes, who was his cat, knew that he had unduly
encouraged them, and MacKenzie always said he could see Mr.
Barnes's eyes convey the warning, "I can do nothing for you. I
warned you not to encourage them. They'll knock you over one
of these days." And when indeed the puppies did knock MacKenzie
over, Mr. Barnes would only shake his head. From that time on,
MacKenzie acknowledged the superior wisdom of all cats.

In the autumn of 1920 I succeeded in securing from the Crown a
sixty-year lease of the Channel Islands of Herm and Jethou, and a
couple of months after I took up residence early in the following
year I acquired a Siamese kitten whom I called Sylvia after the
heroine of my novel *Sylvia Scarlett.*

Some Siberian cats that accompanied
a Russian exile. Artist unknown.

From the first that small Siamese kitten was entirely devoted to me and I loved her just a little more than I have loved any cat. She had a stumpy tail with an unusually pronounced double kink which even as long ago as that would have been regarded with horror by any member of the Siamese Cat fancy. To-day a tiny kink at the very tip of the tail is frowned upon, although it does not actually disqualify the cat who has it from gaining an award when shown.

Let me take this opportunity of saying that I regard the attempt to weed out the kink as a deplorable example of the rage for standardization which already handicaps and may in time arrest the mental development of democracy. The kink of the Siamese tail and the squint in the Siamese eyes do not deserve to be eliminated. There is a pleasant tale about the origin of the kink. A Siamese princess of long ago used to take her favourite cat with her when she bathed in a secluded pool in the royal gardens, and it was her habit before going into the water to remove her rings and slip them over her cat's tail. Then one day in the excitement of seeing a goldfish in the pool the cat swished its tail and as it did so the rings were swished into the pool. To prevent such an accident recurring in the future the princess bent her cat's tail into a kink at the tip so that if it was swished again at the sight of goldfish the rings would stay safely where she had put them.

In those first two or three months on Herm I was much alone and working late at night to finish a novel called *The Seven Ages of Woman* in order to begin the formidable task of writing a trilogy about the life of a Church of England parson. After dinner every night I settled down in the invalid chair in which I have had to write since 1913 to fend off the attacks of an acute sciatica. In this chair after my man had brought in a pint of ale at eleven o'clock Sylvia used to lie beside me without moving until I went off to bed about four or five, when she accompanied me upstairs and got into bed with me. Until Thompson came in last thing at night with the pint of ale it was her habit to use my black Great Dane as a couch. Hamlet was expected to lie outstretched in front of the fire until the time came for him to go off to his kennel with Thompson at eleven o'clock. Siamese cats always enjoy lying with their front paws slightly higher than their backsides. Sylvia found that the stomach of a Great Dane provided her with the perfect medium for this attitude. Hamlet was not expected to move. A disapproving low growl from Sylvia warned him to keep still.

Hamlet: (*with propitiatory thumps of his tail*). Do you mind if I get up for a moment, turn round and lie down again on my other side?

Sylvia: (*growling*). Why do you want to be so fidgety? You'll
           be going off to your kennel in another hour.

Hamlet: Yes, but I'm getting pins and needles.

Sylvia: (*growling again*). Pins and needles, my paws! Do you
           expect me to get out of the comfortable position I'm
           in merely because you have a fancy to lie on your left
           side instead of your right side? Just like a dog! Always
           must fidget.

Hamlet with a deep sigh that was very near to a groan would give up the argument and remain on his right side until Thompson arrived with my nightcap of ale and he was no longer compelled to be an immobile couch for that Siamese kitten.

"Mew!" Sylvia would exclaim as she settled herself down beside me in the chair. "Queer awkward creatures dogs, aren't they? But I must admit that as dogs go Hamlet is not too bad. He's gawky and fidgety and extremely stupid, but he's not a bad old sort."

Sylvia herself had always taken her exercise before we reached the room where I was working. She had her dinner in the kitchen while I was having my soup and always arrived in the dining-room when the parlour-maid brought in the fish or entrée. Then she would jump on the mahogany table and sit for the rest of the meal on a mat which was placed at my left-hand to spare her the discomfort of the bare board. She never moved from her mat until a dish of filberts appeared with dessert. Then a paw was placed on my hand to remind me that it was time for the evening game. As I stripped the nut she would watch me, all tensed for the great moment when I would send the nut rolling down the table to the floor. After a game of football all over the floor of the room she would jump back on the table with the nut in her mouth and again I would send it rolling over the table for another game of football. At last she would tire of the exercise and leaving the nut in a corner she would jump back on the table and tell me that it was time to quit the dining-room and adjourn to the fire in my workroom where Hamlet was expected to remain outstretched on the hearthrug for her to turn him into a couch.

276

Another game she enjoyed was lying on the palms of my hands to be tossed up to the ceiling and caught. She would keep herself stiff all the way up and come down equally stiff on to my hands. She also enjoyed lying on her back and being given a somersault to land on her feet.

I thought it would be good for Sylvia to have a companion of her own age and that spring I bought a blue Persian kitten. She was called Lily after the indolent and beautiful girl who lived with Sylvia Scarlett. As in the book Sylvia Scarlett dominated Lily Haden so Sylvia the kitten dominated Lily the kitten from the start, and that without so much as one angry spit.

One of the obligations in my lease of Herm was to allow the public access to the famous shell beach three times a week on payment of a sixpenny toll of which fourpence was retained by me and twopence by King George V as Duke of Normandy. During that glorious summer of 1921 those visitors were the only cloud upon its azure serenity. Access to the shell beach gave them about a hundred acres of pasturage and a mile of coast to defile with their litter but that toll of sixpence convinced them that they were entitled to wander all over the island. Quiet inoffensive people at home were turned into aggressive savages by the tricky three miles of sea between Guernsey and Herm. Robinson Crusoe did not observe the arrival of a war-canoe on his island with more apprehension than I would watch those visitors disembark in our little harbour.

I must have communicated my feelings to Sylvia. On the three tripper days she was always to be seen in a window of the White House where I was still living while the ugly pseudo-Gothic house at the top of the island occupied by my predecessor Prince Blücher was being made habitable. Later on I opened the Mermaid Tavern for such visitors in the White House, a name which I believe it still retains. As they landed and walked along the quay Sylvia would growl at them until they had disappeared along the road leading to the Shell Beach. However, if those visitors could ignore the sign-post and take the other direction they would constantly do so. On one occasion Sylvia, her stumpy tail bristling, came into the draw-

277

ing room where a friend and I were having our coffee after lunch to announce in contralto Siamese that two of the savages had dared to walk into the White House.

And sure enough a couple of our visitors followed that indignant kitten into the room. When I suggested that this part of the island was private one of them observed with what he evidently hoped was crushing sarcasm,

"I thought we lived in a free country."

There is a Siamese vocal outburst to which "Wow!" is the nearest I can get on the page.

"Wow!" exclaimed Sylvia.

No argument about the degree of freedom enjoyed by Britons ensued because at that moment Hamlet arrived in the room carrying a pair of lacy panties in his mouth.

"My dog evidently thinks so too," I said.

Hamlet had not deprived some bather on the shell beach of her panties. He had found them on a small beach on the far side of the island to bathe from which was not included in the privileges allowed to our invaders for their sixpenny toll, and whatever young woman went back to Guernsey that evening without her panties was silent about their loss.

That cloudless summer of 1921 lingered on well into October, and work on the first volume of my trilogy was sadly behind time when I returned to it that winter and was much interrupted by pain. *The Altar Steps* was a very difficult book to write and without the constant presence of that little cat beside me in my chair I believe I should have abandoned the task of finishing it in time for publication in 1922.

In March it was settled that Sylvia's marriage must be arranged. There was no eligible young Siamese Tom in Guernsey, and I decided to buy one from a breeder in England whose advertisement I had seen in some paper. I was not a member of the Siamese Cat Club at this date; indeed, I was unaware of its existence. Therefore when answering the advertisement of Siamese kittens for sale I did not enquire into the reputation of the breeder.

The British often depict cats in stories and illustrations. This engraving of "The Two Wellers" from Dickens' Pickwick Papers is by Frederick Barnard (1846–1896), English engraver and illustrator.

In due course the husband arrived whose marriage had been arranged with Sylvia in the future. She took one look at him, spat, hurried up to my bedroom, got into bed, went down to the foot of it and bit my toe.

By evening the yellowish froth of gastro-enteritis was round the mouth of the new arrival and within twenty-four hours he was dead. These were the days before inoculation, and few were the Siamese cats that recovered from an attack. It is a highly infectious disease, and for a breeder to send away a kitten which had been exposed to infection in a cattery was disgraceful. Some years later this breeder was censured by the Siamese Cat Club for some breach of cattery etiquette and resigned from it. He then tried to start a rival club, but his malicious enterprise was stillborn.

I have always felt that when Sylvia bit my toe that morning she was trying to warn me of the threat the new arrival was to herself. She had welcomed Lily, and some months ago she had welcomed a Sealyham called Stella to whom she had persistently tried to impart some of her own intelligence. Indeed, the only big creatures she disliked were trippers in a herd.

That new arrival was her death-warrant. A day or two later the menacing yellow froth was oozing from her lips. She was not left alone for a minute during the next forty-eight hours but nothing we could do was able to save that little life. Just before she died she twitched her stumpy tail twice as I leaned over her. It was her last effort to show me she recognized I was doing all I could.

I have never been so much affected by the loss of an animal and as I write about her now nearly forty years later, sitting in the same chair where once upon a time she kept me company through the night as I struggled with *The Altar Steps*, I still miss her, and I have never forgiven that feline breeder who betrayed the code of the Siamese Cat Club.

At the time I could not bear to remain in the White House and although the cottage joined to the Manor House in which I intended to live was not yet ready I moved into it the day after Sylvia died. But I never really recovered on Herm from the loss of Sylvia. I began to feel that the island was unlucky for me, and soon after this I was told something which confirmed this feeling.

My predecessor Prince Blücher von Wahlstatt had been a victim of the hysteria that seizes a country with the outbreak of war and in 1914 he had not been allowed to return, the usual nonsensical fantasies about gun-emplacements and the rest of it being rife. He had married a younger Princess Radziwill whose elder sister married his son at the same time. By this double marriage Prince Blücher became the father-in-law of his sister-in-law and Count Lothair Blücher the son-in-law of his sister-in-law. Count Lothair and Countess Blücher were still living on Guernsey, the Count having been accorded what was held to be the privilege of a commission in a labour battalion but not allowed to serve with the forces in the field during the war. Soon after Sylvia's death I was dining with the Blüchers and the Countess told me that when the news came that Prince and Princess Blücher were not to be allowed to return to the island they loved so much the Princess had wished ill-fortune to the next tenant of the island.

"But she did not know it would be somebody like you or she would never have done what she did."

So far as I was concerned Herm was ill-wished, to use a Cornish phrase, and putting aside any mysterious malign influence I found the financial burden of running the island too much for my pen. One day I appealed to the elemental spirits of the island to send a war profiteer to relieve me of it. Two hours later they sent across in his yacht Sir Percival Perry who had bought the "Slough Dump" and in the following year I was able to transfer to him the lease of Herm and retire myself to the very much smaller island of Jethou. When Sylvia died I gave Lily away because her presence was too poignant a reminder of another's absence. So there was no cat on Jethou when Sylvia the Second arrived as a small kitten.

PRETTY LADY

Helen M. Winslow

An unsympathetic person knows nothing about cats. Cats conceal their characters and shut themselves away from those who dislike them. However, those who love them are constantly instructed, amused, and rewarded. Helen Winslow knew all such pleasures.

She was such a Pretty Lady, and gentle withal; so quiet and eminently ladylike in her behavior, and yet dignified and haughtily reserved as a duchess. Still it is better, under certain circumstances, to be a cat than to be a duchess. And no duchess of the realm ever had more faithful retainers or half so abject subjects.

Do not tell me that cats never love people; that only places have real hold upon their affections. The Pretty Lady was contented wherever I, her most humble slave, went with her. She migrated with me from boarding-house to sea-shore cottage; then to regular housekeeping; up to the mountains for a summer, and back home, a long day's journey on the railway; and her attitude was always "Wheresoever thou goest I will go, and thy people shall be my people."

282

The intellectual cat that appeared in Little Lord Fauntleroy. *The cat was modeled on the cat belonging to the author, Frances Hodgson Burnett (1849–1924), by the painter, R. B. Birch.*

I have known, and loved, and studied many cats, but my knowledge of her alone would convince me that cats love people—in their dignified, reserved way, and when they feel that their love is not wasted; that they reason, and that they seldom act from impulse.

I do not remember that I was born with an inordinate fondness for cats; or that I cried for them as an infant. I do not know, even, that my childhood was marked by an overweening pride in them; this, perhaps, was because my cruel parents established a decree, rigid and unbending as the laws of the Medes and Persians, that we must never have more than one cat at a time. Although this very law may argue that predilection, at an early age, for harboring everything feline which came in my way, which has since become at once a source of comfort and distraction.

After a succession of feline dynasties, the kings and queens of which were handsome, ugly, sleek, forlorn, black, white, deaf, spotted, and otherwise marked, I remember fastening my affections securely upon one kitten who grew up to be the ugliest, gauntest, and dingiest specimen I ever have seen. In the days of his kitten-hood I christened him "Tassie" after his mother; but as time sped on, and the name hardly comported with masculine dignity, this was changed to Tacitus, as more befitting his sex. He had a habit of dodging in and out of the front door, which was heavy, and which sometimes swung together before he was well out of it. As a consequence, a caudal appendage with two broken joints was one of his distinguishing features. Besides a broken tail, he had ears which bore the marks of many a hard-fought battle, and an expression which for general "lone and lorn"-ness would have discouraged even Mrs. Gummidge. But I loved him, and judging from the disconsolate and long-continued wailing with which he filled the house whenever I was away, my affection was not unrequited.

But my real thraldom did not begin until I took the Pretty Lady's mother. We had not been a week in our first house before a handsomely striped tabby, with eyes like beautiful emeralds, who had been the pet and pride of the next-door neighbor for five years, came over and domiciled herself. In due course of time she proudly presented us with five kittens. Educated in the belief that one cat was all that was compatible with respectability, I had four immediately disposed of, keeping the prettiest one, which grew up into the beautiful, fascinating, and seductive maltese "Pretty Lady," with white trimmings to her coat. The mother of Pretty Lady used to

Pretty Lady, by Reginald Dahl.

catch two mice at a time, and bringing them in together, lay one
at my feet and say as plainly as cat language can say, "There, you
eat that one, and I'll eat this," and then seemed much surprised
and disgusted that I had not devoured mine when she had finished
her meal.

We were occupying a furnished house for the summer, however,
and as we were to board through the winter, I took only the kitten
back to town, thinking the mother would return to her former
home, just over the fence. But no. For two weeks she refused all
food and would not once enter the other house. Then I went out

for her, and hearing my voice she came in and sat down before me, literally scolding me for a quarter of an hour. I shall be laughed at, but actual tears stood in her lovely green eyes and ran down her aristocratic nose, attesting her grief and accusing me, louder than her wailing, of perfidy.

I could not keep her. She would not return to her old home. I finally compromised by carrying her in a covered basket a mile and a half and bestowing her upon a friend who loves cats nearly as well as I. But although she was petted, and praised, and fed on the choicest of delicacies, she would not be resigned. After six weeks of mourning, she disappeared, and never was heard of more. Whether she sought a new and more constant mistress, or whether, in her grief at my shameless abandonment of her, she went to some lonely pier and threw herself off the dock, will never be known. But her reproachful gaze and tearful emerald eyes haunted me all winter. Many a restless night did I have to reproach myself for abandoning a creature who so truly loved me; and in many a dream did she return to heap shame and ignominy upon my repentant head.

This experience determined me to cherish her daughter, whom, rather, I cherished as her son, until there were three little new-born kittens, which in a moment of ignorance I "disposed of" at once. Naturally, the young mother fell exceedingly ill. In the most pathetic way she dragged herself after me, moaning and beseeching for help. Finally, I succumbed, went to a neighbor's where several superfluous kittens had arrived the night before, and begged one. It was a little black fellow, cold and half dead; but the Pretty Lady was beside herself with joy when I bestowed it upon her. For two days she would not leave the box where I established their headquarters, and for months she refused to wean it, or to look upon it as less than absolutely perfect. I may say that the Pretty Lady lived to be nine years old, and had, during that brief period, no less than ninety-three kittens, besides two adopted ones; but never did she bestow upon any of her own offspring that wealth of pride and affection which was showered upon black Bobbie.

When the first child of her adoption was two weeks old, I was ill

Kittens Playing, by Pruett Share (1884).

one morning, and did not appear at breakfast. It had always been her custom to wait for my coming down in the morning, evidently considering it a not unimportant part of her duty to see me well launched for the day. Usually she sat at the head of the stairs and waited patiently until she heard me moving about. Sometimes she came in and sat on a chair at the head of my bed, or gently touched my face with her nose or paw. Although she knew she was at liberty to sleep in my room, she seldom did so, except when she had an infant on her hands. At first she invariably kept him in a lower drawer of my bureau. When he was large enough, she removed him to the foot of the bed, where for a week or two her maternal solicitude and sociable habits of nocturnal conversation with her progeny interfered seriously with my night's rest. If my friends used to notice a wild and haggard appearance of unrest about me at certain periods of the year, the reason stands here confessed.

I was ill when black Bobbie was two weeks old. The Pretty Lady waited until breakfast was over, and as I did not appear, came up and jumped on the bed, where she manifested some curiosity as to my lack of active interest in the world's affairs.

"Now, pussy," I said, putting out my hand and stroking her back, "I'm sick this morning. When you were sick, I went and got you a kitten. Can't you get me one?"

This was all. My sister came in then and spoke to me, and the Pretty Lady left us at once; but in less than two minutes she came back with her cherished kitten in her mouth. Depositing him in my neck, she stood and looked at me, as much as to say:—

"There, you can take him awhile. He cured me and I won't be selfish; I will share him with you."

I was ill for three days, and all that time the kitten was kept with me. When his mother wanted him, she kept him on the foot of the bed, where she nursed, and lapped, and scrubbed him until it seemed as if she must wear even his stolid nerves completely out. But whenever she felt like going out she brought him up and tucked him away in the hollow of my neck, with a little guttural noise that, interpreted, meant:—

"There, now you take care of him awhile. I'm all tired out. Don't wake him up."

But when the infant had dropped soundly asleep, she invariably came back and demanded him; and not only demanded, but dragged him forth from his lair by the nape of the neck, shrieking and protesting, to the foot of the bed again, where he was obliged to go through another course of scrubbing and vigorous maternal attentions that actually kept his fur from growing as fast as the coats of less devotedly cared-for kittens grow.

When I was well enough to leave my room, she transferred him to my lower bureau drawer, and then to a vantage-point behind an old lounge. But she never doubted, apparently, that it was the loan of that kitten that rescued me from an untimely grave.

I have lost many an hour of much-needed sleep from my cat's habit of coming upstairs at four A.M. and jumping suddenly upon the bed; perhaps landing on the pit of my stomach. Waking in that fashion, unsympathetic persons would have pardoned me if I had indulged in injudicious language, or had even thrown the cat vio lently from my otherwise peaceful couch. But conscience has not to upbraid me with any of these things. I flatter myself that I bear even this patiently; I remember to have often made sleepy but unpleasant remarks to the faithful little friend whose affection for me and whose desire to behold my countenance was too great to permit her to wait till breakfast time.

If I lay awake for hours afterward, perhaps getting nothing more than literal "cat-naps," I consoled myself with remembering how Richelieu, and Wellington and Mohammed, and otherwise great as well as discriminating persons, loved cats; I remembered, with some stirrings of secret pride, that it is only the artistic nature, the truly aesthetic soul that appreciates poetry, and grace, and all refined beauty, who truly loves cats; and thus meditating with closed eyes, I courted slumber again, throughout the breaking dawn, while the cat purred in delight close at hand.

The Pretty Lady was evidently of Angora or coon descent, as her fur was always longer and silkier than that of ordinary cats. She was fond of all the family. When we boarded in Boston, we kept her in a front room, two flights from the ground. Whenever any of us came in the front door, she knew it. No human being could have told, sitting in a closed room in winter, two flights up, the identity of a person coming up the steps and opening the door. But the Pretty Lady, then only six months old, used to rouse from her nap in a big chair, or from the top of a folding bed, jump down, and be at the hall door ready to greet the incomer, before she was halfway up the stairs. The cat never got down for the wrong person, and she never neglected to meet any and every member of our family who might be entering. The irreverent scoffer may call it "instinct," or talk about the "sense of smell." I call it sagacity.

One summer we all went up to the farm in northern Vermont, and decided to take her and her son, "Mr. McGinty," with us. We put them both in a large market-basket and tied the cover securely. On the train Mr. McGinty manifested a desire to get out, and was allowed to do so, a stout cord having been secured to his collar first,

Cat's World, by Henriette Ronner.

and the other end tied to the car seat. He had a delightful journey, once used to the noise and motion of the train. He sat on our laps, curled up on the seat and took naps, or looked out of the windows with evident puzzlement at the way things had suddenly taken to flying; he even made friends with the passengers, and in general amused himself as any other traveler would on an all-day's journey by rail, except that he did not risk his eyesight by reading newspapers. But the Pretty Lady had not travelled for some years, and did not enjoy the trip as well as formerly; on the contrary she curled herself into a round tight ball in one corner of the basket till the journey's end was reached.

Once at the farm she seemed contented as long as I remained with her. There was plenty of milk and cream, and she caught a great many mice. She was far too dainty to eat them, but she had an inherent pleasure in catching mice, just like her more plebeian sisters; and she enjoyed presenting them to Mr. McGinty or me, or some other worthy object of her solicitude.

She was at first afraid of "the big outdoors." The wide, wind-blown spaces, the broad, sunshiny sky, the silence and the roominess of it all, were quite different from her suburban experiences; and the farm animals, too, were in her opinion curiously dangerous objects. Big Dan, the horse, was truly a horrible creature; the rooster was a new and suspicious species of biped, and the bleating calves objects of her direst hatred.

The pig in his pen possessed for her the most horrid fascination. Again and again would she steal out and place herself where she could see that dreadful strange, pink, fat creature inside his own quarters. She would fix her round eyes widely upon him in blended fear and admiration. If the pig uttered the characteristic grunt of his race, the Pretty Lady at first ran swiftly away; but afterward she used to turn and gaze anxiously at us, as if to say:—

"Do you hear that? Isn't this a truly horrible creature?" and in other ways evince the same sort of surprise that a professor in the Peabody Museum might, were the skeleton of the megatherium suddenly to accost him after the manner peculiar to its kind.

It was funnier, even, to see Mr. McGinty on the morning after

291

his arrival at the farm, as he sallied forth and made acquaintance with other of God's creatures than humans and cats, and the natural enemy of his kind, the dog. In his suburban home he had caught rats and captured on the sly many an English sparrow. When he first investigated his new quarters on the farm, he discovered a beautiful flock of very large birds led by one of truly gorgeous plumage.

"Ah!" thought Mr. McGinty, "this is a great and glorious country, where I can have such birds as these for the catching. Tame, too. I'll have one for breakfast."

So he crouched down, tiger-like, and crept carefully along to a convenient distance and was preparing to spring, when the large and gorgeous bird looked up from his worm and remarked:—

"Cut-cut-cut, ca-dah-cut!" and, taking his wives, withdrew toward the barn.

Mr. McGinty drew back amazed. "This is a queer bird," he seemed to say; "saucy, too. However, I'll soon have him," and he crept more carefully than before up to springing distance, when again this most gorgeous bird drew up and exclaimed, with a note of annoyance:—

"Cut-cut-cut, ca-dah-cut! What ails that old cat, anyway?" And again he led his various wives barnward.

Mr. McGinty drew up with a surprised air, and apparently made a cursory study of the leading anatomical features of this strange bird; but he did not like to give up, and soon crouched and prepared for another onslaught. This time Mr. Chanticleer allowed the cat to come up close to his flock, when he turned and remarked in the most amicable manner, "Cut-cut-cut-cut!" which interpreted seemed to mean: "Come now; that's all right. You're evidently new here; but you'd better take my advice and not fool with me."

Anyhow, with this, down went McGinty's hope of a bird breakfast "to the bottom of the sea," and he gave up the hunt. He soon made friends, however, with every animal on the place, and so endeared himself to the owners that he lived out his days there with a hundred acres and more as his own happy hunting-ground.

Not so, the Pretty Lady. I went away on a short visit after a few weeks, leaving her behind. From the moment of my disappearance she was uneasy and unhappy. On the fifth day she disappeared. When I returned and found her not, I am not ashamed to say that I hunted and called her everywhere, nor even that I shed a few tears when days rolled into weeks and she did not appear, as I realized that she might be starving, or have suffered tortures from some larger animal.

There are many remarkable stories of cats who find their way home across almost impossible roads and enormous distances. There is a saying, believed by many people, "You can't lose a cat," which can be proved by hundreds of remarkable returns. But the Pretty Lady had absolutely no sense of locality. She had always lived in-doors and had never been allowed to roam the neighborhood. It was five weeks before we found trace of her, and then only by accident. My sister was passing a field of grain, and caught a glimpse of a small creature which she at first thought to be a woodchuck. She turned and looked at it, and called "Pussy, pussy," when with a heart-breaking little cry of utter delight and surprise, our beloved cat came toward her. From the first, the wide expanse of the country had confused her; she had evidently "lost her bearings" and was probably all the time within fifteen minutes' walk of the farm-house.

When found, she was only a shadow of herself, and for the first and only time in her life we could count her ribs. She was wild with delight, and clung to my sister's arms as though fearing to lose her; and in all the fuss that was made over her return, no human being could have showed more affection, or more satisfaction at finding her old friends again.

That she really was lost, and had no sense of locality to guide her home, was proven by her conduct after she returned to her Boston home. I had preceded my sister, and was at the theatre on the evening when she arrived with the Pretty Lady. The latter was carried into the kitchen, taken from her basket, and fed. Then, instead of going around the house and settling herself in her old home, she went into the front hall which she had left four months before, and seated herself on the spot where she always watched and waited when I was out. When I came home at eleven, I saw through the screen door her "that was lost and is found." She had been waiting to welcome me for three mortal hours.

I wish those people who believe cats have no affection for people could have seen her then. She would not leave me for an instant, and manifested her love in every possible way; and when I retired for the night, she curled up on my pillow and purred herself contentedly to sleep, only rising when I did. After breakfast that first morning after her return, she asked to be let out of the back door, and made me understand that I must go with her. I did so, and she explored every part of the back yard, entreating me in the same way she called her kittens to keep close by her. She investigated our own premises thoroughly and then crept carefully under the fences on either side into the neighbor's precincts where she had formerly visited in friendly fashion; then she came timidly back, all the time keeping watch that she did not lose me. Having finished her tour of inspection, she went in and led me on an investigating trip all through the house, smelling of every corner and base-board, and insisting that every closet door should be opened, so that she might smell each closet through in the same way. When this was done, she settled herself in one of her old nooks for a nap and allowed me to leave.

But never again did she go out of sight of the house. For more than a year she would not go even into a neighbor's yard, and when she finally decided that it might be safe to crawl under the fences on to other territory, she invariably turned about to sit facing the house, as though living up to a firm determination never to lose sight of it again. This practice she kept up until at the close of her last mortal sickness, when she crawled into a dark place under a neighboring barn and said good-by to earthly fears and worries forever.

Requiescat in pace, my Pretty Lady. I wish all your sex had your gentle dignity, and grace, and beauty, to say nothing of your faithfulness and affection. Like Mother Michel's "Monmouth," it may be said of you:

She was merely a cat,
But her Sublime Virtues place her on a level with
The Most Celebrated Mortals,
and
In Ancient Egypt
Altars would have been Erected to her
Memory.

The Cat's Doll,
by Margaret Webb.

MY MOTHER'S CAT

Louise Chandler Moulton

Louise Chandler Moulton collected poets and cats the way other people collected china. She was one of those charming Bostonians of the nineteenth century who knew everybody from Whitman to Whistler.

She was deeply concerned, as so many of the good women of Boston were in those days, with animal welfare, and all her cats were happy ones.

My mother had a cat that lived to be twenty-five years old. He was faithful and fond, and a great pet in the family, of course. About two years before his death, a new kitten was added to the family. This kitten, named Jim, immediately conceived the greatest affection for old Jack, and as the old fellow's senses of sight and smell failed so that he could not go hunting himself, Jim used to do it for both. Every day he brought Jack mice and squirrels and other game as long as he lived. Then, too, he used to wash Jack, lapping him all over as a mother cat does her kitten. He did this, too, as long as he lived. The feebler old Jack grew the more Jim did for him, and when Jack finally died of old age, Jim was inconsolable.

Sara and Friend. Artist unknown.

DEATH OF A FAVORITE

J. F. Powers

That very great writer Flannery O'Connor—(she never wrote a short story about a cat; we wished she had)—once said about J. F. Powers that not only was he an extraordinary writer, but he had made the cat an "Intelligence" in some of his great short stories.

The Fritz of this story is one of our favorite cats. He always listens quietly and wisely to conversations that span the philosophy of Arthur Koestler to baseball scores. He knows the ropes; everybody who comes in contact with him is obviously a poor second. This is a cat who has the ability to cope with this world . . . as well as the next.

I had spent most of the afternoon mousing—a matter of sport with me and certainly not of diet—in the sunburnt fields that begin at our back door and continue hundreds of miles into the Dakotas. I gradually gave up the idea of hunting, the grasshoppers convincing me that there was no percentage in stealth. Even to doze was difficult, under such conditions, but I must have managed it. At least I was late coming to dinner, and so my introduction to the two missionaries took place at table. They were surprised, as most visitors are, to see me take the chair at Father Malt's right.

Father Malt, breaking off the conversation (if it could be called that), was his usual dear old self. "Fathers," he said, "meet Fritz."

I gave the newcomers the first good look that invariably tells me whether or not a person cares for cats. The mean old buck in charge of the team did not like me, I could see, and would bear watching. The other one obviously did like me, but he did not appear to be long enough from the seminary to matter. I felt that I had broken something less than even here.

"My assistant," said Father Malt, meaning me, and thus unconsciously dealing out our fat friend at the other end of the table. Poor Burner! There was a time when, thinking of him, as I did now, as the enemy, I could have convinced myself I meant something else. But he *is* the enemy, and I was right from the beginning, when it could only have been instinct that told me how much he hated me even while trying (in his fashion!) to be friendly. (I believe his prejudice to be acquired rather than congenital, and very likely, at this stage, confined to me, not to cats as a class—there *is* that in his favor. I intend to be fair about this if it kills me.)

My observations of humanity incline me to believe that one of us —Burner or I—must ultimately prevail over the other. For myself, I should not fear if this were a battle to be won on the solid ground of Father Malt's affections. But the old man grows older, the grave beckons to him ahead, and with Burner pushing him from behind, how long can he last? Which is to say: How long can *I* last? Unfortunately, it is naked power that counts most in any rectory, and as things stand now, I am safe only so long as Father Malt retains it here. Could I—this impossible thought is often with me now—could I effect a reconciliation and alliance with Father Burner? Impossible! Yes, doubtless. But the question better asked is: *How* impossible? (Lord knows I would not inflict this line of reasoning upon myself if I did not hold with the rumors that Father Burner will be the one to succeed to the pastorate.) For I do like it here. It is not at all in my nature to forgive and forget, certainly not as regards

299

Father Burner, but it is in my nature to come to terms (much as nations do) when necessary, and in this solution there need not be a drop of good will. No dog can make that statement, or take the consequences, which I understand are most serious, in the world to come. Shifts and ententes. There is something fatal about the vocation of favorite, but it is the only one that suits me, and, all things considered—to dig I am not able, to beg I am ashamed—the rewards are adequate.

"We go through Chicago all the time," said the boss missionary, who seemed to be returning to a point he had reached when I entered. I knew Father Malt would be off that evening for a convention in Chicago. The missionaries, who would fill in for him and conduct a forty hours' devotion on the side, belonged to an order just getting started in the diocese and were anxious to make a good impression. For the present, at least, as a kind of special introductory offer, they could be had dirt-cheap. Thanks to them, pastors who'd never been able to get away had got a taste of Florida last winter.

"Sometimes we stay over in Chicago," bubbled the young missionary. He was like a rookie ballplayer who hasn't made many road trips.

"We've got a house there," said the first, whose name in religion, as they say, was—so help me—Philbert. Later, Father Burner would get around it by calling him by his surname. Father Malt was the sort who wouldn't see anything funny about "Philbert," but it would be too much to expect him to remember such a name.

"What kind of a house?" asked Father Malt. He held up his hearing aid and waited for clarification.

Father Philbert replied in a shout, "The Order owns *a house* there!"

Father Malt fingered his hearing aid.

Father Burner sought to interpret for Father Philbert. "I think, Father, he wants to know what it's made out of."

"Red brick—it's red brick," bellowed Father Philbert.

"*My* house is red brick," said Father Malt.

300

"I *noticed* that," said Father Philbert.

Father Malt shoved the hearing aid at him.

"I know it," said Father Philbert, shouting again.

Father Malt nodded and fed me a morsel of fish. Even for a Friday, it wasn't much of a meal. I would not have been sorry to see this housekeeper go.

"All right, all right," said Father Burner to the figure lurking behind the door and waiting for him, always the last one, to finish. "She stands and looks in at you through the crack," he beefed. "Makes you feel like a condemned man." The housekeeper came into the room, and he addressed the young missionary (Burner was a great one for questioning the young): "Ever read any books by this fella Koestler, Father?"

"The Jesuit?" the young one asked.

"Hell, no, he's some kind of a writer. I know the man you mean, though. Spells his name different. Wrote a book—apologetics."

"That's the one. Very—"

"Dull."

"Well . . ."

"This other fella's not bad. He's a writer who's ahead of his time —about fifteen minutes. Good on jails and concentration camps. You'd think he was born in one if you ever read his books." Father Burner regarded the young missionary with absolute indifference. "But you didn't."

"No. Is he a Catholic?" inquired the young one.

"He's an Austrian or something."

"Oh."

The housekeeper removed the plates and passed the dessert around. When she came to Father Burner, he asked her privately, "What is it?"

"Pudding," she said, not whispering, as he would have liked.

"*Bread* pudding?" Now he was threatening her.

"Yes, Father."

Father Burner shuddered and announced to everybody, "No dessert for me." When the housekeeper had retired into the kitchen, he said, "Sometimes I think he got her from a hospital and some-times, Father, I think she came from one of *your* fine institutions"—this to the young missionary.

Father Philbert, however, was the one to see the joke, and he laughed.

"My God," said Father Burner, growing bolder. "I'll never forget the time I stayed at your house in Louisville. If I hadn't been there for just a day—for the Derby, in fact—I'd have gone to Rome about it. I think I've had better meals here."

At the other end of the table, Father Malt, who could not have heard a word, suddenly blinked and smiled; the missionaries looked to him for some comment, in vain.

"He doesn't hear me," said Father Burner. "Besides, I think he's listening to the news."

"I didn't realize it was a radio too," said the young missionary.

"Oh, hell, yes."

"I think he's pulling your leg," said Father Philbert.

"Well, I thought so," said the young missionary ruefully.

"It's an idea," said Father Burner. Then in earnest to Father Philbert, whom he'd really been working around to all the time—the young one was decidedly not his type—"You the one drivin' that new Olds, Father?"

"It's not mine, Father," said Father Philbert with a meekness that would have been hard to take if he'd meant it. Father Burner understood him perfectly, however, and I thought they were two persons who would get to know each other a lot better.

"Nice job. They say it compares with the Cad in power. What do you call that color—oxford or clerical gray?"

"I really couldn't say, Father. It's my brother's. He's a layman in Minneapolis—St. Stephen's parish. He loaned it to me for this little trip."

Father Burner grinned. He could have been thinking, as I was, that Father Philbert protested too much. "Thought I saw you go by earlier," he said. "What's the matter—didn't you want to come in when you saw the place?"

302

Father Philbert, who was learning to ignore Father Malt, laughed discreetly. "Couldn't be sure this was it. That house on the *other* side of the church, now—"

Father Burner nodded. "Like that, huh? Belongs to a Mason."

Father Philbert sighed and said, "It would."

"Not at all," said Father Burner. "I like 'em better than K.C.s." If he could get the audience for it, Father Burner enjoyed being broad-minded. Gazing off in the direction of the Mason's big house, he said, "I've played golf with him."

The young missionary looked at Father Burner in horror. Father Philbert merely smiled. Father Burner, toying with a large crumb, propelled it in my direction.

"Did a bell ring?" asked Father Malt.

"His P.A. system," Father Burner explained. "Better tell him," he said to the young missionary. "You're closer. He can't bring me in on those batteries he uses."

"No bell," said the young missionary, lapsing into basic English and gestures.

Father Malt nodded, as though he hadn't really thought so.

"How do you like it?" said Father Burner.

Father Philbert hesitated, and then he said, "Here you mean?"

"I wouldn't ask you that," said Father Burner, laughing. "Talkin' about that Olds. Like it? Like the Hydramatic?"

"No kiddin,' Father. It's not mine," Father Philbert protested.

"All right, all right," said Father Burner, who obviously did not believe him. "Just so you don't bring up your vow of poverty." He looked at Father Philbert's uneaten bread pudding—"Had enough?" —and rose from the table blessing himself. The other two followed when Father Malt, who was feeding me cheese, waved them away. Father Burner came around to us, bumping my chair—intentionally, I know. He stood behind Father Malt and yelled into his ear, "Any calls for me this aft?" He'd been out somewhere, as usual. I often thought he expected too much to happen in his absence.

"There was something . . ." said Father Malt, straining his memory, which was poor.

"*Yes?*"

"Now I remember—they had the wrong number."

Father Burner, looking annoyed and downhearted, left the room.

"They said they'd call back," said Father Malt, sensing Father Burner's disappointment.

I left Father Malt at the table reading his Office under the orange light of the chandelier. I went to the living room, to my spot in the window from which I could observe Father Burner and the missionaries on the front porch, the young one in the swing with his breviary—the mosquitoes, I judged, were about to join him—and the other two just smoking and standing around, like pool players waiting for a table. I heard Father Philbert say, "Like to take a look at it, Father?"

"Say, that's an idea," said Father Burner.

I saw them go down the front walk to the gray Olds parked at the curb. With Father Burner at the wheel they drove away. In a minute they were back, the car moving uncertainly—this I noted with considerable pleasure until I realized that Father Burner was simply testing the brakes. Then they were gone, and after a bit, when they did not return, I supposed they were out killing poultry on the open road.

That evening, when the ushers dropped in at the rectory, there was not the same air about them as when they came for pinochle. Without fanfare, Mr. Bauman, their leader, who had never worked any but the center aisle, presented Father Malt with a travelling bag. It was nice of him, I thought, when he said, "It's from all of us" for it could not have come from all equally. Mr. Bauman, in hardware, and Mr. Keller, the druggist, were the only ones well off, and must have forked out plenty for such a fine piece of luggage, even after the discount.

Father Malt thanked all six ushers with little nods in which there was no hint of favoritism. "Ha," he kept saying. "You shouldn'a done it."

The ushers bobbed and ducked, dodging his flattery, and kept up a mumble to the effect that Father Malt deserved everything they'd ever done for him and more. Mr. Keller came forward to instruct Father Malt in the use of the various clasps and zippers. Inside the bag was another gift, a set of military brushes, which I could see they were afraid he would not discover for himself. But he unsnapped a brush, and, like the veteran crowd-pleaser he was, swiped once or twice at his head with it after spitting into the bristles. The ushers all laughed.

"Pretty snazzy," said the newest usher—the only young blood among them. Mr. Keller had made him a clerk at the store, had pushed through his appointment as alternate usher in the church, and was gradually weaning him away from his motorcycle. With Mr. Keller, the lad formed a block to Mr. Bauman's power, but he was perhaps worse than no ally at all. Most of the older men, though they pretended a willingness to help him meet the problems of an usher, were secretly pleased when he bungled at collection time and skipped a row or overlapped one.

Mr. Keller produced a box of ten-cent cigars, which, as a *personal* gift from him, came as a bitter surprise to the others. He was not big enough, either, to attribute it to them too. He had anticipated their resentment, however, and now produced a bottle of milk of magnesia. No one could deny the comic effect, for Father Malt had been known to recommend the blue bottle from the confessional.

"Ha!" said Father Malt, and everybody laughed.

"In case you get upset on the trip," said the druggist.

"You know it's the best thing," said Father Malt in all seriousness, and then even he remembered he'd said it too often before. He passed the cigars. The box went from hand to hand, but, except for the druggist's clerk, nobody would have one.

Father Malt, seeing this, wisely renewed his thanks for the bag, insisting upon his indebtedness until it was actually in keeping with the idea the ushers had of their own generosity. Certainly none of them had ever owned a bag like that. Father Malt went to the housekeeper with it and asked her to transfer his clothes from the old bag, already packed, to the new one. When he returned, the ushers were still standing around feeling good about the bag and not so good about the cigars. They'd discuss that later. Father Malt urged them to sit down. He seemed to want them near him as long as possible. They *were* his friends, but I could not blame Father Burner for avoiding them. He was absent now, as he usually managed to be when the ushers called. If he ever succeeded Father Malt, who let them have the run of the place, they would be the first to suffer—after me! As Father Malt was the heart, they were the substance of a parish that remained rural while becoming increasingly suburban. They dressed up occasionally and dropped into St. Paul and Minneapolis, "the Cities," as visiting firemen into Hell, though it would be difficult to imagine any other place as graceless and far-gone as our own hard little highway town—called Sherwood but about as sylvan as a tennis court.

They were regular fellows—not so priestly as their urban colleagues—loud, heavy of foot, wearers of long underwear in wintertime and iron-gray business suits the year round. Their idea of a good time (pilsner beer, cheap cigars smoked with the bands left on, and pinochle) coincided nicely with their understanding of "doing good" (a percentage of every pot went to the parish building fund). Their wives, also active, played cards in the church basement and sold vanilla extract and chances—mostly to each other, it appeared—with all revenue over cost going to what was known as "the missions." This evening I could be grateful that time was not going to permit the usual pinochle game. (In the midst of all their pounding—almost as hard on me as it was on the dining-room table —I often felt they should have played on a meat block.)

The ushers, settling down all over the living room, started to talk about Father Malt's trip to Chicago. The housekeeper brought in a round of beer.

"How long you be gone, Father—three days?" one of them asked.

Father Malt said that he'd be gone about three days.

"Three days! This is Friday. Tomorrow's Saturday. Sunday. Monday." Everything stopped while the youngest usher counted on his fingers. "Back on Tuesday?"

306

Father Malt nodded.

"Who's takin' over on Sunday?"

Mr. Keller answered for Father Malt. "He's got some missionary fathers in."

"Missionaries!"

The youngest usher then began to repeat himself on one of his two or three topics. "Hey, Father, don't forget to drop in the U.S.O. if it's still there. I was in Chi during the war," he said, but nobody would listen to him.

Mr. Bauman had cornered Father Malt and was trying to tell him where that place was—that place where he'd eaten his meals during the World's Fair; one of the waitresses was from Minnesota. I'd had enough of this—the next thing would be a diagram on the back of an envelope—and I'd heard Father Burner come in earlier. I went upstairs to check on him. For a minute or two I stood outside his room listening. He had Father Philbert with him, and, just as I'd expected, he was talking against Father Malt, leading up to the famous question with which Father Malt, years ago, had received the Sherwood appointment from the Archbishop: "Have dey got dere a goot meat shop?"

Father Philbert laughed, and I could hear him sip from his glass and place it on the floor beside his chair. I entered the room, staying close to the baseboard, in the shadows, curious to know what they were drinking. I maneuvered myself into position to sniff Father Philbert's glass. To my surprise, Scotch. Here was proof that Father Burner considered Father Philbert a friend. At that moment I could not think what it was he expected to get out of a lowly missionary. My mistake, not realizing then how correct and prophetic I'd been earlier in thinking of them as two of a kind. It seldom happened that Father Burner got out the real Scotch for company, or for himself *in* company. For most guests he had nothing—a safe policy, since a surprising number of temperance cranks passed through the rectory—and for unwelcome guests who would like a drink he kept a bottle of "Scotch-type" whiskey, which was a smooth, smoky blend of furniture polish that came in a fancy bottle, was offensive even when watered, and cheap, though rather hard to get since the end

307

of the war. He had a charming way of plucking the rare bottle from a bureau drawer, as if this were indeed an occasion for him; even so, he would not touch the stuff, presenting himself as a chap of simple tastes, of no taste at all for the things of this world, who would prefer, if anything, the rude wine made from our own grapes —if we'd had any grapes. Quite an act and one he thoroughly enjoyed, holding his glass of pure water and asking, "How's your drink, Father? Strong enough?"

The housekeeper, appearing at the door, said there'd been a change of plans and some of the ushers were driving Father Malt to the train.

"Has he gone yet?" asked Father Burner.

"Not yet, Father."

"Well, tell him goodbye for me."

"Yes, Father."

When she had gone, he said, "I'd tell him myself, but I don't want to run into that bunch."

Father Philbert smiled. "What's he up to in Chicago?"

"They've got one of those pastors' and builders' conventions going on at the Stevens Hotel."

"Is he building?"

"No, but he's a pastor and he'll get a lot of free samples. He won't buy anything."

"Not much has been done around here, huh?" said Father Philbert.

He had fed Father Burner the question he wanted. "He built that fish pond in the back yard—for his minnows. That's the extent of the building program in his time. Of course he's only been here a while."

"How long?"

"Fourteen years," said Father Burner. *He* would be the greatest builder of them all—if he ever got the chance. He lit a cigarette and smiled. "What he's really going to Chicago for is to see a couple of ball games."

Father Philbert did not smile. "Who's playing there now?" he said.

A little irritated at this interest, Father Burner said, "I believe it's the Red Sox—or is it the Reds? Hell, how do I know?"

"Couldn't be the Reds," said Father Philbert. "The boy and I were in Cincinnati last week and it was the start of a long home stand for them."

"Very likely," said Father Burner.

While the missionary, a Cardinal fan, analyzed the pennant race in the National League, Father Burner sulked. "What's the best train out of Chicago for Washington?" he suddenly inquired.

Father Philbert told him what he could, but admitted that his information dated from some years back. "We don't make the run to Washington any more."

"That's right," said Father Burner. "Washington's in the American League."

Father Philbert laughed, turning aside the point that he traveled with the Cardinals. "I thought you didn't know about these things," he said.

"About these things it's impossible to stay ignorant," said Father Burner. "Here, and the last place, and the place before that, and in the seminary—a ball, a bat, and God. I'll be damned, Father, if I'll do as the Romans do."

"What price glory?" inquired Father Philbert as if he smelt heresy.

"I know," said Father Burner. "And it'll probably cost me the red hat." A brave comment, perhaps, from a man not yet a country pastor, and it showed me where his thoughts were again. He did not disguise his humble ambition by speaking lightly of an impossible one. "Scratch a prelate and you'll find a second baseman," he fumed.

Father Philbert tried to change the subject. "Somebody told me Father Malt's the exorcist for the diocese."

"Used to be." Father Burner's eyes flickered balefully.

"Overdid it, huh?" asked Father Philbert—as if he hadn't heard!

"Some." I expected Father Burner to say more. He could have told some pretty wild stories, the gist of them all that Father Malt,

309

as an exorcist, was perhaps a little quick on the trigger. He had stuck pretty much to livestock, however, which was to his credit in the human view.

"Much scandal?"

"Some."

"Nothing serious, though?"

"No."

"Suppose it depends on what you call serious."

Father Burner did not reply. He had become oddly morose. Perhaps he felt that he was being catered to out of pity, or that Father Philbert, in giving him so many opportunities to talk against Father Malt, was tempting him.

"Who plays the accordion?" inquired Father Philbert, hearing it downstairs.

"He does."

"Go on!"

"Sure."

"How can he hear what he's playing?"

"What's the difference—if he plays an accordion?"

Father Philbert laughed. He removed the cellophane from a cigar, and then he saw me. And at that moment I made no attempt to hide. "There's that damn cat."

"His assistant!" said Father Burner with surprising bitterness. "Coadjutor with right of succession."

Father Philbert balled up the cellophane and tossed it at the wastebasket, missing.

"Get it," he said to me, fatuously.

I ignored him, walking slowly toward the door.

Father Burner made a quick movement with his feet, which were something to behold, but I knew he wouldn't get up, and took my sweet time.

Father Philbert inquired, "Will she catch mice?"

She! Since coming to live at the rectory, I've been celibate, it's true, but I daresay I'm as manly as the next one. And Father Burner, who might have done me the favor of putting him straight, said nothing.

"She looks pretty fat to be much of a mouser."

I just stared at the poor man then, as much as to say that I'd think one so interested in catching mice would have heard of a little thing called the mousetrap. After one last dirty look, I left them to themselves—to punish each other with their company.

I strolled down the hall, trying to remember when I'd last had a mouse. Going past the room occupied by the young missionary, I smiled upon his door, which was shut, confident that he was inside hard at his prayers.

The next morning, shortly after breakfast, which I took, as usual, in the kitchen, I headed for the cool orchard to which I often repaired on just such a day as this one promised to be. I had no appetite for the sparrows hopping from tree to tree above me, but there seemed no way to convince them of that. Each one, so great is his vanity, thinks himself eminently edible. Peace, peace, they cry, and there is no peace. Finally, tired of their noise, I got up from the matted grass and left, levelling my ears and flailing my tail, in a fake dudgeon that inspired the males to feats of stunt flying and terrorized the young females most delightfully.

I went then to another favorite spot of mine, that bosky strip of green between the church and the brick sidewalk. Here, however, the horseflies found me, and as if that were not enough, visions of stray dogs and children came between me and the kind of sleep I badly needed after an uncommonly restless night.

When afternoon came, I remembered that it was Saturday, and that I could have the rectory to myself. Father Burner and the missionaries would be busy with confessions. By this time the temperature had reached its peak, and though I felt sorry for the young missionary, I must admit the thought of the other two sweltering in the confessionals refreshed me. The rest of the afternoon I must have slept something approaching the sleep of the just.

I suppose it was the sound of dishes that roused me. I rushed into the dining room, not bothering to wash up, and took my customary place at the table. Only then did I consider the empty chair next to me—the utter void. This, I thought, is a foreshadowing of what I

311

must someday face—this, and Father Burner munching away at the other end of the table. And there was the immediate problem: no one to serve me. The young missionary smiled at me, but how can you eat a smile? The other two, looking rather wilted—to their hot boxes I wished them swift return—talked in expiring tones of reserved sins and did not appear to notice me. Our first meal together without Father Malt did not pass without incident, however. It all came about when the young missionary extended a thin sliver of meat to me.

"Hey, don't do that!" said Father Philbert. "You'll never make a mouser out of her that way."

Father Burner, too, regarded the young missionary with disapproval.

"Just this one piece," said the young missionary. The meat was already in my mouth.

"Well, watch it in the future," said Father Philbert. It was the word "future" that worried me. Did it mean that he had arranged to cut off my sustenance in the kitchen too? Did it mean that until Father Malt returned I had to choose between mousing and fasting?

I continued to think along these melancholy lines until the repast, which had never begun for me, ended for them. Then I whisked into the kitchen, where I received the usual bowl of milk. But whether the housekeeper, accustomed as she was to having me eat my main course at table, assumed there had been no change in my life, or was now acting under instructions from these villains, I don't know. I was too sickened by their meanness to have any appetite. When the pastor's away, the curates will play, I thought. On the whole I was feeling pretty glum.

It was our custom to have the main meal at noon on Sundays. I arrived early, before the others, hungrier than I'd been for as long as I could remember, and still I had little or no expectation of food at this table. I was there for one purpose—to assert myself—and possibly, where the young missionary was concerned, to incite sympathy for myself and contempt for my persecutors. By this time I knew that to be the name for them.

They entered the dining room, just the two of them.

"Where's the kid?" asked Father Burner.

"He's not feeling well," said Father Philbert.

I was not surprised. They'd arranged between the two of them to have him say the six- and eleven-o'clock Masses, which meant, of course, that he'd fasted in the interval. I had not thought of him as the hardy type, either.

"I'll have the housekeeper take him some beef broth," said Father Burner. He suddenly whirled and swept me off my chair. Then he picked it up and placed it against the wall. Then he went to the lower end of the table, removed his plate and silverware, and brought them to Father Malt's place. Talking and fuming to himself, he sat down in Father Malt's chair. I did not appear very brave, I fear, cowering under mine.

Father Philbert, who had been watching with interest, now greeted the new order with a cheer. "Attaboy, Ernest!"

Father Burner began to justify himself. "More light here," he said, and added, "Cats kill birds," and for some reason he was puffing.

"If they'd just kill mice," said Father Philbert, "they wouldn't be so bad." He had a one-track mind if I ever saw one.

"Wonder how many that black devil's caught in his time?" said Father Burner, airing a common prejudice against cats of my shade (though I do have a white collar). He looked over at me. "Sssssss," he said. But I held my ground.

"I'll take a dog any day, " said the platitudinous Father Philbert.

"Me, too."

After a bit, during which time they played hard with the roast, Father Philbert said, "How about taking her for a ride in the country?"

"Hell," said Father Burner. "He'd just come back."

"Not if we did it right, she wouldn't."

"Look," said Father Burner. "Some friends of mine dropped a cat off the high bridge in St. Paul. They saw him go under in mid-channel. I'm talking about the Mississippi, understand. Thought they'd never lay eyes on that animal again. That's what they thought.

He was back at the house before they were." Father Burner paused —he could see that he was not convincing Father Philbert—and then he tried again. "That's a fact, Father. They might've played a quick round of golf before they got back. Cat didn't even look damp, they said. He's still there. Case a lot like this. Except now they're afraid of *him*."

To Father Burner's displeasure, Father Philbert refused to be awed or even puzzled. He simply inquired: "But did they use a bag? Weights?"

"Millstones," snapped Father Burner. "Don't quibble."

Then they fell to discussing the burial customs of gangsters— poured concrete and the rest—and became so engrossed in the matter that they forgot all about me.

Over against the wall, I was quietly working up the courage to act against them. When I felt sufficiently lionhearted, I leaped up and occupied my chair. Expecting blows and vilification, I encountered only indifference. I saw then how far I'd come down in their estimation. Already the remembrance of things past—the disease of noble politicals in exile—was too strong in me, the hope of restoration unwarrantably faint.

At the end of the meal, returning to me, Father Philbert remarked, "I think I know a better way." Rising, he snatched the

Trouble for a nineteenth-century cat.
Pictures drawn by Frank Dellon.

crucifix off the wall, passed it to a bewildered Father Burner, and, saying "Nice Kitty," grabbed me behind the ears. "Hold it up to her," said Father Philbert. Father Burner held the crucifix up to me. "See that?" said Father Philbert to my face. I miaowed. "Take that!" said Father Philbert, cuffing me. He pushed my face into the crucifix again. "See that?" he said again, but I knew what to expect next, and when he cuffed me, I went for his hand with my mouth, pinking him nicely on the wrist. Evidently Father Burner had begun to understand and appreciate the proceedings. Although I was in a good position to observe everything, I could not say as much for myself. "Association," said Father Burner with mysterious satisfaction, almost with zest. He poked the crucifix at me. "If he's just smart enough to react properly," he said. "Oh, she's plenty

315

smart," said Father Philbert, sucking his wrist and giving himself, I hoped, hydrophobia. He scuffed off one of his sandals for a paddle. Father Burner, fingering the crucifix nervously, inquired, "Sure it's all right to go on with this thing?" "It's the intention that counts in these things," said Father Philbert. "Our motive is clear enough." And they went at me again.

After that first taste of the sandal in the dining room, I foolishly believed I would be safe as long as I stayed away from the table; there was something about my presence there, I thought, that brought out the beast in them—which is to say very nearly all that was in them. But they caught me in the upstairs hall the same evening, one brute thundering down upon me, the other sealing off my only avenue of escape. And this beating was worse than the first —preceded as it was by a short delay that I mistook for a reprieve until Father Burner, who had gone downstairs muttering something about "leaving no margin for error," returned with the crucifix from the dining room, although we had them hanging all over the house. The young missionary, coming upon them while they were at me, turned away. "I wash my hands of it," he said. I thought he might have done more.

Out of mind, bruised of body, sick at heart, for two days and nights I held on, I know not how or why—unless I lived in hope of vengeance. I wanted simple justice, a large order in itself, but I would never have settled for that alone. I wanted nothing less than my revenge.

I kept to the neighborhood, but avoided the rectory. I believed, of course, that their only strategy was to drive me away. I derived some little satisfaction from making myself scarce, for it was thus I deceived them into thinking their plan to banish me successful. But this was my single comfort during this hard time, and it was as nothing against their crimes.

I spent the nights in the open fields. I reeled, dizzy with hunger, until I bagged an aged field mouse. It tasted bitter to me, this stale provender, and seemed, as I swallowed it, an ironic concession to

316

the enemy. I vowed I'd starve before I ate another mouse. By way of retribution to myself, I stalked sparrows in the orchard—hating myself for it but persisting all the more when I thought of those bird-lovers, my persecutors, before whom I could stand and say in self-redemption, "You made me what I am now. You thrust the killer's part upon me." Fortunately, I did not flush a single sparrow. Since *my* motive was clear enough, however, I'd had the pleasure of sinning against them and their ideals, the pleasure without the feathers and mess.

On Tuesday, the third day, all caution, I took up my post in the lilac bush beside the garage. Not until Father Malt returned, I knew, would I be safe in daylight. He arrived along about dinner-time, and I must say the very sight of him aroused a sentiment in me akin to human affection. The youngest usher, who must have had the afternoon off to meet him at the station in St. Paul, carried the new bag before him into the rectory. It was for me an act symbolic of the counter-revolution to come. I did not rush out from my hiding place, however. I had suffered too much to play the fool now. Instead I slipped into the kitchen by way of the flap in the screen door, which they had not thought to barricade. I waited under the stove for my moment, like an actor in the wings.

Presently I heard them tramping into the dining room and seating themselves, and Father Malt's voice saying, "I had a long talk with the Archbishop." (I could almost hear Father Burner praying, Did he say anything about *me?*) And then, "Where's Fritz?"

"He hasn't been around lately," said Father Burner cunningly. He would not tell the truth and he would not tell a lie.

"You know, there's something mighty funny about that cat," said Father Philbert. "We think she's possessed."

I was astonished, and would have liked a moment to think it over, but by now I was already entering the room.

"Possessed!" said Father Malt. "Aw, no!"

"Ah, yes," said Father Burner, going for the meat right away. "And good riddance."

And then I miaowed and they saw me.

"Quick!" said Father Philbert, who made a nice recovery after involuntarily reaching for me and his sandal at the same time. Father Burner ran to the wall for the crucifix, which had been, until now, a mysterious and possibly blasphemous feature of my beatings—the crucifix held up to me by the one not scourging at the moment, as if it were the will behind my punishment. They had schooled me well, for even now, at the sight of the crucifix, an undeniable fear was rising in me. Father Burner handed it to Father Malt.

"Now you'll see," said Father Philbert.

"We'll leave it up to you," said Father Burner.

I found now that I could not help myself. What followed was hidden from them—from human eyes. I gave myself over entirely to the fear they'd beaten into me, and in a moment, according to their plan, I was fleeing the crucifix as one truly possessed, out of the dining room and into the kitchen, and from there, blindly, along the house and through the shrubbery, ending in the street, where a powerful gray car ran over me—and where I gave up the old ghost for a new one.

Simultaneously, reborn, redeemed from my previous fear, identical with my former self, so far as they could see, and still in their midst, I padded up to Father Malt—he still sat gripping the crucifix —and jumped into his lap. I heard the young missionary arriving from an errand in Father Philbert's *brother's* car, late for dinner he thought, but just in time to see the stricken look I saw coming into the eyes of my persecutors. This look alone made up for everything I'd suffered at their hands. Purring now, I was rubbing up against the crucifix, myself effecting my utter revenge.

"What have we done?" cried Father Philbert. He was basically an emotional dolt and would have voted then for my canonization.

"I ran over a cat!" said the young missionary excitedly. "I'd swear it was this one. When I looked, there was nothing there!"

"Better go upstairs and rest," growled Father Burner. He sat down—it was good to see him in his proper spot at the low end of the table—as if to wait a long time, or so it seemed to me. I found

318

myself wondering if I could possibly bring about his transfer to another parish—one where they had a devil for a pastor and several assistants, where he would be able to start at the bottom again.

But first things first, I always say, and all in good season, for now Father Malt himself was drawing my chair up to the table, restoring me to my rightful place.

A particular favorite
—his cat Foss,
by Edward Lear.

319

Foss Couchant

Foss, a untin.

Foss
rampant

Foss dansant.

MISS SPOT AND OTHERS

Harriet Prescott Spofford

What a grande dame *she was, Mrs. Spofford! One of the literary lights of New England, Mrs. Spofford was one of the first to establish the fact that a woman could have a literary life quite independent of family or social foibles. Her cats were just as individualistic, each a very* grand chat, *indeed.*

As for my own cats,—their name has been legion, although a few remain preëminent. There was Miss Spot who came to us already named, preferring our domicile to the neighboring one she had. Her only son was so black that he was known as Ink Spot, but her only daughter was so altogether ideal and black, too, that she was known as Beauty Spot. Beauty Spot led a sorrowful life, and was fortunately born clothed in black or her mourning would have been expensive, as she was always in a bereaved condition, her drowned offspring making a shoal in the Merrimac, although she had always plenty left. She solaced herself with music. She would never sit in any one's lap but mine, and in mine only when I sang; and then only when I sang "The Last Rose of Summer." This is really true. But she would spring into my husband's lap if he whistled. She

321

Cat and Birds, by Harrison Weir.

would leave her sleep reluctantly, start a little way, and retreat, start and retreat again, and then give one bound and light on his knee or his arm and reach up one paw and push it repeatedly across his mouth like one playing the jew's-harp; I suppose to get at the sound. She always went to walk with us and followed us wherever we went about the island.

Lucifer and Phosphor have been our cats for the last ten years: Lucifer, entirely black, Phosphor, as yellow as saffron, a real golden fleece. My sister lived in town and going away for the summer left her cat in a neighbor's care, and the neighbor moved away meanwhile and left the cat to shift for herself. She went down to the apothecary's, two blocks away or more. There she had a family of kittens, but apparently came up to reconnoitre, for on my sister's return, she appeared with one kitten and laid it down at Kate's feet; ran off, and in time came with another which she left also, and so on until she had brought up the whole household. Lucifer was one of them.

He was as black as an imp and as mischievous as one. His bounds have always been tremendous: from the floor to the high mantel, or to the top of a tall buffet close under the ceiling. And these bounds of his, together with a way he has of gazing into space with his soulful and enormous yellow eyes, have led to a thousand tales as to his nightly journeyings among the stars; hurting his foot slumping through the nebula in Andromeda; getting his supper at a place in the milky way, hunting all night with Orion, and having awful fights with Sirius. He got his throat cut by alighting on the North Pole one night, coming down from the stars. The reason he slumps through the nebula is on account of his big feet; he has six toes (like the foot in George Augustus Sala's drawing) and when he walks on the top of the piazza you would think it was a burglar.

Lucifer's Mephistophelian aspect is increased not only by those feet, but by an arrow-pointed tail. He sucks his tail,—alas, and alas! In vain have we peppered it, and pepper-sauced it, and dipped it in Worcestershire sauce and in aloes, and done it up in curl papers, and glued on it the fingers of old gloves. At last we gave it up in despair, and I took him and put his tail in his mouth and told him to take his pleasure,—and that is the reason, I suppose, that he attaches himself particularly to me. He is very near-sighted with those magnificent orbs, for he will jump into any one's lap, who wears a black gown, but jump down instantly, and when he finds my lap curl down for a brief season. But he is not much of a lap-loving cat. He puts up his nose and smells my face all over in what he means for a caress, and is off. He is not a large eater, although he has been known to help himself to a whole steak at the table, being alone in the dining room; and when poultry are in the larder he is insistent till satisfied. But he wants his breakfast early. If the second girl, whose charge he is, does not rise in season, he mounts two flights of stairs and seats himself on her chest until she does rise. Then if she does not wait on him at once, he goes into the drawing-room, and springs to the top of the upright piano, and deliberately knocks off the bric-a-brac, particularly loving to encounter and floor a brass dragon candlestick. Then he springs to the mantel-shelf if he has not been seized and appeased, and repeats operations, and has even carried his work of destruction around the room to the top of a low bookcase and has proved himself altogether the wrong sort of person in a china-shop.

However, it is conceded in the family that Phosphor is not a cat merely: he is a person, and Lucifer is a spirit. Lucifer seldom purrs —I wonder if that is a characteristic of black cats? A little thread of sound, and only now and then, when very happy and loving, a rich, full strain. But Phosphor purrs like a windmill, like an electric car, like a tea-kettle, like a whole boiled dinner. When Phosphor came, Lucifer, six weeks her senior (Phosphor's excellencies always incline one to say "she" of him), thought the little live yellow ball was made only for him to play with, and he cuffed and tossed him around for all he was worth, licked him all over twenty times a day, and slept with his arms about him. During those early years Phosphor never washed himself, Lucifer took such care of him, and they were a lovely sight in each other's arms asleep. But of late years a coolness has intervened, and now they never speak as they pass by. They sometimes go fishing together, Lucifer walking off majestically alone, always dark, mysterious, reticent, intent on his own affairs, making you feel that he has a sort of lofty contempt for yours. Sometimes, the mice depositing a dead fish in the crannies of the rocks, Lucifer appears with it in the twilight, gleaming silver-white in his jaws, and the great eyes gleaming like fire-balls above it. Phosphor is, however, a mighty hunter: mice, rats by the score, chipmunks,— all is game that comes to his net. He has cleaned out whole colonies of catbirds (for their insolence), and eaten every golden robin on the island.

It used to be very pretty to see them, when they were little, as El Mahdi, the peacock, spread his great tail, dart and spring upon it, and go whirling round with it as El Mahdi, fairly frantic with the little demons that had hold of him, went skipping and springing round and round. But although so fierce a fighter, so inhospitable to every other cat, Phosphor is the most affectionate little soul. He is still very playful, though so large, and last summer to see him bounding on the grass, playing with his tail, turning somersaults all by himself, was quite worth while.

When we first happened to go away in his early years he wouldn't speak to us when we came back, he felt so neglected. I went away for five months once, before Lucifer was more than a year old. He got into no one's lap while I was gone, but the moment I sat down on my return, he jumped into mine, saluted me, and curled himself down for a nap, showing the plainest recognition. Now when one comes back, Phosphor is wild with joy—always in a well-bred way. He will get into your arms and on your shoulder and rub his face. around, and before you know it his little mouth is in the middle of your mouth as much like a kiss as anything can be. Perhaps it isn't so well bred, but his motions are so quick and perfect it seems so. When you let him in he curls into heaps of joy, and fairly stands on his head sometimes. He is the most responsive creature, always ready for a caress, and his wild, great amber eyes beam love, if ever love had manifestation. His beauty is really extraordinary; his tail a real wonder. Lucifer, I grieve to say, looks very moth-eaten. Phosphor wore a bell for a short time once—a little Inch-Cape Rock bell—but he left it to toll all winter in a tall tree near the drawing-room window.

A charm of cats is that they seem to live in a world of their own, just as much as if it were a real dimension of space.

ON OBSERVING HIS CATS

Andrew Lang

Andrew Lang, that great Scotsman, had a delightful instinct for fraternity with man or cat. As a folklorist, he was well aware of cats' supernatural aspects. (He himself had such a wide-ranging interest in witches and specters that his friends often laughed at him.) He could never resist a ghost, but he also could never resist the meow of a poor lost kitten. He had many cats, and loved them all.

From the dawn of creation, the cat has known his place, and he has kept it, practically untamed and unspoiled by man. He has *retenue*. Of all animals, he alone attains to the Contemplative Life. He regards the wheel of existence from without, like the Buddha. There is no pretence of sympathy about the cat. He lives alone, aloft, sublime, in a wise passiveness. He is excessively proud, and, when he is made the subject of conversation, will cast one glance of scorn, and leave the room in which personalities are bandied. All expressions of emotion he scouts as frivolous and insincere, except, indeed, in the ambrosial night, when, free from the society of mankind, he pours forth his soul in strains of unpremeditated art. The paltry pay and

Illustrations by H. J. Ford
from Andrew Lang's The Yellow Fairy Book.

paltry praise of humanity he despises, like Edgar Poe. He does not
exhibit the pageant of his bleeding heart; he does not howl when
people die, nor explode in cries of delight when his master returns
from a journey. With quiet courtesy, he remains in his proper and
comfortable place, only venturing into view when something he
approves of, such as fish or game, makes its appearance. On the
rights of property he is firm. If a strange cat enters his domain, he
is up in claws to resist invasion. It was for these qualities, probably,
that the cat was worshipped by the ancient Egyptians.

Everyone is aware that a perfectly comfortable, well-fed cat will occasionally come to his house and settle there, deserting a family by whom it is lamented, and to whom it could, if it chose, find its way back with ease. This conduct is a mystery which may lead us to infer that cats form a great secret society, and that they come and go in pursuance of some policy connected with education, or perhaps with witchcraft. We have known a cat to abandon his home for years. Once in six months he would return, and look about him with an air of some contempt. "Such," he seemed to say, "were my humble beginnings."

A cat in an Irish household in the last century. Artist unknown.

RUMPEL

Robert Southey

Robert Southey, Poet Laureate of England, friend of the great,
master of literature, was but a plaything to his cats. This eulogy to
a remarkable cat has found some sympathetic readers and a few dis-
senters—Agnes Repplier, for one, who pointed out, correctly, we
think, that cats do not like coy names. And poor Rumpel most cer-
tainly must have suffered from a surfeit of love.

This day poor Rumpel was found dead, after as long and happy a
life as cat could wish for, if cats form wishes on that subject. His full
titles were: The Most Noble, the Archduke Rumpelstiltzchen,
Marcus Macbum, Earl Tomlefnagne, Baron Raticide, Waowhler
and Scratch. There should be a court-mourning in Catland, and if
the Dragon (your pet cat) wear a black ribbon round his neck, or a
band of crape à la militaire round one of his forepaws it will be but
a becoming mark of respect. . . . I believe we are each and all,
servants included, more sorry for his loss, or, rather, more affected
by it, than any of us would like to confess.

*The cat was often used in children's books at the time of Robert Southey
(1774–1843). Many such books were published by Mary Shelley's step-
mother, Mary Godwin.* Dame Wiggins and Her Seven Wonderful Cats
*was written "Principally by a Lady of Ninety." First published in the
eighteenth century, it was a favorite of adults and children.*

THE LAST WORDS

Thomas Janvier

Thomas Janvier, biographer and artist extraordinaire of Greenwich Village, knew intimately the cats of what he called "the most attractive portion of New York." We know from experience of our cats and others that there seems to be a protecting spirit of grace that extends from person to puss in that village of the mind.

It is a happy fact that even the least of us—drawing closer as did the blessed Saint Francis of Assisi to our brethren, the beasts and the fishes and the birds—may in some measure forestall the millennium in our lives. And also it is true that in so doing we may at the same time hasten by a fractional part, the revival universal of the gracious epoch when man and the so-called lower orders of animals once more shall be on terms of cordial fellowship; when, most joyous of all the joyous sights of that reunion, Homo and Felis shall stand friendly together, hand clasping paw.

THE ACHIEVEMENT
OF THE CAT

Saki

The British have had a long and noble love for the cat, and as Hillaire Belloc said, "If it be true that nations have the cats they deserve, then the English people deserve well of cats, for there are none so prosperous or so friendly in the world."

This charming envoi by Saki is a British poem to the achievement of the fabulous feline.

In the political history of nations it is no uncommon experience to find states and peoples which but a short time since were in bitter conflict and animosity with each other, settled down comfortably on terms of mutual goodwill and even alliance. The natural history of the social developments of species affords a similar instance in the coming-together of two once warring elements, now represented by civilized man and the domestic cat. The fiercely waged struggle which went on between humans and felines in those far-off days when sabre-toothed tiger and cave lion contended with primeval man, has long ago been decided in favour of the most fitly equipped combatant—the Thing with a Thumb—and the descendants of the

332

Fish-Day by Meredith Nugent.

dispossessed family are relegated today, for the most part, to the waste lands of jungle and veld, where an existence of self-effacement is the only alternative to extermination. But the *felis catus,* or whatever species was the ancestor of the modern domestic cat (a vexed question at present), by a master-stroke of adaptation avoided the ruin of its race, and "captured" a place in the very keystone of the conqueror's organization.

For not as a bond-servant or dependent has this proudest of mammals entered the human fraternity; not as a slave like the beasts of burden, or a humble camp-follower like the dog. The cat is domestic only as far as suits its own ends; it will not be kennelled or harnessed nor suffer any dictation as to its goings out or comings in. Long contact with the human race has developed in it the art of diplomacy, and no Roman Cardinal of mediæval days knew better how to ingratiate himself with his surroundings than a cat with a saucer of cream on its mental horizon. But the social smoothness, the purring innocence, the softness of the velvet paw may be laid aside at a moment's notice, and the sinuous feline may disappear, in deliberate aloofness, to a world of roofs and chimney-stacks, where the human element is distanced and disregarded. Or the innate savage spirit that helped its survival in the bygone days of tooth and claw may be summoned forth from beneath the sleek exterior, and the torture-instinct (common alone to human and feline) may find free play in the death-throes of some luckless bird or rodent. It is, indeed, no small triumph to have combined the untrammelled liberty of primeval savagery with the luxury which only a highly developed civilization can command; to be lapped in the soft stuffs that commerce has gathered from the far ends of the world; to bask in the warmth that labour and industry have dragged from the bowels of the earth; to banquet on the dainties that wealth has bespoken for its table, and withal to be a free son of nature, a mighty hunter, a spiller of life-blood. This is the victory of the cat.

But besides the credit of success the cat has other qualities which compel recognition. The animal which the Egyptian worshipped as divine, which the Romans venerated as a symbol of liberty, which Europeans in the ignorant Middle Ages anathematized as an agent of demonology, has displayed to all ages two closely blended characteristics—courage and self-respect. No matter how unfavorable the circumstances, both qualities are always to the fore.

Confront a child, a puppy, and a kitten with a sudden danger; the child will turn instinctively for assistance, the puppy will grovel in abject submission to the impeding visitation, the kitten will brace its tiny body for a frantic resistance. And disassociate the luxury-loving cat from the atmosphere of social comfort in which it usually contrives to move, and observe it critically under the adverse conditions of civilization—that civilization which can impel a man to the degradation of clothing himself in tawdry ribald garments and capering mountebank dances in the streets for the earning of the few coins that keep him on the respectable, or non-criminal, side of society. The cat of the slums and alleys, starved, outcast, harried, still keeps amid the prowlings of its adversity the bold, free, panther-tread with which it paced of yore the temple courts of Thebes, still displays the self-reliant watchfulness which man has never taught it to lay aside.

And when its shifts and clever managings have not sufficed to stave off inexorable fate, when its enemies have proved too strong or too many for its defensive powers, it dies fighting to the last, quivering with the choking rage of mastered resistance, and voicing in its death-yell that agony of bitter remonstrance which human animals, too, have flung at the powers that may be; the last protest against a destiny that might have made them happy—and has not.

A contribution to Century *magazine by Laura Richards.*

BIOGRAPHICAL NOTES

JAMES HERRIOT, Scottish writer and veterinarian, lives and works in northern England. He came upon the literary scene in 1972 with *All Creatures Great and Small,* an extraordinary collection of stories of his early years. His succeeding books deal with his continuing encounters with men and beasts.

SARAH ORNE JEWETT, American writer, was born in Maine, in 1849. She wrote many sketches and stories of New England life. She died in 1909.

LILIAN JACKSON BRAUN has worked as a journalist for many years. She is also the "Good Living" editor of the Detroit *Free Press* and the owner of two Siamese cats.

MICHAEL JOSEPH was the director of his own literary agency and publishing house and wrote a number of books on the art of writing. However, his real interest in life (and only recreation) was cats.

HECTOR HUGH MUNRO, who wrote under the name of "Saki," was born in Burma in 1870 where his father was an inspector-general. In 1904 he began writing the delightful stories that were to make his reputation. He was killed in action in the First World War.

ROBERTSON DAVIES, Canadian novelist, playwright, and educator, was born in 1913 in Thamesville, Ontario, and educated at Queen's University and at Oxford. He has achieved international recognition with his major work, the trilogy composed of *Fifth Business, The Manticore,* and *World of Wonders.*

HELEN M. WINSLOW, American author, editor and publisher, was born in 1851 and died in 1938.

HERODOTUS, Greek historian of the fifth century B.C., was born in Asia Minor. His great work is a history of the Greek-Persian wars from 500 to 479 B.C.

JEROME K. JEROME, English humorist, was born in 1859 in Staffordshire, England, and died in 1927. His most famous book, *Three Men in a Boat,* sold over a million copies in America.

EDEN PHILLPOTTS, English novelist and playwright, was born in Rajputawa Province, India, in 1862. He was the author of regional and historical novels, mystery stories, short stories, poems, and plays. He died in 1960.

PIERRE LOTI was the pen name of Louis Marie Julien Viaud, French naval officer and novelist, born in 1850. His journeys in waters near Japan, Senegal, and Tonkin provided background for his novels. He died in 1923.

L. P. HARTLEY, British author, was born in 1895. A noted novelist of English country life, he also wrote a number of excellent horror stories. He died in 1972.

FRANCIS BUCKLAND, naturalist and writer, was born (1826) and educated at Oxford where his father was a canon of Christ Church. He studied medicine in London, and was assistant-surgeon in the Life Guards. He also founded and edited *Land and Water.* Buckland died in 1880.

AGNES REPPLIER, American essayist and biographer, was born in Philadelphia, Pennsylvania, in 1855 and died there in 1950. A prolific writer, she produced over twenty volumes of essays and biographies. Miss Repplier received many awards and honors during her lifetime.

THOMAS JANVIER, American writer, was born in Philadelphia, Pennsylvania, in 1849. He wrote many stories about New York, where he lived from 1884 until his death in 1913.

CHARLES DUDLEY WARNER, American essayist, novelist, and editor, was born in Plainfield, Massachusetts, in 1829. He often wrote and lectured on social reform. He died in 1900.

JAMES THURBER, one of America's best-loved humorists, was born in Columbus, Ohio, in 1894. Though dogged by progressive loss of vision and eventual blindness, he continued to write and was the author of more than twenty books. He died in 1962.

JOHN COLEMAN ADAMS, American clergyman and author, was born in Malden, Massachusetts, in 1849, and died in Hartford, Connecticut, in 1922.

ELEANOR FARJEON, British writer, was born in London in 1881. Miss Farjeon was a prolific writer of fantasies, verse, and plays, and is considered one of England's most distinguished writers for children. She died in 1965.

JOHN OXENFORD, English playwright and critic, was born in 1812 and died in 1877. He was drama critic on *The London Times*.

BRYAN MACMAHON, Irish writer and educator, was born and lives in Listowel, County Kerry. His short stories have been collected in *The Lion Tamer* (1949) and *The Red Petticoat* (1955).

BILL NYE, American humorist, was born in 1850. He founded and edited the *Laramie Boomerang*, where his humorous pieces were first published. Later he was on the staff of the New York *World* and lectured extensively. He died in 1896.

CHARLES ANDERSON DANA, American newspaper editor, was born in 1819. He was the owner and editor of the New York *Sun* from 1868 until his death in 1897.

JULIAN RALPH, American journalist, was born in New York City in 1853. He was on the staff of the New York *World* (1872), the New York *Daily Graphic* (1873–75) and the New York *Sun* (1875–95). He died in 1903.

WILLIAM WINTLE, British writer of the late Victorian period, collected old British folk songs for publication. His stories of the weird and macabre were originally written to entertain young relatives.

AGNES A. SANDHAM was a contributor to several of the leading nineteenth-century magazines.

SAMUEL LOVER, novelist, songwriter, and portrait painter, was born in Dublin, son of a stockbroker, in 1797. He joined with Charles Dickens in founding *Bentley's Magazine*. He died in 1868.

MARY F. HONEYMAN was a regular contributor to *St. Nicholas* magazine.

HARRIET BEECHER STOWE, American author, was born in Litchfield, Connecticut, in 1811. Her famous book *Uncle Tom's Cabin* (1854) helped to solidify sentiment in the North against slavery. She died in 1896.

WILLIAM ROSSETTI, critic and biographer, was born in London in 1829, a brother of Dante Gabriel and Christina Rossetti. Besides writing art criticism, he edited the works of his brother and sister and published a series of books on English poets. He died in 1919.

HENRY SLESAR was born in Brooklyn, New York, in 1927. He has written over five hundred short stories, novels, and novellas, and some fifty plays for television.

MADAME ADÈLE MICHELET, French writer, was born in 1826 and died in 1899. She also collaborated with her husband Jules, who was a noted French historian.

OLIVER HERFORD, British writer and illustrator, was born in 1863 and died in 1935. He was the author of numerous whimsical works illustrated with his own drawings, including the *Rubaiyat of a Persian Kitten* (1904).

EDNA DEAN PROCTOR, American author, was born in Henniker, New Hampshire, in 1829. She was a lifelong friend of the American Indian, and many of her writings deal with their problems. She died in 1923.

ALGERNON BLACKWOOD, British novelist and short story writer, was born in Kent in 1869, the son of Sir Arthur Blackwood and Sidney, Duchess of Manchester. His macabre stories are considered among the best of the genre. He died in 1951.

COMPTON MACKENZIE, English novelist, was born in West Hartlepool in 1883. His novel *Tight Little Island* was made into a very successful motion picture. He was knighted in 1952, and died in 1972.

Louise Chandler Moulton, American poet, was born in Pomfret, Connecticut, in 1835. Her collected verse appeared in *The Poems and Sonnets of Louise Chandler Moulton* (1909). She died in 1909.

James Farl Powers, American writer, was born in Jacksonville, Illinois, in 1917. His novels and short stories have won many awards, including the 1963 National Book Award.

Harriet Prescott Spofford, American novelist and poet, was born in 1835. Among her books are *New England Legends* (1871), *Poems* (1881), and *In Titian's Garden and Other Poems* (1897). She died in 1921.

Andrew Lang, Scottish scholar, folklorist, and poet, was born in Selkirk in 1844 and died in 1912. He is best known for his series of *Fairy Books,* called by the names of different colors.

Robert Southey, British poet, was born in Bristol in 1774 and died in 1843. He held the office of Poet Laureate from 1813 until his death.